OPERATIONS RESEARCH AND QUANTITATIVE ECONOMICS

An Elementary Introduction

ECONOMICS HANDBOOK SERIES

SEYMOUR E. HARRIS, EDITOR

OPERATIONS RESEARCH
AND QUANTITATIVE ECONOMICS

An Elementary Introduction

Translated from the Dutch. *VOORSPELLEN EN BESLISSEN*

HENRI THEIL

JOHN C. G. BOOT

TEUN KLOEK

Econometric Institute
Netherlands School of Economics
Rotterdam

1965

McGRAW-HILL BOOK COMPANY, New York • St. Louis
San Francisco • Toronto
London • Sydney

**OPERATIONS RESEARCH
AND QUANTITATIVE ECONOMICS**

An Elementary Introduction

Library of Congress Catalog Card Number 65-16155

63892

67890MP7210

PROLOGUE

The increasing importance of mathematics is one of the interesting aspects of the world of today. One does not risk being accused of great exaggeration by stating that in former days the study of mathematics was a closed system. The field was there to be studied in high school and college; if somebody wanted to go more deeply into the matter, he could certainly do so, but his job would simply be that of a high school or college teacher helping the next generation to get acquainted with the field. Nowadays, however, we are accustomed to the idea that mathematics is being applied in a great many areas—a development that is very much stimulated by new mathematical techniques as well as by the electronic computer. To mention just one example: Thanks to computers, the courses of astronauts speeding through space at about 20,000 miles per hour can be calculated with an accuracy of a few seconds.

Most of the earlier applications of mathematics were in the physical sciences. One important new field is *econometrics*, which is concerned with the mathematical and statistical aspects of economics. It dates back to the middle of the nineteenth century, when European statisticians started to analyze budget data of family households. An even more recent development is *operations research*, which is concerned with the mathematical aspects of company management, such as efficient planning and inventory control. The main origin of operations research (or OR, as it is frequently called[1]) was in World War II during the period when Britain had to fight alone. The decision was made to mobilize science for the purpose of efficient ocean transports, fighting submarines, effective bombing, etc. The analysts were of various backgrounds (mathematicians, physicists, biologists, etc.); several of them turned to management problems after the war.

The purpose of this book is to present a survey of the methods and accomplishments of econometrics and operations research at a nontechnical level. Indeed, one glance through the pages of this book shows that there are few formulas and rather few symbols. The use of mathe-

---

[1] Management science (MS) is a closely related area, but somewhat broader.

matics and symbols cannot be avoided completely, of course.   However, we require the reader to know little.   He should know, for example, that x and y stand for variables (things that can vary, such as the level of production from month to month) and a and b for constants, such as 3 and -5; and that $y = a + bx$ is a linear equation, represented by a straight line in a plane, and that $y = a + bx + cx^2$ is a quadratic equation, which is represented by a curve.   He should remember what a square root is and realize that the square of a number is never negative. That is all, and even some of these matters are explained in an elementary way in Chap. 1.

The book will not really make the reader an expert in econometrics or operations research.   To become an expert, academic study at the graduate level is required.   The book addresses itself to the layman-reader who wants an understandable survey of the area; to the undergraduate student who wants to be informed about the field before deciding on his graduate specialization; and to the graduate student who does not want to specialize in mathematical methods but (correctly!) feels that it would be unwise to be unaware of what is going on in the area.   To achieve this goal, we have written thirteen short chapters, which are reproduced schematically on page vii.   The letters right below the boxes are indicative of the level of difficulty. A chapters are not difficult at all, B chapters are a little less easy, and C chapters are still a little less easy. It is to be noticed that the level of difficulty does not necessarily coincide with the amount of mathematics used.   For example, in Chap. 2 (a B chapter) the difficulty is mainly that the story is rather long, so that some effort is required to follow the argument.   In Chap. 12 (a C chapter) the line of reasoning is rather abstract, but the mathematics involved is not at all difficult.

The chapters are connected by arrows.   When an arrow runs from one chapter to another, it is strongly advised to read the one before the other. Thus, Chap. 1 should be read before Chap. 2, Chaps. 3 and 4 before Chap. 5; but Chap. 3 can be read without first reading Chaps. 1 and 2, Chap. 4 can be read without first reading the first three chapters, and so on.   This is not to say that in Chap. 4 no reference is made to the first three chapters at all.   Such references do occur, but their main function is to formulate the link between Chap. 4 and the earlier chapters; there need be no loss of understanding if these earlier chapters have not been read.   Note that two arrows are dashed.   This means that the indicated order is advised, and can be disregarded only at some loss of understanding.   The arrow scheme shows that no chapter requires more than two chapters of prerequisite reading.

Students in business and industrial engineering whose interest is confined to company management problems may want to read the following chapters:

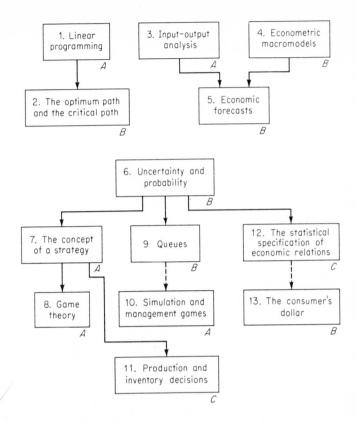

Students in economics whose interest is in econometrics rather than management problems may decide to read the following chapters:

The book ends with an epilogue, a bird's-eye view of the topics and examples discussed. One can easily form an impression of the contents of this book by reading the epilogue first.

HENRI THEIL

JOHN C. G. BOOT

TEUN KLOEK

ACKNOWLEDGMENTS

Many others contributed to this book besides the three authors. Useful suggestions and substantive corrections were made by just about all staff members of the Econometric Institute in Rotterdam. We are also indebted to several readers of the Dutch version of this book, who were kind enough to send us their comments.

Thanks are due to Mrs. Cynthia van Schilfgaarde, Rotterdam, and Mrs. Evelyn Reymond, New York, who helped translate the Dutch into proper American English. It was as pleasant as it was instructive for the authors to cooperate with them. Miss Cok Berger made proofreading a delight rather than a chore by typing the manuscript very neatly on an old-fashioned typewriter. Several graduate students of the Netherlands School of Economics also helped proofread; we are grateful for their assistance.

HENRI THEIL
JOHN C. G. BOOT
TEUN KLOEK

CONTENTS

1

Linear Programming

1-1. The Structure of a Linear Programming Problem

We shall base our opening discussion of a linear programming problem on an investigation made by G. J. Stigler. As many housewives have done, he wanted to determine the cheapest menu sufficient to keep a person alive and healthy for a year. Such a menu clearly has to satisfy a number of nutritional requirements: it should contain sufficient vitamins, fats, proteins, calories, minerals, etc.—in all, there were nine such requirements. The menu was to be chosen from 77 different foods. The prices of these foods were known, as were their nutrient contents. Computations based on these data showed that the cheapest menu satisfying all nine requirements consisted of nine dishes. This correspondence in numbers is, as will be shown below, no mere coincidence. The diet included only wheat flour, corn meal, evaporated milk, peanut butter, lard, beef liver, cabbage, potatoes, and spinach. It is not a very palatable menu. By taking into consideration such factors as taste and variety, it is possible to obtain a more gastronomically pleasing menu, but the cost will then, of course, be higher. Incidentally, the solution of a variant of this problem—determining a menu with as few calories as possible which satisfies all nutritional requirements—can be found weekly in the women's magazines.

The *structure* of the problem is as follows: The unknowns are the quantities of the various foods to be purchased. In mathematics such unknowns are conventionally indicated by a symbol, such as x. The quantities of the 77 different foods, then, will be denoted by x_1, x_2, . . . , x_{77}. If the first food is cod-liver oil, the second radishes, . . . , and the last red beets, x_1 stands for the number of bottles of cod-liver oil, x_2 for the number of bunches of radishes, . . . , and x_{77} for the number of pounds of red beets to be bought. We indicate these various quantities by x_i; the index i can take the values 1 through 77.

The problem will now be formulated mathematically. The object

1

is to discover the cheapest menu possible, and thus the first problem is to find an expression for the cost. Let the prices of the various commodities be designated by p_i. Obviously p_1 stands for the price in dollars of a bottle of cod-liver oil, p_2 the price of a bunch of radishes, . . . , and p_{77} the price of a pound of red beets. It is then easy to see that x_1 bottles of cod-liver oil will cost p_1x_1 dollars. Similarly, x_2 bunches of radishes will cost p_2x_2 dollars, and together these will cost $p_1x_1 + p_2x_2$ dollars. The total cost of the purchase of x_1 bottles of cod-liver oil, x_2 bunches of radishes, . . . , and x_{77} pounds of red beets then amounts to

$$C = p_1x_1 + p_2x_2 + \cdots + p_{77}x_{77}$$

This is called the *objective function*. The value C is to be minimized. The objective function is *linear* in the unknowns x_i; that is, it is of the form "p_1 times x_1 plus p_2 times x_2 plus . . . ," where the prices p_1, p_2, . . . , p_{77} are known numbers.[1]

How can the problem of minimizing the objective function be solved? Perhaps one would think that all x_i should be equal to zero, so that one buys nothing at all. The cost is then very low indeed, in fact, zero. But such a "menu" would not satisfy the nutritional requirements, the so-called *side conditions*. As an example, consider the caloric requirement. Doctors have found that an adult requires at least 800,000 calories a year. It is known that a bottle of cod-liver oil contains c_1 calories, a bunch of radishes c_2, . . . , a pound of red beets c_{77}. If one buys x_1 bottles of cod-liver oil, x_2 bunches of radishes, . . . , and x_{77} pounds of red beets, one has a total of

$$c_1x_1 + c_2x_2 + \cdots + c_{77}x_{77}$$

calories. This total should amount to at least 800,000, so we write for

---

[1] A linear function (without "constant term") of a number of variables x_1, x_2, . . . has the following simple property. If we double the value of all variables, the value of the function is doubled; thus

$$p_1(2x_1) + p_2(2x_2) + \cdots + p_{77}(2x_{77}) = 2p_1x_1 + 2p_2x_2 + \cdots + 2p_{77}x_{77}$$
$$= 2(p_1x_1 + p_2x_2 + \cdots + p_{77}x_{77}) = 2C$$

Similarly, of course, if we replace x_i by $7x_i$, the value of the function becomes seven times as large. A *quadratic function* does not possess this property. For example, $3y^2$ is a quadratic function of y. Replacing y by $2y$ gives as the new value for the function

$$3(2y)^2 = 3 \times 2^2 \times y^2$$

which is four times rather than twice as large.

the caloric requirement

$$c_1x_1 + c_2x_2 + \cdots + c_{77}x_{77} \geq 800,000$$

Similar restrictions hold for vitamins, fats, proteins, etc., giving in total nine side conditions. Notice that the left-hand side of such a side condition is, just like the objective function, linear in the values x_i.

We are nearly there, but not quite. It still must be explicitly stipulated that the x_i values cannot be negative. Obviously, we cannot buy negative amounts of cod-liver oil or a negative number of red beets, but the mathematical apparatus is not concerned with the question of whether restrictions are obvious or not. Thus we impose explicitly

$$x_i \geq 0 \qquad \text{for } i = 1, 2, \ldots, 77$$

All this says is that the amounts purchased of each of the 77 foods must be either zero or positive. These restrictions are known as *nonnegativity conditions*.

The linear programming problem has now been formulated. The problem is to determine the values of a number of unknowns. The unknowns are the 77 quantities of the various foods to be bought. These quantities are controlled; that is, they can be determined by the person for whom the problem is a real problem (in our case the housewife). This person must decide upon the values of these unknowns, which are therefore referred to as *decision variables*. On what criterion is the decision based? The decision is made in such a way that a *linear objective function is minimized*. In our example, the total cost of the diet is to be minimized. However, this minimization does not proceed unconditionally, for the solution has to satisfy (1) the nonnegativity conditions for all decision variables and (2) the side constraints. In our example the constraints have the form of inequalities determined by the requirements concerning calories, proteins, etc. A certain linear expression in the decision variables must be *at least equal to* some given number. This number may be zero (as in the case of nonnegativity conditions) or 800,000 (as in our calorie constraint) or any other number. Actually, it could also be an inequality of the form *at most equal to*. This would be the case if there had been a restriction of the form "it is medically undesirable for a person to consume *more than* two million calories per year." As stated, all these inequalities are *linear* in the decision variables.

It may happen that the objective function is to be *maximized* rather than *minimized*. However, it is important to realize that the difference is mathematically irrelevant, because minimizing the cost is equivalent to maximizing minus the cost.   An example of maximization follows now.

1-2. The Production of Radios

A problem of smaller dimensions (with 2 rather than 77 decision variables) will help us to illustrate the solution technique.   Suppose that a radio manufacturer turns out only two types of radios, a standard model guaranteeing perfect sound reproduction and a large luxury model with more knobs and dials—the latest word in radio technique.   These radios are sold at a profit of \$20 and \$30, respectively.   The decision variables are the *number* of standard radios r_1 and the *number* of luxury radios r_2 to be produced daily.   If the producer makes r_1 standard radios and r_2 luxury radios, he makes a daily profit of

$$20r_1 + 30r_2$$

measured in dollars.   This function, his total profit, is what he wants to maximize.   (It goes without saying that r_1 and r_2 cannot be negative.) Although one might think that the manufacturer should produce only the more profitable luxury radios, capacity limitations make this impossible.

Imagine then that the production takes place on two conveyor belts— one belt for the cheap standard radio and the other for the elaborate luxury model.   The capacity of these belts is limited.   No more than 7 standard radios can be produced daily:

$$r_1 \leq 7$$

The other belt has a production capacity of 5 luxury radios per day, so that we have

$$r_2 \leq 5$$

Moreover, there is a side constraint, because the total labor supply is limited.   If this were not the case, the manufacturer would no doubt produce up to capacity, that is, 7 standard and 5 luxury radios each day. There are only 12 employees in the factory, however, so the available labor amounts to 12 man-days.   It requires 1 man-day to make a standard radio and 2 man-days for a luxury radio.   If r_1 standard models and r_2 luxury models are assembled per day, the total program requires $1r_1 + 2r_2$ man-days.   Thus we are confronted with the side constraint

$$r_1 + 2r_2 \leq 12$$

This constraint prevents the manufacturer from producing up to the capacity of the conveyor belts, that is, up to $r_1 = 7$ and $r_2 = 5$. Such a program would require $1 \times 7 + 2 \times 5 = 17$ man-days, 5 more than are available. It is possible, for example, to produce 4 standard and 4 luxury radios, so that all employees are busy ($1 \times 4 + 2 \times 4 = 12$). Both belts then have excess capacity, and the total profit amounts to $20 \times 4 + 30 \times 4 = \$200$ a day.

It is easy to verify that we have here an example of a linear programming problem. We have two decision variables r_1 and r_2 which the manufacturer can decide upon as he sees fit—within certain limits. These limits are determined on the one hand by the nonnegativity conditions ($r_1 \geq 0$ and $r_2 \geq 0$) and on the other hand by the capacity of the belts ($r_1 \leq 7, r_2 \leq 5$) and the limited supply of manpower ($r_1 + 2r_2 \leq 12$). All three side constraints are linear in r_1 and r_2. The objective function $20r_1 + 30r_2$, the value of which we want to maximize, is also linear in r_1 and r_2. Thus, we have a linear programming problem.

1-3. An Illustration

When there are only two decision variables, it pays off handsomely to present the problem graphically, as we can then see the problem more clearly. Let us draw (Fig. 1-1) a coordinate system with two perpen-

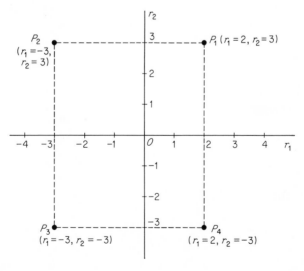

FIG. 1-1

dicular axes. Along the horizontal axis we measure r_1, along the vertical axis r_2. Consider then the point P_1. With the help of the dashed lines which have been drawn from this point parallel to the axes, we see that

P_1 is 2 units from the vertical axis and 3 units from the horizontal axis. This implies that P_1 is the graphic representation of the production program $r_1 = 2$, $r_2 = 3$.   Each point in the plane represents a production program, and each production program is represented by a point in this plane.   However, some points represent rather unusual production programs.   At point P_2, for example, we have $r_1 = -3$ and $r_2 = 3$. Apparently at P_2 a negative number of standard radios is produced, which is both impossible and mathematically excluded by the non-negativity conditions.   This holds for all points to the left of the vertical axis.   The condition $r_1 \geq 0$ requires that the point be on or to the right of the vertical axis.   Analogously, the constraint $r_2 \geq 0$ requires that the point be on or above the horizontal axis.   The points P_3 and P_4 violate

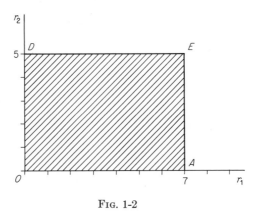

Fig. 1-2

this requirement: since their r_2 value is negative, they lie below the horizontal axis.

The two nonnegativity conditions together require that the solution be sought on or above the horizontal axis and on or to the right of the vertical axis.   This area is further restricted, however, for we must take into account the capacity restrictions of the conveyor belts, $r_1 \leq 7$ and $r_2 \leq 5$.   The point P_1 of our figure, where $r_1 = 2$, $r_2 = 3$, satisfies these inequalities.   If we had chosen a point more than 7 to the right of the vertical axis or more than 5 above the horizontal axis, we should have been in trouble, since the associated production program could not be realized.   These considerations lead to Fig. 1-2, in which the freedom of choice is limited to the shaded rectangle.

Let us once again carefully indicate how the shaded rectangle has been constructed.   The rectangle is determined by its four sides, and these sides correspond in turn to the four restrictions $r_1 \geq 0$, $r_2 \geq 0$, $r_1 \leq 7$, $r_2 \leq 5$.   In order to indicate the restriction $r_1 \leq 7$, we first draw the line along which $r_1 = 7$. This is the line AE in Fig. 1-2. For each point on AE we have $r_1 = 7$. Should we continue the line indefinitely upward and downward, it would divide the plane into two parts. Only one part is allowed by the side constraint $r_1 \leq 7$; the other part is not admissible, because $r_1 > 7$ holds for all its points. We should take a similar approach to the other inequality restrictions, first drawing the line where the corresponding equality holds. This line partitions the plane into two parts, one of which consists of all admissible points and the other of only inadmissible points.

We shall use the same procedure in drawing the constraint limiting the amount of man-days available, that is, the constraint $r_1 + 2r_2 \leq 12$.

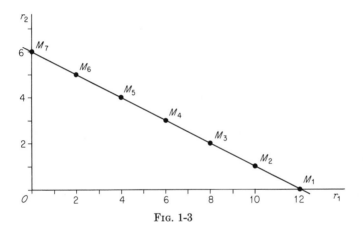

Fig. 1-3

It is rather easy to find a number of combinations of values for r_1 and r_2 such that $r_1 + 2r_2 = 12$. For example,

$$r_1 = 12, r_2 = 0 \ (12 + 2 \times 0 = 12); M_1$$
$$r_1 = 10, r_2 = 1 \ (10 + 2 \times 1 = 12); M_2$$
$$r_1 = 8, r_2 = 2 \ (8 + 2 \times 2 = 12); M_3$$
$$r_1 = 6, r_2 = 3 \ (6 + 2 \times 3 = 12); M_4$$
$$r_1 = 4, r_2 = 4 \ (4 + 2 \times 4 = 12); M_5$$
$$r_1 = 2, r_2 = 5 \ (2 + 2 \times 5 = 12); M_6$$
$$r_1 = 0, r_2 = 6 \ (0 + 2 \times 6 = 12); M_7$$

Thus, we have seven different production programs, indicated in Fig. 1-3 by the points M_1 through M_7. We see that all points lie on a straight line, which is a general property of linear equations in two variables. For example, the equations $6r_1 + r_2 = 18$ and $27r_1 + 3r_2 = 81$ are also represented by a straight line in a plane.

Because a straight line is fully determined by two points, it can be easily constructed. Generally, the easiest procedure is to determine (1) the value of r_1 when r_2 equals 0 and (2) the value of r_2 when r_1 equals 0. From these two points we can construct the whole line. In our example it would have sufficed to determine M_1 ($r_1 = 12$ when $r_2 = 0$) and M_7 ($r_2 = 6$ when $r_1 = 0$).

We now have the line M_1M_7 consisting of points for which $r_1 + 2r_2 = 12$. This line partitions the plane into two sections. For all points in the one section we have $r_1 + 2r_2 < 12$; this is the side in which we are interested. For all points in the other section we have $r_1 + 2r_2 > 12$; this is the inadmissible area. All that remains is to determine which section is the admissible one. This can simply be accomplished by verifying

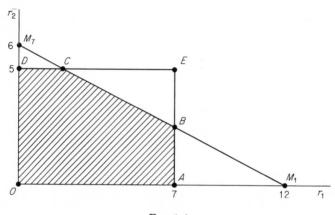

Fig. 1-4

whether the origin O (where the axes intersect and where $r_1 = 0$, $r_2 = 0$) is in the admissible or in the inadmissible section. If O lies in the admissible half, then the section containing O is the part in which we are interested. This is the case here, because $0 + 2 \times 0 < 12$. Thus for our problem we must be *under* the line M_1M_7 in Fig. 1-3.

It is time to combine the results. In view of the nonnegativity conditions and the limited capacities of the belts we cannot select a point lying outside the shaded rectangle of Fig. 1-2. Also, the point we choose must be under the line M_1M_7 to satisfy the restriction regarding the limited supply of labor. Combining these conditions, we obtain Fig. 1-4. The admissible region, or *feasible* region, has shrunk to a pentagon $OABCD$. All points outside the pentagon are inadmissible. For example, if we begin at the origin O, we can travel no further to the right than point A; if we were to proceed further, the capacity restriction of the conveyor belt for standard radios would be violated. Likewise, moving from A to B, we cannot proceed further than B, because we have no more than 12 man-days. Moving on the line BC we must stop at C, where $r_1 = 2$, $r_2 = 5$. We cannot continue further because of the capacity of the luxury conveyor belt. Left of C we find D, to the left of which the number of standard radios would be negative.

This takes care of the nonnegativity conditions and the side constraints. Our problem is to select from this feasible region a point that provides maximum profit. Consider now the objective function $20r_1 + 30r_2$ and the special case of a profit of \$60 a day. In other words, let us determine by what combinations of values r_1 and r_2 we have $20r_1 + 30r_2 = 60$. Since this is again a linear equation, it can be represented by a straight

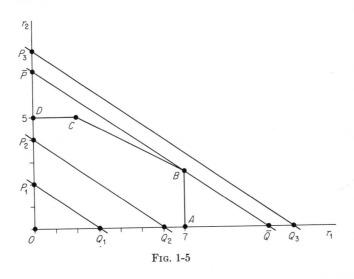

Fig. 1-5

line—the straight line through P_1 (where $r_1 = 0$, $r_2 = 2$) and Q_1 (where $r_1 = 3$, $r_2 = 0$) in Fig. 1-5. For each point on the line P_1Q_1 the total profit equals \$60 a day. The line P_1Q_1 lies partly inside and partly outside the feasible region. In the latter case the corresponding production program cannot be realized, of course.

Next consider a profit of \$120 a day. This is obtained at Q_2, where $r_1 = 6$, $r_2 = 0$, or at P_2, where $r_2 = 4$, $r_1 = 0$. Similarly, the profit is \$120 daily for all points on the line P_2Q_2. The straight line P_2Q_2 is parallel to P_1Q_1, but further from the origin. This is geometrically equivalent to stating that the profit is higher. (At the origin itself we have a zero profit.) Obviously, we want the profit line to be as far as possible from the origin, but this cannot be done blindly. Take the line P_3Q_3: For all points on P_3Q_3 we have a profit of no less than \$240, but the line has *no* point in common with the feasible region. Hence,

not a single feasible production schedule exists which yields a profit of
$240 a day. What we need to find is the profit line which is as far as
possible from the origin, but has at least one point in common with the
feasible region. This is the line $\bar{P}\bar{Q}$, and the point in question is B, which
therefore constitutes the solution to the linear programming problem.
The profit at B is $215 a day, for $7 \times 20 + 2\frac{1}{2} \times 30 = \$215$. The
maximum attainable profit is therefore $215 per day, obtained by pro-
ducing 7 standard and $2\frac{1}{2}$ luxury radios daily (5 luxury radios per 2 days).

1-4. The Solution for Different Profit Margins

Our problem has thus been solved graphically. In fact, not only *this*
problem has been solved, but also a whole class of problems obtained
by taking different values for the profit per standard or luxury radio.

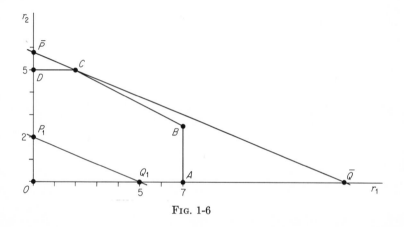

FIG. 1-6

For example, if the profit per standard radio remains $20, but the luxury
radio commands a profit of $50, a new objective function $20r_1 + 50r_2$
must be maximized. The lines PQ then become a little flatter (see
Fig. 1-6), and the new solution is C ($r_1 = 2, r_2 = 5$) rather than B ($r_1 = 7$,
$r_2 = 2\frac{1}{2}$). In the new solution 2 standard and 5 luxury radios are
produced, and the profit amounts to $2 \times 20 + 5 \times 50 = \$290$ a day.
The profit in B is only $7 \times 20 + 2\frac{1}{2} \times 50 = \$265$ a day. In the new
solution more luxury radios are produced at the expense of the number
of standard radios that are manufactured. That stands to reason, for
the profitability of luxury radios has increased compared with that of
the standard radios.

A rather remarkable situation arises when the profit margin of luxury
radios becomes $40. The expression to be maximized then becomes
$20r_1 + 40r_2$, and the profit lines PQ are parallel to BC. If one shifts
the profit line away from the origin, there will be a moment when this

line coincides with the line BC (see Fig. 1-7). Further shifts away from the origin give profit lines that have *no* point in common with the feasible region. Hence the line BC is as far away from O as is feasible. Each point on this line BC, including the points B and C themselves, gives an equal profit. At B, $7 \times 20 + 2\frac{1}{2} \times 40 = \$240$; at C, $2 \times 20 + 5 \times 40 = \$240$; and again at N on the line BC, corresponding with $r_1 = 4, r_2 = 4$, the total profit is $4 \times 20 + 4 \times 40 = \$240$. When the profit for luxury radios is \$40 and for standard radios \$20, the optimum production program is not unique. There are numerous solutions, all leading to the same total profit.

To conclude our graphical exercises, let us briefly summarize the results. In all cases which were investigated, the solution lies on the *boundary*

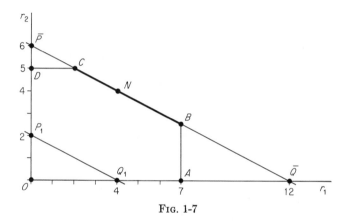

FIG. 1-7

of the feasible region, not somewhere in the middle of it. This is invariably the case in linear programming. Moreover, the solution is usually at a corner point, such as B or C. The solution may, by chance, consist of a whole line segment, but even then there is at least one corner point solution (in our example both B and C). We conclude that whatever the profit margins, the solution always includes a corner point of the feasible region.

1-5. Slack Variables

Truly interesting linear programming problems involve more than just two decision variables. Such problems, which cannot be graphically illustrated, will be our present concern.

Consider an arbitrary side condition, such as

$$x_1 + 2x_2 + 3x_3 + 4x_4 + 5x_5 \le 19$$

which might be interpreted as follows. Suppose one has only \$19 to spend on entertainment.   With that amount of money one can go

x_5 times to a restaurant, which costs \$5
x_4 times to a concert, which costs \$4
x_3 times to a theater, which costs \$3
x_2 times to a movie, which costs \$2
x_1 times to a coffee shop, which costs \$1

These variables have to be nonnegative, because one obviously cannot
go to the movies a negative number of times.   It follows from the side
constraint that one cannot go twice to a restaurant ($x_5 = 2$), twice to a
concert ($x_4 = 2$), and once to a movie ($x_2 = 1$).   Such a program requires
$2 \times 1 + 4 \times 2 + 5 \times 2 = \$20$, whereas only \$19 is available.   But
one can easily do everything once, because

$$1 \times 1 + 2 \times 1 + 3 \times 1 + 4 \times 1 + 5 \times 1 = \$15$$

which leaves \$4.

We shall now introduce a sixth variable x_6, which stands for the number
of dollars *not* spent.   The side condition is then written as an *equality*:

$$(x_1 + 2x_2 + 3x_3 + 4x_4 + 5x_5) + x_6 = 19$$

The expression in parenthesis stands for the amount of money spent,
x_6 for the dollars left over, and together they add up to \$19.   Thus, we
have transformed an inequality ($\leq$) into an equality ($=$).   This formulation as an equality is fully equivalent to the original formulation as an
inequality.   The newly introduced variable x_6 is called a *slack variable*.
When $x_6 = 0$, the full amount of money available has been spent; when
$x_6 > 0$, money is left over; $x_6 < 0$ can never occur, for this would mean
that more than \$19 was spent.   Thus, just like the original decision
variables, a slack variable cannot be negative.

By introducing slack variables we can reformulate *all* side conditions
as equalities rather than inequalities.   In the example of the radio producer, we can introduce a slack variable r_3 with the interpretation, "idle
capacity of the conveyor belt for standard radios."   Instead of

$$r_1 \leq 7$$

we then have

$$r_1 + r_3 = 7$$

stating that the sum of the *used* and *unused* capacity of that belt equals 7. Similarly, by introducing the slack variables r_4 (unused capacity on the belt for luxury radios) and r_5 (unused manpower), we obtain two other equations. As a whole,

$$
\begin{aligned}
r_1 \quad\quad + r_3 \quad\quad\quad\quad &= 7 \\
r_2 \quad + r_4 \quad &= 5 \\
r_1 + 2r_2 \quad\quad\quad + r_5 &= 12
\end{aligned}
$$

This is a system of three equations in five unknowns.   We are interested only in solutions which have nonnegative values for each of the variables, as those are the only feasible solutions.   Each such solution corresponds to a point in the pentagon of Fig. 1-4.   Conversely, every point of the

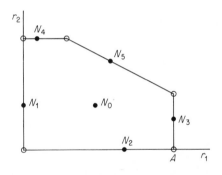

Fig. 1-8

shaded pentagon corresponds to a nonnegative solution of the equation system.   An important point to notice in this context is that for all points *within* the pentagon (*not* on the boundary), the values of the five unknowns are *positive* (not zero).   We can clarify this with an illustration (see Fig. 1-8).   For N_0 within the pentagon, all five unknowns are positive.   This is immediately evident for r_1 and r_2.   Moreover, N_0 is to the left of the vertical capacity restriction of the belt for standard radios and below the horizontal capacity restriction for the belt of luxury radios.   At N_0 both belts thus have capacity to spare, and hence r_3 and r_4 are positive. Finally, N_0 lies under the sloping line which represents the limited availability of labor.   Some labor is left idle; thus r_5 is positive also.   By contrast, at N_1 the value of r_1 is zero: no standard radios are produced. Similarly, at N_2, N_3, N_4, and N_5 all variables are positive except, respectively, r_2, r_3, r_4, and r_5, which are zero.   Thus on the sides of the pentagon one variable is exactly zero.   The corner points are situated on two sides, and for these points two variables are zero, the remaining three positive. For example, at the corner point A, $r_2 = r_3 = 0$ and r_1, r_4, and r_5 are positive.

As we have seen before, the (or at least a) solution of a linear programming problem corresponds to a corner point. We have just observed that in such a corner point only three of the five variables are positive, whereas two variables are zero. The number three is exactly equal to the number of side conditions. *This result always obtains:* When we have n decision variables and m side constraints giving rise to m slack variables ($n = 2$, $m = 3$ in the radio example), we have $n + m$ variables in total; at any corner point, m of those $n + m$ variables are positive, and the remaining n are equal to zero. There are exactly the same number of strictly positive variables in the solution of a linear programming problem as there are side constraints.

We began this chapter with a discussion of a diet problem. In that problem we had 77 decision variables; hence $n = 77$. There were 9 side constraints; hence $m = 9$. Thus there are also 9 slack variables, and the total number of variables equals $n + m = 77 + 9 = 86$. The cheapest menu contained only 9 dishes. All $77 - 9 = 68$ other foods and the 9 slack variables were exactly equal to zero in the solution. Obviously, it need not necessarily be the case that all slack variables are zero and only decision variables positive. There may also be positive slack variables in the solution, which would imply that the cheapest menu contains, for example, more than the minimum required number of calories. This would be the case if the other side constraints for fats and proteins, etc., resulted in a menu of more than the minimum required calories. If this were true, the menu would have less than 9 dishes, that is, less than 9 positive decision variables.

In this diet example the inequality restrictions were of the type "at least equal to" ($\geq$) rather than, as in the radio example, "at most equal to" ($\leq$). The slack variable is then deducted rather than added, but otherwise the procedure is exactly the same. Thus, the side constraint

$$7x_1 + 3x_2 + 2x_3 \geq 4$$

is equivalent to

$$7x_1 + 3x_2 + 2x_3 - x_4 = 4 \qquad x_4 \geq 0$$

The slack variable is then interpreted as "the extra amount of something" rather than "the unused amount of something."

1-6. The Approach of the Simplex Technique

Now we have reached the stage where we can concentrate on the actual algebraic solution technique, rather than the pictorial method which we used in the radio example.   The graphical procedure breaks down when the number of decision variables exceeds three.   It is not our intention, however, to discuss the algebra in detail; instead, we want to emphasize the basic ideas behind the approach.

We have a total of $n + m$ decision variables plus slack variables.   We are looking for corner points, and we know that in such a corner point m variables are positive and the remaining n all equal zero.   Moreover, we have m linear equations in these $n + m$ variables.   By equating n of the variables to zero, we are left with a system of m linear equations in m

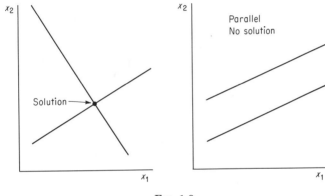

F<small>IG</small>. 1-9

unknowns.   The solution to this system then automatically gives us a corner point.   A system of m linear equations in m unknowns usually has exactly one solution.

To show this, we start by considering two linear equations in two unknowns.   When we plot the equations on a graph, we obtain two straight lines, and the unique solution is their point of intersection (see Fig. 1-9).   Difficulties only arise when, by chance, the lines run parallel or coincide.   Similarly, three linear equations in three unknowns usually have exactly one solution.   By eliminating one of the unknowns, we arrive at a situation of two equations in two unknowns.   Proceeding in this way we can conclude that, quite generally, m linear equations in m unknowns have exactly one solution.   There are, of course, exceptions— to be compared with parallel or coinciding lines—but these will not be discussed.

The procedure as outlined above is still rather laborious, because the

n variables which are chosen to be equal to zero can be chosen in many different ways. In the radio example there are $2 + 3 = 5$ variables, two of which are to be zero. By proceeding systematically we can easily enumerate all possible ways of choosing two out of five variables—mathematicians can show that there are 10 such combinations.[1] Each of the 10 systems of three equations with three unknowns must be solved in turn. Sometimes the solution gives negative values for some variables; such solutions need not be further considered. Each of the nonnegative solutions is substituted into the objective function, and the optimum solution is the one in which the objective function has the highest value.

There exists a much faster method of finding the solution to a linear programming problem. This method is known as the *simplex technique*, which is characterized by the following two properties:

1. Initially, one must find a nonnegative solution with n variables equal to zero. This is practically always the solution in which all n decision variables are equal to zero and all m slack variables are positive. In our example $r_1 = r_2 = 0, r_3 = 7, r_4 = 5, r_5 = 12$. In other words, one begins at the origin, where no radios are being produced.

2. One continues by switching variables which are zero (r_1, r_2) and variables which are positive (r_3, r_4, r_5). In each step one positive variable is exchanged for one zero variable, in such a way that the nonzero variables do not become negative *and* in such a way that the value of the objective function increases (at least does not decrease). If this last condition cannot be fulfilled—if all possible switches decrease the value of the objective function—the solution has been found.

These are the basic principles of the simplex technique. Usually there are from m to $2m$ switches before the solution has been reached. Proceeding according to the simplex rules, one finds consecutively (with $p = \text{profit} = 20r_1 + 30r_2$):

(1) $\qquad\qquad r_1 = 0, r_2 = 0, r_3 = 7, r_4 = 5, r_5 = 12$
$\qquad\qquad\qquad$ (the origin O, $p = 0$)

(2) $\qquad\qquad r_1 = 0, r_2 = 5, r_3 = 7, r_4 = 0, r_5 = 2$
$\qquad\qquad\qquad$ (the point D, $p = 150$)

---

[1] One may be inclined to think that there are only five such combinations because Fig. 1-8 contains only five corner points. There are, however, more, because there is also an intersection between the vertical axis and the line representing the labor restriction, and so on. (Of the mentioned 10 possibilities, two are missing in this case, because there are two pairs of parallel lines.)

(3) $r_1 = 2, r_2 = 5, r_3 = 5, r_4 = 0, r_5 = 0$
                       (the point C, $p = 190$)
(4) $r_1 = 7, r_2 = 2\frac{1}{2}, r_3 = 0, r_4 = 2\frac{1}{2}, r_5 = 0$
                       (the point B, $p = 215$).

Thus the maximum value has been found after four steps. Using the simplex technique, one moves from one corner point to an adjacent corner point in such a way that the value of the objective function increases, as illustrated in Fig. 1-10.

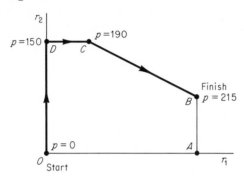

FIG. 1-10

1-7. What Is the Price of a Side Constraint?

In the example of the radio manufacturer the best production schedule turned out to be $r_1 = 7$, $r_2 = 2\frac{1}{2}$ ($r_3 = 0$, $r_4 = 2\frac{1}{2}$, $r_5 = 0$). Such a production program uses the full capacity of the belt for standard radios, the available labor is also fully occupied, but the belt for luxury radios operates at only 50 per cent of capacity. Even if the producer had a larger capacity available for the production of luxury radios, his maximum profit would not increase, since there is already idle capacity in the present situation. Thus, an extra unit capacity on the luxury belt is of *no value* to the producer; indeed, one unit capacity less on that belt would not cost him a penny.

The situation is different for the standard radio belt. If on this belt 8 instead of 7 radios could be produced per day, the solution would certainly be changed. When in Fig. 1-5 the line AB is moved one unit to the right, the new optimum solution is clearly to produce 8 standard and 2 luxury radios daily. (One cannot continue to produce $2\frac{1}{2}$ luxury radios in view of the labor restriction.) The total profit now adds up to

$$8 \times 20 + 2 \times 30 = \$220 \text{ a day}$$

This is $5 more than the $215 profit in the previous situation, so we conclude that one extra unit capacity on the belt of standard radios has a value of $5 a day.   Labor also has a definite value for the manufacturer. One extra man-day enables him to produce 7 standard and 3 luxury radios.   (It can be verified graphically that this is indeed the optimum production program if 13 man-days are available.)   This leads to a profit of $7 \times 20 + 3 \times 30 = \$230$, i.e., an extra profit of $15 per day.   We conclude that one man-day has a value of $15 for this manufacturer.   If he can employ an extra man for less than $15 a day, he is well advised to do so.

An analogous line of reasoning can be given for the diet problem.   We had to find the cheapest menu satisfying a number of minimum requirements for calories, etc.   It is now quite legitimate to ask how much cheaper the menu would be if we were willing to relax these requirements. For example, assume that we should be willing to accept a menu with one less calorie.   The cost of the new optimum menu will then probably be lower.   If it becomes a penny cheaper, the cost of the last calorie is one penny.   On the other hand, it is possible that the cost of the menu does not decrease.   This happens when as a result of the requirements for vitamins, proteins, etc., the original requirement of 800,000 calories is more than fulfilled.   In such a case the same menu will be bought even if we relax the calorie requirement, for the calorie restriction does not increase the cost of the menu.   In short, the restriction costs nothing.

The simplex technique has the admirable quality of giving, together with the solution, the price or cost of the restrictions as well.   That is, the following question is answered: "If one more unit of some scarce resource were available, by how much would the value of the objective function increase?"   Or: "If one less unit of some requirement were needed, by how much would the value of the objective function decrease?"   Such a price is invariably zero if in the optimum solution the slack variable associated with the restriction is positive rather than zero, for in that case the restriction is amply satisfied and does not cost a penny.

We emphasize that we are concerned here with small additions or reductions, indicated by *one* unit more or less.   Suppose that the radio producer employs 10 extra men for a total of $100 a day.   He believes this to be profitable, because one extra employee enables him to make an extra profit of $15.   Does it necessarily follow, however, that when one employee increases profits by $15 a day, 10 employees will increase the profit by $150?   No, not necessarily, because it is possible (and likely, in the case of large changes) that side conditions that were originally amply satisfied will become bottlenecks.   This is the case here.   As long as a new employee can be put to work at the belt for luxury radios, he can be gainfully employed and contributes an extra $15 to the daily profit—but this can only be done on a limited scale.   If five more men are offered a job, the luxury belt—as the belt for standard radios—is occupied to capacity. There are then 17 employees in total, both belts are fully used, and further additions to the labor force do not increase the profit. In view of this type of problem, i.e., new bottlenecks, only small additions or deductions of any one factor can be considered.

1-8. Betting at Saratoga

A linear programming problem is characterized by three requirements:

1. There should be a function, linear in a number of decision variables, which has to be maximized or minimized.
2. These decision variables may not assume negative values.
3. They must satisfy a number of linear side conditions, usually in the form of inequalities. (Sometimes a number of side conditions are in the form of equations. We can then save the trouble of introducing slack variables, but the problem is not essentially altered.)

These requirements determine the structure of the problem. However simple this structure may be, it leaves ample opportunity for a whole range of problems in vastly different areas. Often the most difficult exercise is to recognize a given problem as a linear programming problem. After this has been done and the problem has been formulated correctly in the linear programming framework, the actual solution is usually a matter of routine. We shall give two examples, in which we emphasize the formulation of the problem.

Our first example is betting at Saratoga. The crux of the matter is to pinpoint the horse that will win. One can bet on that horse, and if it wins, a certain multiple of the original stake is paid out. If the horse loses, the stake is lost. Suppose that four horses are running—White, Brown, Grey, and Dapple. The payoff is such that a one-dollar bet on

White, if White wins, pays out $3
Brown, if Brown wins, pays out $4
Grey, if Grey wins, pays out $5
Dapple, if Dapple wins, pays out $6

The net profit on the dollar bet is the payoff minus the original dollar.

Let us assume that you have $57 at your disposal. The question "to bet or not to bet" has been answered in the affirmative, and the only question remaining, therefore, is how to bet. That depends on your expectations. If you are *certain* that Brown will win, you should, of course, bet $57 on Brown. But you may not be so clairvoyant. It may well be that you do not have the foggiest notion which horse will win. What should you do then? Perhaps you reason, as an optimist, that since you do not know anything anyway, it is nice to bet on Dapple. After all, if Dapple wins, you get paid out $57 \times 6 = \$342$ for a \$57 bet. No other horse gives such favorable odds, but this should also make you suspicious. Apparently the experts do not have much faith in Dapple. According to this argument, it might be wise to bet on White, the horse which the experts judge most likely to win. But even if you bet on White, the chances are that you will lose \$57. And if you win, your net profit is only \$114. Just imagine your frustration when you bet on White and it turns out that, after all, Dapple does win the race. You could have won $342 - 57 = \$285$, and you let the opportunity slip by.

But now consider the following line of reasoning. Because you have no idea whatsoever which horse will win, you are well advised to provide for the most unfavorable situation that may arise. Pessimistic? Conservative? Yes, somewhat. If you decide to insure your house against fire, however, you cover yourself against the most unfavorable situation that may occur. This philosophy will determine our action; it leads to a rather beautiful linear programming problem.

The decision variables in this problem are the amounts of money to bet on White, Brown, Grey, and Dapple. For these amounts we write x_W, x_B, x_G, and x_D. They cannot be negative and have to satisfy

$$x_W + x_B + x_G + x_D = 57$$

because your total capital is \$57. The objective is to bet in such a way as to maximize the net profit even if the horse you would least like to win in fact does win. In more technical terms, we want to maximize the minimum gain.

Let us first express the net profit when one bets x_W on White, x_B on Brown, x_G on Grey, and x_D on Dapple. The profit obviously depends upon the winning horse. If White wins, only the dollars bet on White result in a payoff. The payoff is $3x_W$, because the odds for White are 3 to 1. A net profit of $3x_W - 57$ remains after deducting the original outlay for the bet. (This profit is negative when x_W is smaller than 19; in that case it is a loss.) If we repeat this argument for the other three possibilities, we get the following results:

If White wins, the profit equals $3x_W - 57$
If Brown wins, the profit equals $4x_B - 57$
If Grey wins, the profit equals $5x_G - 57$
If Dapple wins, the profit equals $6x_D - 57$

The object is to determine x_W, x_B, x_G, and x_D so as to maximize the minimum of these four possible profits. We shall write M for this minimum. The four profits are each at least equal to M, as follows from the definition of a minimum. Thus

$$3x_W - 57 \geq M$$
$$4x_B - 57 \geq M$$
$$5x_G - 57 \geq M$$
$$6x_D - 57 \geq M$$

Introducing nonnegative slack variables y_W, y_B, y_G, and y_D, we obtain

$$3x_W - 57 - y_W = M$$
$$4x_B - 57 - y_B = M$$
$$5x_G - 57 - y_G = M$$
$$6x_D - 57 - y_D = M$$

Adding these four equations, we get

$$3x_W + 4x_B + 5x_G + 6x_D - 228 - y_W - y_B - y_G - y_D = 4M$$

We can simplify this result a little bit by taking into account that the x values add up to 57; hence

$$228 = 4x_W + 4x_B + 4x_G + 4x_D$$

Substituting this result into the previous equation gives us

$$4M = -x_W + x_G + 2x_D - y_W - y_B - y_G - y_D$$

Thus we can express M in the decision and slack variables as follows:

$$M = \tfrac{1}{4}(-x_W + x_G + 2x_D - y_W - y_B - y_G - y_D)$$

This is the objective function to be maximized.

The problem has now been formulated as a linear programming problem. We have a linear objective function which must be maximized subject to side conditions.[1] Although we are actually more concerned with the

---

[1] There are four side conditions. The first states that the x values add up to 57. The other three imply that

$$3x_W - 57 - y_W \quad 4x_B - 57 - y_B \quad 5x_G - 57 - y_G \quad 6x_D - 57 - y_D$$

are all equal to each other, because they are all equal to M.

formulation than with the solution of the problem, it might be interesting
to note that the optimum solution is

$x_W = 20$ (the profit is $3x_W - 57 = 60 - 57 = 3$ if White wins)
$x_B = 15$ (the profit is $4x_B - 57 = 60 - 57 = 3$ if Brown wins)
$x_G = 12$ (the profit is $5x_G - 57 = 60 - 57 = 3$ if Grey wins)
$x_D = 10$ (the profit is $6x_D - 57 = 60 - 57 = 3$ if Dapple wins)

If \$57 is divided in this way, one can be sure to receive \$60, whichever
horse wins. One can then be certain of a profit of \$3. This can be com-
pared with fire insurance on your house for \$30,000. The risk of losing
\$30,000 is exchanged for the certainty of losing the insurance premium.
In the chapter on game theory we shall come back to this point.

1-9. A Manufacturer

Our second example concerns a manufacturer who wants to minimize
his production cost. To prevent complications, assume that only one
product is being produced and that the demand for the product is known
in advance:

20 units in the first quarter
30 units in the second quarter
50 units in the third quarter
60 units in the fourth quarter

This cycle repeats itself every year. There is a seasonal pattern, stable
in the course of time. The pattern of demand is depicted in Fig. 1-11.

Each year the manufacturer must produce $20 + 30 + 50 + 60 = 160$
units. The manufacturer's objective is to schedule the production over
the various quarters so as to minimize the production cost. His decision
variables are the level of production in each quarter. These decision
variables will be indicated by $x(t)$; thus $x(1)$ is the production volume in
the first quarter, $x(2)$ in the second quarter, . . . , $x(17)$ in the seven-
teenth quarter. Since there is periodicity in the problem, the decisions
will be the same from year to year; hence $x(1) = x(5)$, $x(2) = x(6)$, etc.
There are then really only four decision variables, $x(1)$ to $x(4)$, and we
note at the outset that none of these variables can assume negative values.

Two types of production costs can be distinguished. The first includes
the overhead and the costs associated with the physical production of
160 units. These costs cannot be influenced by the decision variables
here considered and can therefore be disregarded in the present problem.
The second category can be influenced by the choice of the values for the

decision variables and consists of two parts:

1. *Inventory costs:* Each unit remaining in inventory at the end of a quarter costs \$8. The initial inventory, that is, the inventory at the beginning of the first quarter, is zero.[1]

2. *Adjustment costs:* At the beginning of each quarter t, the machines have to be adjusted to the production level in that quarter $x(t)$. Each unit difference in the production level of two consecutive quarters costs the manufacturer \$5. If $x(3) = 50$ and $x(4) = 40$, this change costs the manufacturer $(50 - 40) \times 5 = \$50$. These costs are the same in the reverse case, when the production increases from $x(3) = 40$ to $x(4) = 50$.

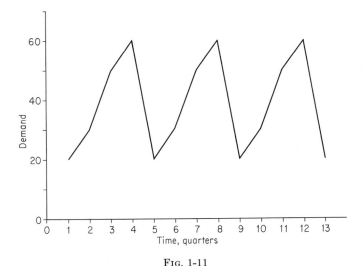

FIG. 1-11

Let us now imagine that the manufacturer has employed two university graduates, an economist and an engineer, to advise him on the production schedule. The economist has been taught that inventories are costly, and he is inclined to advise that, in each quarter, production should equal demand. The engineer has learned in college that it is extremely convenient for the production manager to leave the level of output unchanged through time. He advises the production of 40 units per quarter, hence 160 over the whole year.

What is the cost of each of these plans? The economist's suggestion would lead to zero inventory costs, but to substantial adjustment costs. To be specific, from the first to the second quarter demand, and hence production, would increase by 10 units, from 20 to 30. This costs

---

[1] There is no need for a buffer stock when demand is known.

$10 \times 5 = \$50$.   From the second to the third quarter there is an increase of 20 units (from 30 to 50), hence \$100 in adjustment costs.   There are \$50 in adjustment costs from the third to the, fourth quarter when production rises from 50 to 60 units.   From the fourth to the fifth quarter demand, and hence production, diminishes by 40 units (from 60 to 20), which results in adjustment costs of \$200.   The total yearly adjustment costs add up to

$$50 + 100 + 50 + 200 = \$400$$

Since inventory costs have been avoided, this is also the total production cost (which is defined here as the sum of inventory and adjustment costs).

The engineer's program avoids adjustment costs but results in rather large inventory costs.   To determine these, one must first compute the inventory at the end of each quarter.   The initial inventory equals zero. During the first quarter 40 units are produced, of which only 20 are sold. The remaining 20 units make up the inventory at the end of the first quarter.   Thus, we begin the second quarter with 20 units.   During that second quarter, once again 40 units are produced, of which 30 are sold. The remainder of 10 is added to the initial inventory of 20, resulting in a final inventory of $20 + 10 = 30$ at the end of the second quarter.   In the third and fourth quarters the production of 40 units is less than sales (50 and 60, respectively), and the balance is supplied from the inventory. At the end of the fourth quarter the inventory is zero again, and the cycle starts anew.   A complete survey of the first four quarters is given below:

Quarter	Sales	Production	Inventory at the end of quarter (initial inventory + production − sales)
1	20	40	$0 + 40 - 20 = 20$
2	30	40	$20 + 40 - 30 = 30$
3	50	40	$30 + 40 - 50 = 20$
4	60	40	$20 + 40 - 60 = 0$

The final inventories of the four successive quarters are thus 20, 30, 20, and 0.   Since the cost per unit is \$8, yearly inventory costs are

$$8 \times 20 + 8 \times 30 + 8 \times 20 + 8 \times 0 = \$560$$

Adjustment costs are zero in this case, so that \$560 is the total production cost.

These are the two extreme cases.   We can reasonably assume that the optimum will be a mixture of the two programs. We shall then have *some* inventory costs and *some* adjustment costs, but their *sum* will be less than the $400 of the one extreme and certainly less than the $560 of the other extreme. To find this optimum, we must first express the inventory and adjustment costs in terms of the decision variables $x(t)$. The inventory costs can be determined from the following table:

Quarter	Sales	Production	Inventory at the end of quarter (initial inventory + production − sales)
1	20	$x(1)$	$0 + x(1) - 20 = x(1) - 20$
2	30	$x(2)$	$[x(1) - 20] + x(2) - 30 = x(1) + x(2) - 50$
3	50	$x(3)$	$[x(1) + x(2) - 50] + x(3) - 50 = x(1) + x(2) + x(3) - 100$
4	60	$x(4)$	$[x(1) + x(2) + x(3) - 100] + x(4) - 60 = 0$

The final inventory at the end of the last quarter is always zero, since $x(1) + x(2) + x(3) + x(4) = 160$. Because each unit in inventory at the end of a quarter costs $8, the total inventory costs per year equal

$$8[x(1) - 20 + x(1) + x(2) - 50 + x(1) + x(2) + x(3) - 100]$$
$$= 24x(1) + 16x(2) + 8x(3) - 1{,}360$$

This is the expression which gives the inventory costs in terms of the decision variables. It may be verified that if $x(1) = x(2) = x(3) = x(4) = 40$, the costs are $560.

The adjustment costs are determined by the differences in production in successive quarters, $x(2) - x(1)$, $x(3) - x(2)$, $x(4) - x(3)$, and $x(5) - x(4)$. We must first determine the sign (plus, zero, or minus) of these successive differences. Can we say something about the sign of $x(2) - x(1)$ in the optimum production schedule? Take the case $x(1) = 40$, $x(2) = 20$, so that production in the first quarter exceeds production in the second quarter. Let us compare this case with $x(1) = 30$, $x(2) = 30$ when the total production during the two quarters is also 60, but now differently distributed over the two quarters. The latter case is clearly more advantageous from the point of view of adjustment costs between the two quarters (zero as compared to $100), but it is also more advantageous as far as inventory costs are concerned. To verify this, we should realize that the inventory at the end of the second quarter is the same in both cases. The difference is to be found in the inventory at the end of the first quarter, which equals $x(1) - 20$. This inventory is larger in the first case when $x(1) = 40$ than in the second case when $x(1) = 30$. Thus, from the point of view of both adjustment costs and inventory costs, the second schedule is to be preferred. Quite generally, as far as adjustment costs are concerned, the production schedule should be as constant as possible, and, as far as inventory costs are concerned, production should coincide with the demand—or at least move as much as possible in the same direction, surely not in the opposite direction.

These considerations (whose rigor could be improved, but only at the expense of many more lines) lead to the conclusion that in the optimal solution $x(2)$ will not be less than $x(1)$. Thus, there will be adjustment costs equal to $5[x(2) - x(1)]$ and *not* $5[x(1) - x(2)]$. The adjustment costs for the next two quarters equal $5[x(3) - x(2)]$ and $5[x(4) - x(3)]$, respectively. The sales increase during these quarters, and hence, if $x(3)$ differs from $x(2)$, it will be higher; if $x(4)$ differs from $x(3)$, it will also be higher. In the fifth quarter sales drop sharply from 60 to 20; hence production will (if anything) decrease, and the adjustment costs will equal $5[x(4) - x(5)]$ rather than $5[x(5) - x(4)]$. When we recall that $x(5)$ equals $x(1)$, we find that the total adjustment costs for the year are

$$5[x(2) - x(1) + x(3) - x(2) + x(4) - x(3) + x(4) - x(1)]$$
$$= -10x(1) + 10x(4)$$

Again, it can be verified that when $x(1) = 20$, $x(2) = 30$, $x(3) = 50$, and $x(4) = 60$, the result is \$400.

The sum of inventory and adjustment costs equals

$$24x(1) + 16x(2) + 8x(3) - 1{,}360 - 10x(1) + 10x(4)$$
$$= 14x(1) + 16x(2) + 8x(3) + 10x(4) - 1{,}360$$

This is the linear objective function which is to be minimized. The number 1,360 is a constant which plays no role in the minimization process, since it cannot be influenced by the decision variables.

To show that we do indeed have a linear programming problem with four decision variables, we must still consider the side conditions. The nonnegativity conditions have already been mentioned. There is also the condition that the sum of the decision variables should equal 160, which is a linear equation. Furthermore, when we assume that inventories cannot be negative, we have the restrictions

$$\begin{aligned} x(1) &\geq 20 \\ x(1) + x(2) &\geq 50 \\ x(1) + x(2) + x(3) &\geq 100 \end{aligned}$$

These linear inequalities follow immediately from the formulas for final inventory which have been derived on page 25. Finally, we added the following constraints at the beginning of page 26:

$$x(2) \geq x(1) \quad x(3) \geq x(2) \quad x(4) \geq x(3) \quad x(4) \geq x(1)$$

These are all linear inequalities, so that we have indeed a linear programming problem.

The solution can be calculated by the simplex procedure. The result is that 25 units should be produced in the first two quarters and 55 units in the last two quarters. This implies that adjustment costs are incurred only twice a year—at the end of the second and fourth quarters. Adjustment costs each time are $5 \times 30 = \$150$; the total adjustment costs are therefore equal to \$300 per year. The inventory survey is as follows:

Quarter	Sales	Production	Inventory at the end of quarter (initial inventory + production − sales)
1	20	25	0 + 25 − 20 = 5
2	30	25	5 + 25 − 30 = 0
3	50	55	0 + 55 − 50 = 5
4	60	55	5 + 55 − 60 = 0

The inventory costs are $8(5 + 0 + 5 + 0) = \$80$ a year. Total production cost is then $300 + 80 = \$380$ a year. This is \$20 below the cost

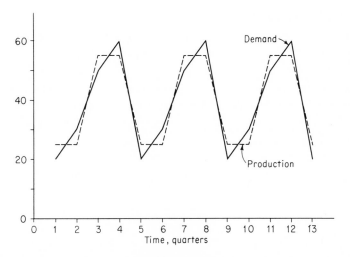

Fig. 1-12

suggested by the economist, which resulted from a complete adaptation of production to sales in each quarter.   Figure 1-12 is a graph of demand and production through time.

Literature

The simplex technique is due to G. B. Dantzig [1].   Actually, the Russian mathematician L. Kantorovich had given a closely related solution technique as early as 1939, but this passed unnoticed in the West until about 1955.   His original work has now been translated [2].   The diet problem is taken from Stigler [3].   The production scheduling problem was first discussed by Hoffman and Jacobs [4] and since then by many others.   The betting problem is, to the best of our knowledge, due to Vajda [5].   Vajda's book may serve as an introduction to linear programming.   A somewhat easier and very lucid text has been written by Gass [6].   Charnes and Cooper [7] have written a standard work with many applications and examples and complete references (up to 1960).   A more recent book by Dantzig [8] is also required reading for all professionals in the field.

[1] G. B. Dantzig, "Maximization of a Linear Function of Variables Subject to Linear Inequalities," chap. 21, in T. C. Koopmans (ed.), *Activity Analysis of Production and Allocation*, John Wiley & Sons, Inc., New York, 1951.
[2] L. Kantorovich, "Mathematical Methods of Organizing and Planning Production," *Management Science*, vol. 6 (1960), pp. 366–422.
[3] G. J. Stigler, "The Cost of Subsistence," *Journal of Farm Economics*, vol. 27 (1945), pp. 303–314.
[4] A. J. Hoffman and W. W. Jacobs, "Smooth Patterns of Production," *Management Science*, vol. 1 (1954), pp. 86–91.
[5] S. Vajda, *Mathematical Programming*, Addison-Wesley Publishing Company, Inc., Reading, Mass., 1961.
[6] S. I. Gass, *Linear Programming*, McGraw-Hill Book Company, New York, 1958; 2d ed., 1964.
[7] A. Charnes and W. W. Cooper, *Management Models and Industrial Applications of Linear Programming*, John Wiley & Sons, Inc., New York, 1961, 2 vols.
[8] G. B. Dantzig, *Linear Programming and Extensions*, Princeton University Press, Princeton, N.J., 1963.

The textbooks discuss much more than linear programming, the simplex technique, and some applications.   For example, they discuss *degeneracy* and the difficulties to which that gives rise.   Degeneracy occurs when at a certain moment *less than m* (the number of side conditions) variables are positive, rather than *exactly m*, as usual. They also discuss *integer programming*, a programming problem in which the decision variables can only assume integer values.   This frequently arises in practice, because half a plane cannot fly and half a salesman cannot travel.   They also discuss extensions to quadratic programming, which differs from linear programming in that the objective function is quadratic.

The textbooks explain other solution techniques besides the simplex solution. Some of these are very efficient for specific problems, such as the transportation problem which we shall discuss at length in Chap. 2.

2

The Optimum Path and the Critical Path

2-1. Fire!

We shall begin this chapter by sketching the outline of an important application of linear programming. Our example will be a transportation problem. Although this type of problem can be solved with the help of the conventional simplex technique, more efficient methods have been developed, which we shall discuss and illustrate.

In the city of Phoenix, Arizona (the example is fictitious), there are three fire stations, located in the southern, eastern, and western parts of the city. These stations have 2, 3, and 4 fire engines, respectively, which can leave at a half minute's notice. For a small fire 1 fire engine is sufficient; for a normal fire 3 fire engines will do; for a real conflagration 5 fire engines are required. (These 5 cannot all come from the same station, since even the largest contains only 4 fire engines.)

There is also, of course, a superintendent of the fire brigade. He is at the town hall behind a desk with three telephones—a green one for a small fire, a white one for a middle-sized fire, and a red one for a major fire. The chief's duty consists of directing the fire engines to the fires. He will phone the fire station closest to the fire so as to have the fire engines at the spot as fast as possible.

At a certain moment—which the fire chief will long, long remember— the three telephones ring simultaneously. The green one reports a small fire in the center of town, the white one reports a middle-sized fire in the southern part, and the red one reports a huge fire in the northern part. The fire chief is now faced with the question of how to direct the fire engines out of the various stations to the respective fires so as to minimize the total number of miles to be driven. Hence, it is a minimization problem. Moreover, there are side conditions, which we shall formulate by referring to the following table:

		Center fire 1, 1	South fire 2, 3	North fire 3, 5
South station 1	2	5	2	9
East station 2	3	3	8	6
West station 3	4	2	5	7

In this table we have written in the left-hand column the number of fire engines available in each station. In the top row we have recorded the number of engines required at each fire. In the table the distances have been given. The distance between the east station and the north fire, for example, is 6 miles; between the west station and the south fire, 5 miles.

The decision variables of this problem are the *number* of engines to be directed from a given station to a given fire. To keep the notation manageable, we shall indicate the south, east, and west stations by 1, 2, and 3, respectively, as indicated in the table. Also, the center, south, and north fires will be indicated by 1, 2, and 3. Then we write x_{11} for the number of engines directed from the south station to the center fire. The *first* index tells *from* which station the engine is being sent; the *second* index states *to* which fire the engine is being sent. Thus, x_{23} stands for the number of engines directed from east station 2 to north fire 3.

The objective function can now be formulated with the aid of the nine decision variables x_{11}, x_{12}, . . . , x_{33} and the data given in the table. We see immediately that the x_{11} engines that go from 1 to 1 each travel 5 miles, hence $5x_{11}$ miles in total. The x_{12} engines from 1 to 2 each drive 2 miles, $2x_{12}$ in total, and so on. In the end all distances have to be added. The objective function, which gives the total number of miles to be driven, is then

$$5x_{11} + 2x_{12} + 9x_{13} + 3x_{21} + 8x_{22} + 6x_{23} + 2x_{31} + 5x_{32} + 7x_{33}$$

This function is to be minimized. The side conditions can be easily formulated. All engines will have to leave their stations, because there are 9 engines required at the fires, and there are, in total, 9 engines in the stations. We have now as constraints:

$$x_{11} + x_{12} + x_{13} = 2 \qquad (1)$$
(the number of engines directed from south station 1 is 2)
$$x_{21} + x_{22} + x_{23} = 3 \qquad (2)$$
(the number of engines directed from east station 2 is 3)
$$x_{31} + x_{32} + x_{33} = 4 \qquad (3)$$
(the number of engines directed from west station 3 is 4)

These are the conditions which follow from the number of engines in the stations. Furthermore, we have similar restrictions because of the number of engines required at the various fires:

$$x_{11} + x_{21} + x_{31} = 1 \qquad (4)$$
(the number of engines to be sent to center fire 1 is 1)
$$x_{12} + x_{22} + x_{32} = 3 \qquad (5)$$
(the number of engines to be sent to south fire 2 is 3)
$$x_{13} + x_{23} + x_{33} = 5 \qquad (6)$$
(the number of engines to be sent to north fire 3 is 5)

Finally, the decision variables cannot be negative. It is thus a clear example of a linear programming problem. The side conditions are ·already formulated as equations rather than inequalities. We know from the previous chapter that inequalities are, with the help of slack variables, reformulated as equations. This step can be omitted here, as we have no need for slack variables.

It seems that we have a problem with nine nonnegative decision variables and six side conditions, but this is not quite true. For *one* of the side conditions follows automatically given the remaining *five*, so that in fact we have only five side conditions. This can be seen as follows: When we add the first three side conditions and deduct the fourth and the fifth, we get the sixth. In other words, we can confine ourselves to the first five side conditions; the sixth is then automatically satisfied. (We can also take the last five rather than the first five side constraints. The first then automatically follows.[1])

Thus, we have a linear programming problem with nine variables and five equalities as side conditions. From the previous chapter we then know that in the solution we shall have five positive variables—the other four will be zero. However, should the fire chief try to solve this problem with the aid of the conventional simplex technique, not only the burning houses themselves but all adjacent buildings will have burnt to ashes before even one engine leaves its station. A faster method is required. This method will also show that the solution always consists of integer numbers, which is very fortunate. Just suppose for an instant that the linear programming solution showed that $1\frac{1}{2}$ engines should go from the south station to the south fire and the remaining $\frac{1}{2}$ engine from the south station to the center fire. How would we have interpreted this result? Luckily, this will never happen in a transportation problem.

---

[1] The argument is slightly different when there are more fire engines than needed to fight the fires. This case can be simply dealt with when we introduce slack variables standing for the number of engines kept in the stations.

We have constructed a somewhat farfetched example of a transportation problem, but one should realize, this example notwithstanding, that the problem is of a general nature. (For example, how many tankers will transport how much oil from which source to which refinery?) Quite generally, whenever there are different production centers and distribution centers managed by the same company, there are transportation problems.

2-2. The Northwest Corner Rule

One of the convenient aspects of a transportation problem is that it is very easy to find an initial solution which (1) satisfies all side conditions and (2) has as many positive variables as there are side conditions. (Recall that the number of side conditions is one less than the number of stations plus the number of fires.) We can illustrate this with the fire example if we make, once again, a table with the available fire engines in the left-hand column and the required number of fire engines in the top row.

	1	3	5
2	.	.	.
3	.	.	.
4	.	.	.

The numbers with which we replace the dots are the numbers of fire engines which go from a given station to a given fire. These are the values for the decision variables, and we select them according to the aptly named northwest corner rule. We start at the northwest point, corresponding to x_{11}, the number of engines that go from station 1 to fire 1. We then move to the right and down, until we are at x_{33}, the number of engines going from station 3 to fire 3. The procedure, which will be explained in detail below, derives its importance from its simplicity.

Station 1 contains 2 fire engines; fire 1 needs 1 engine. For the first step we send the maximum, in this case 1 engine, hence $x_{11} = 1$. Fire 1 is now taken care of and should not receive any further engines from the other fire stations. This completes the first column, and the table now looks as follows:

	1	3	5
2	1	.	.
3	0	.	.
4	0	.	.

For the second step we observe that station 1 still contains 1 fire engine. This is sent to fire 2, so that a 1 appears immediately to the right of the 1 in the given table. There are no more engines left at station 1, so the first row is now complete, as well as the first column. In full we have:

	1	3	5
2	1	1	0
3	0	·	·
4	0	·	·

In the third step the new northwest corner is the point x_{22}. Fire 2 has already received 1 engine from station 1, so it needs 2 more. These are available from station 2, so we fill in $x_{22} = 2$. The second column is now also complete, since fire 2 has received the required 3 engines:

	1	3	5
2	1	1	0
3	0	2	·
4	0	0	·

In the fourth step we send the remaining engine of station 2 to fire 3. The second row is then complete, and station 2 is empty:

	1	3	5
2	1	1	0
3	0	2	1
4	0	0	·

In the fifth and last step we dispatch 4 fire engines from station 3 to fire 3. The whole table is then complete:

	1	3	5
2	1	1	0
3	0	2	1
4	0	0	4

We thus have indeed a solution with exactly five positive numbers. We add the following comments:

1. We cannot in the first step fill in a 2 in the northwest corner, so as to make the first row complete, for then $x_{11} = 2$, but $x_{11} + x_{21} + x_{31} = 1$, so x_{21} or x_{31} would be negative.   In other words, of the two, row or column, we complete the one requiring the smallest number to be completed.[1]

2. Because at each stage either a row or a column is completed, there are, at most, six positive numbers.   We showed above, however, that as soon as five side conditions are satisfied, the sixth is automatically satisfied.   Hence, when we complete the fifth side constraint, the sixth is completed at the same step, so we have at most five positive numbers in the end.

Other examples:

	4	1	2	10			4	1	2	10
2	·	·	·	·		2	2	0	0	0
6	·	·	·	·	→	6	2	1	2	1
9	·	·	·	·		9	0	0	0	9

	1	2	8			1	2	8
5	·	·	·		5	1	2	2
4	·	·	·	→	4	0	0	4
1	·	·	·		1	0	0	1
1	·	·	·		1	0	0	1

In both examples the sum of the numbers in the left-hand column equals the sum of the numbers in the top row.   In both, the number of stations plus the number of fires equals seven.   We need not be surprised that there are six positive numbers in the answer.

The northwest corner rule is quite simple, but totally disregards the given distances.   It is therefore to be expected that the solution reached requires too much travel.   In the present case, the solution given under the fifth step is $x_{11} = 1$, $x_{12} = 1$, $x_{22} = 2$, $x_{23} = 1$, and $x_{33} = 4$, while $x_{13} = x_{21} = x_{31} = x_{32} = 0$.   The total number of miles required for this solution is

$$5 \times 1 + 2 \times 1 + 8 \times 2 + 6 \times 1 + 7 \times 4 = 57$$

The question comes to mind whether it is possible to find an initial solu-

---

[1] It can happen that a row and a column need the same number to be completed. This happens invariably in the last step, but sometimes also in the middle.   If this happens, the procedure continues by considering routinely the point in the northwest corner which is not yet filled in.   The final solution has then, however, less than five positive numbers.   This leads to some complications, which are not very serious.

tion which requires fewer miles.   To find this, we use the given table of distances:

	1	3	5
2	5	2	9
3	3	8	6
4	2	5	7

	1	3	5
2	·	·	·
3	·	·	·
4	·	·	·

It stands to reason to begin with the shortest route; in this case there are two shortest routes, from station 1 to fire 2 and from station 3 to fire 1. We choose the first and make $x_{12} = 2$, so as to complete the first row. Having filled in x_{12}, we try to complete either the first row or the second column; i.e., we continue until one of them is complete.   In this example, as the first row is completed first, we next want to complete the second column by making x_{22} or x_{32} positive.   Of these two we choose the one with the shorter distance, in this case x_{32}.   (The distance 5 is less than the distance 8.)   Quite generally, after starting at the shortest route, we continue by dispatching engines (1) *from* that station in which some engines remained at the end of the previous step or *to* that fire which received some but not enough engines at the end of the previous step and (2) along the shortest possible route.   Thus, in two consecutive steps we remain either in the same row or in the same column—which, incidentally, we also do in the northwest corner rule.   Following these instructions, we easily obtain as the result:

	1	3	5
2	0	2	0
3	0	0	3
4	1	1	2

The total distance in miles needed for this program is

$$2 \times 2 + 6 \times 3 + 2 \times 1 + 5 \times 1 + 7 \times 2 = 43$$

which is, compared with 57, a rather substantial improvement.   Can it still be improved upon, or is this the optimum solution?   This is the question that will concern us in the next section.

2-3. Conditions for the Optimum Solution

The following theorem is used to verify whether a given solution is the optimum one: The optimum solution of a transportation problem does not change when *all* numbers in a row or a column of the table of distances are increased or decreased by the same number. Take, for example, our original table of distances:

$$
\begin{array}{c|ccc}
 & 1 & 3 & 5 \\
\hline
2 & 5 & 2 & 9 \\
3 & 3 & 8 & 6 \\
4 & 2 & 5 & 7 \\
\end{array}
\qquad \text{(I)}
$$

If we deduct 2 from all entries in the bottom row, we obtain:

$$
\begin{array}{c|ccc}
 & 1 & 3 & 5 \\
\hline
2 & 5 & 2 & 9 \\
3 & 3 & 8 & 6 \\
4 & 0 & 3 & 5 \\
\end{array}
\qquad \text{(II)}
$$

According to our theorem, the optimum solution of problems (I) and (II) is the same. That is, in both (I) and (II) we need to send the same number of fire engines from each station to each fire. In fact, if we deduct 4 from all entries in the top row and add 1 to all numbers in the second column, we get the result:

$$
\begin{array}{c|ccc}
 & 1 & 3 & 5 \\
\hline
2 & 1 & -1 & 5 \\
3 & 3 & 9 & 6 \\
4 & 0 & 4 & 5 \\
\end{array}
\qquad \text{(III)}
$$

The optimum solution of (III) is the same as the one for (I) or (II). It may seem rather foolish to work with negative distances (from station 1 to fire 2), but it should be considered merely as a mathematical manipulation which happens to be convenient for our present purposes. We shall see that the signs (plus, zero, or minus) of an adapted distance scheme determine whether a solution is the optimum one.

Why does the optimum solution not change when a constant is added to or deducted from each number in a row or column of the distance table? Consider the objective function associated with the original distance table:

$$
5x_{11} + 2x_{12} + 9x_{13}
$$
$$
+3x_{21} + 8x_{22} + 6x_{23}
$$
$$
+2x_{31} + 5x_{32} + 7x_{33}
$$

The objective function of the modified table (II) is exactly the same, apart from the fact that the following expression (which concerns the bottom row) should be deducted:

$$2x_{31} + 2x_{32} + 2x_{33} = 2(x_{31} + x_{32} + x_{33})$$

This is just a complicated way of writing $2 \times 4 = 8$, however, because the sum of all x values in the bottom row necessarily has to equal 4 (there are 4 engines in station 3). Thus, the objective function of (II) can be derived from the objective function of (I) by simply deducting 8. This result is independent of the way in which the engines are directed; it is valid for each possible solution, whether optimum or not, all of which become 8 miles shorter. Moreover, it is then easy to see that the optimum solution does not change either; only the value of the optimum solution is 8 lower in case (II). For table (III) the reasoning is analogous. The objective function of (III) is obtained from the objective function of (II) by deducting

$$4(x_{11} + x_{12} + x_{13}) = 4 \times 2 = 8$$

and adding

$$1(x_{12} + x_{22} + x_{32}) = 1 \times 3 = 3$$

These are constants, independent of the values we give to the decision variables, and hence again the optimum solution does not change.

Suppose now that we want to find out whether a given transportation schedule is the optimum solution. The above theorem will be used to transform the distance table in such a way that the routes actually used in the solution considered have a "distance" of zero. Then the signs of the "distances" of the routes which are *not* used will be considered. At this stage it might already be obvious that if all distances not used are positive, the solution is the optimum one. Let us proceed step by step, however.

Our starting point is the distance table (I) and the solution given at the end of the preceding section, which we shall refer to as the initial solution:

Distance table				*Initial solution*		
	1	3	5		1	3	5
2	5	2	9	2	0	2	0
3	3	8	6	3	0	0	3
4	2	5	7	4	1	1	2

In the first instance we are interested only in the distances of the routes which are actually used. For the time being we disregard the other distances, and we add to the table a right-hand column and a bottom row consisting of points:

	1	3	5	
2		2		·
3			6	·
4	2	5	7	·
	·	·	·	

By adding and deducting constant numbers from the distances in each row and column, we want to make these distances all equal to zero. As we just saw, this does not influence the optimum solution. To this end, we replace the first point in the bottom row with an *arbitrary* number, for which we conveniently and conventionally pick zero. This gives:

	1	3	5	
2		2		·
3			6	·
4	2	5	7	·
	0	·	·	

We now observe that if the distance of 2 miles from station 3 to fire 1 is to become zero, this can be achieved by deducting 2 from the third row, which is indicated as follows:

	1	3	5	
2		2		·
3			6	·
4	2	5	7	2
	0	·	·	

This is interpreted in the sense that the distance of 2 miles from station 3 to fire 1 is split up into a number 2 for the third row and a number 0 for the first column. *Given* the number 2 in the third row, we need a 3 in the second column so as to split up the distance of 5 miles from station 3 to fire 2, for 2 + 3 = 5. Similarly, given the 2 in the third row, we need a 5 in the third column, for $7 = 2 + 5$. Thus:

	1	3	5	
2		2		·
3			6	·
4	2	5	7	2
	0	3	5	

Two more steps are required. The point in the second row should be equal to 1, because the distance of 6 miles from station 2 to fire 3 is split up as $5 + 1$; the first row gets a -1, so as to split up the 2 into 3 and -1. The result is:

	1	3	5	
2		2		-1
3			6	1
4	2	5	7	2
	0	3	5	

The points have been filled in. Each number within the table is equal to the number to the right of its row plus the number at the bottom of its column. Given that the first number in the bottom row is chosen as zero, numbers can be easily and uniquely specified in a certain order to replace the remaining row and column points. Indeed, we might as well have chosen the number 3 for the first number in the bottom row, for the choice is arbitrary. Then the following scheme would result:

	1	3	5	
2		2		-4
3			6	-2
4	2	5	7	-1
	3	6	8	

All numbers in the bottom row are now 3 higher, and all numbers in the right-hand column 3 lower. The arbitrary element of choice is explained by the circumstance that there are six points which are to be filled in, while there are only five numbers in the table proper.

We now return to the complete distance table, which we border with the previously found numbers:

	1	3	5	
2	5	2	9	−1
3	3	8	6	1
4	2	5	7	2
	0	3	5	

We proceed by deducting from all distances the corresponding row and column constants. The distance 8 from station 2 to fire 2 is thus diminished by $3 + 1$ and hence becomes 4. The complete adapted distance table is now:

	1	3	5
2	$5 - (-1) - 0 = 6$	$2 - (-1) - 3 = 0$	$9 - (-1) - 5 = 5$
3	$3 - 1 - 0 = 2$	$8 - 1 - 3 = 4$	$6 - 1 - 5 = 0$
4	$2 - 2 - 0 = 0$	$5 - 2 - 3 = 0$	$7 - 2 - 5 = 0$

or, more concisely,

	1	3	5
2	6	0	5
3	2	4	0
4	0	0	0

This distance table has zeros for all actually used routes. This is not surprising, for the row and column numbers were constructed with precisely this purpose in mind. Moreover, the transportation problem associated with this distance table has the same optimum solution as that of the original distance table. This follows from the theorem which states that the optimum solution of two tables is identical when one table has been derived from the other by increasing or decreasing all the numbers in a given row or column by the same amount. This new, transformed transportation problem has a very simple solution. Consider the objective function

$$6x_{11} + 0x_{12} + 5x_{13}$$
$$+2x_{21} + 4x_{22} + 0x_{23}$$
$$+0x_{31} + 0x_{32} + 0x_{33}$$

The minimum value that this objective function can assume is zero. A negative value is impossible because of the nonnegativity restrictions on the x values, which are multiplied here by numbers which are either positive or zero. The objective function can, however, take on the value zero. To this end we must ensure that all the x values associated with positive coefficients (x_{11}, x_{13}, x_{21}, x_{22}) are zero. Our initial solution precisely satisfies this requirement. The solution is

$$x_{12} = 2 \qquad x_{23} = 3 \qquad x_{31} = 1 \qquad x_{32} = 1 \qquad x_{33} = 2$$

while all other decision variables are zero. Thus, only x values associated with zero distances are nonzero. The initial solution is the optimum solution of the transformed transportation problem and, therefore, also of the original transportation problem.

The solution has been found. We know that the minimum number of miles to be driven is 43, and we also know how to verify whether a given solution to a transportation problem is the optimum solution. We transform the distance table in such a way that the routes to be used have a "distance" of zero. When the unused routes all have a positive (or zero) distance in the transformed table, we have the optimum solution. When there are negative distances, however, we can further improve the solution.

2-4. How to Find the Optimum Solution

In order to prevent misunderstandings, we emphasize that the method by which the initial solution was constructed need not necessarily lead directly to the optimum solution. If it does not, improvements must be made on the initial solution step by step until the optimum solution is reached. To show how this is done, we shall use as the initial solution the transportation schedule obtained by the application of the northwest corner rule:

Distance table

	1	3	5
2	5	2	9
3	3	8	6
4	2	5	7

Initial solution

	1	3	5
2	1	1	0
3	0	2	1
4	0	0	4

The first step consists of verifying whether we have the optimum solution. (In the present case this is a little superfluous, because we have already found a better solution.) Thus, we take the distance table, omit the entries representing unused routes, and compute the bottom row and right-hand column numbers by splitting up the remaining distances. The result is:

	1	3	5
2	5	2		5
3		8	6	11
4			7	12
0	−3	−5

The numbers in the margin are found in the order 0, 5, −3, 11, −5, and 12. We now go back to the complete distance table and deduct from each distance the corresponding row and column numbers. The result is:

	1	3	5
2	5 − 5 − 0 = 0	2 − 5 − (−3) = 0	9 − 5 − (−5) = 9
3	3 − 11 − 0 = −8	8 − 11 − (−3) = 0	6 − 11 − (−5) = 0
4	2 − 12 − 0 = −10	5 − 12 − (−3) = −4	7 − 12 − (−5) = 0

or, in short,

	1	3	5
2	0	0	9
3	−8	0	0
4	−10	−4	0

This new table has three negative "distances." The associated objective function is

$$0x_{11} + 0x_{12} + 9x_{13}$$
$$-8x_{21} + 0x_{22} + 0x_{23}$$
$$-10x_{31} - 4x_{32} + 0x_{33}$$

Apparently we can decrease the value of this function by making x_{21}, x_{31}, or x_{32} positive. (In the initial solution they are all zero.) The first question is which of the three should be made positive. We choose x_{31} because it is multiplied by the largest negative number (−10). The second question is how large x_{31} should be made. The answer is that x_{31} should be made as large as possible, since every extra increase reduces the value of our objective function. However, the side constraints and, in particular, the nonnegativity conditions must be kept in mind.

We reconsider the initial solution and attach a plus sign to the zero of x_{31} to indicate that it will be increased to a positive value:

	1	3	5
2	1	1	0
3	0	2	1
4	0^+	0	4

When one or more fire engines are sent from station 3 to fire 1, there are two immediate consequences. In the first place, fewer engines need to go from other stations to fire 1; in the second place, fewer engines can go to the other fires from station 3. To indicate these consequences, we write:

	1	3	5
2	1^-	1	0
3	0	2	1
4	0^+	0	4^-

Two minus signs have been attached to numbers which should be reduced. Obviously we cannot further diminish the number of engines sent from station 2 to fire 1, for this is already zero. We cannot decorate zeros with minus signs. Apparently, then, we should reduce x_{11} and x_{33}. If x_{11} is reduced (by sending fewer engines from station 1 to fire 1), more engines must be directed from station 1 to the other fires. Similarly, if x_{33} is reduced (because station 3 sends fewer engines to fire 3), extra engines are needed for fire 3 from other stations. Thus we get the following schedule:

	1	3	5
2	1^-	1^+	0
3	0	2	1^+
4	0^+	0	4^-

(We could, of course, have attached a plus sign to the zero at the top, but we already have a zero with a plus at the bottom left. For reasons which will become clear below, we confine ourselves to at most one zero with a plus sign.) Thus, we have a nearly complete "ring dance" of pluses and minuses. Still, we must remember that sending more engines from station 1 to fire 2 (the plus of $x_{12} = 1$) reduces the number sent to fire 2 from other stations and that sending more fire engines from station 2 to fire 3 (the plus of $x_{23} = 1$) reduces the number of engines sent from station 2 to other fires. In both these cases, a minus sign must be attached to the center element $x_{22} = 2$:

	1	3	5
2	1^-	1^+	0
3	0	2^-	1^+
4	0^+	0	4^-

The ring dance is now complete. We began by attaching a plus sign to a zero, and now we end up with exactly one plus and one minus sign in each row and column. How far can we now increase x_{31}? Remember that only the minuses are potentially dangerous. For every engine added to x_{31}, we must remove one engine from each route to which a minus sign has been attached. Apparently, then, we can increase x_{31} only by the lowest number to which a minus has been attached, lest this lowest number become negative. Here, this lowest number is 1 (top left). Therefore, x_{31} is increased from 0 to 1, all other routes with a plus sign are increased by 1, and all routes with a minus are decreased by 1. The result is:

	1	3	5
2	0	2	0
3	0	1	2
4	1	0	3

The total distance in miles equals

$$2 \times 2 + 8 \times 1 + 6 \times 2 + 2 \times 1 + 7 \times 3 = 47$$

which is 10 miles shorter than the initial northwest corner solution.[1]

Has the optimum solution been found? To answer this question,

---

[1] It will now be clear why we wanted to attach a plus to only *one* zero value. If there had been two, two numbers would have become positive in the new schedule. This is counterbalanced by only one positive number which becomes zero. The number of positive variables would have been six rather than the required five, whereas we recall from Chap. 1 that in the solution the number of positive variables is at most equal to the number of side conditions.

first consider the adapted distance schedule:

	1	3	5
2		2	−5
3		8	6	1
4	2		7	2
	0	7	5

We find:

	1	3	5
2	$5 - (-5) - 0 = 10$	$2 - (-5) - 7 = 0$	$9 - (-5) - 5 = 9$
3	$3 - 1 - 0 = 2$	$8 - 1 - 7 = 0$	$6 - 1 - 5 = 0$
4	$2 - 2 - 0 = 0$	$5 - 2 - 7 = -4$	$7 - 2 - 5 = 0$

There is still one negative "distance," the −4 at x_{32}. We must thus increase x_{32}:

	1	3	5
2	0	2	0
3	0	1	2
4	1	0^+	3

This leads to the following ring dance of pluses and minuses:

	1	3	5
2	0	2	0
3	0	1^-	2^+
4	1	0^+	3^-

We can now increase x_{21} to 1 at most, because the *lowest* number with an attached minus sign is 1. So we find:

	1	3	5
2	0	2	0
3	0	0	3
4	1	1	2

This is the optimum solution, as we have already established.

2-5. The Quiz

Each of four participants in a quiz team must answer questions on one particular topic. The four topics are geography (G), history (H), music (M), and sports (S). The four participants are Mr. Adams (A), Mr. Bartleson (B), Mr. Crommelin (C), and Mr. Dailey (D). Each of the four has some ability in each of these fields, but their abilities on specific topics vary. We assume that this ability is graded from zero—no competence whatsoever—to 10—a near-perfect knowledge. The abilities of A, B, C, and D can now be summarized in a table as follows:

	A	B	C	D
G	8	8	4	9
H	6	8	5	7
M	5	8	5	8
S	8	9	7	4

Apparently, Mr. Bartleson is the star performer, while Mr. Crommelin is a little shaky.

Each of the participants must answer questions in one and only one field. The problem is to distribute the various topics among the participants so as to ensure the best performance of the entire team. We assume, more precisely, that the performance of each participant in each field coincides with his grade, so that if Mr. Adams has to answer questions in the field of history, he—and hence the team—will score 6 points. The total performance of the team is measured by the sum of the individual scores. We now number both the participants and the subjects (in alphabetical order) from 1 to 4 and write $6x_{21}$ for the points scored in the field of history (2) by Mr. Adams (1). If indeed Mr. Adams takes history, $x_{21} = 1$. If not, $x_{21} = 0$. The same rule applies to all other x values. The objective function then reads:

$$8x_{11} + 8x_{12} + 4x_{13} + 9x_{14}$$
$$+6x_{21} + 8x_{22} + 5x_{23} + 7x_{24}$$
$$+5x_{31} + 8x_{32} + 5x_{33} + 8x_{34}$$
$$+8x_{41} + 9x_{42} + 7x_{43} + 4x_{44}$$

This objective function is linear in each of the 16 nonnegative decision variables. The constraints state that each participant must tackle one and only one topic. For example, a possible solution might be:

$$
\begin{array}{c|cccc}
 & A & B & C & D \\
 & 1 & 1 & 1 & 1 \\
\hline
G\ 1 & 1 & 0 & 0 & 0 \\
H\ 1 & 0 & 1 & 0 & 0 \\
M\ 1 & 0 & 0 & 0 & 1 \\
S\ 1 & 0 & 0 & 1 & 0 \\
\end{array}
$$

In this example geography is entrusted to Mr. Adams, Mr. Bartleson is in charge of history, Mr. Crommelin tackles the sports questions, and music is left to Mr. Dailey. It is easy to see that the structure of this problem is in complete correspondence to that of a conventional transportation problem. If we were to consider G, H, M, and S as four fire stations, each having one fire engine, and A, B, C, and D as four small fires, there would be a correspondence in interpretation as well.

The solution given in the example happens to be the optimum. The total score equals $8 + 8 + 7 + 8 = 31$, the maximum possible. The derivation of this result will not be given here. The number of side constraints equals $4 + 4 - 1 = 7$, and the number of positive variables equals only 4, which has some implications for the computations.

2-6. The Critical Path

In the quiz problem the concepts of routes and distances seemed irrelevant or at least farfetched. We now return to those concepts, with the purpose of finding not the shortest, but rather the longest, path to the destination. In doing so, we leave the area of linear programming. Instead of transportation problems proper, we shall study more general organization problems. "Organization," as used here, has to be interpreted broadly. On the one hand, one can think about the planning of an ordinary day (making a pot of coffee, going to work, walking the dog, . . .) or a less ordinary day (birthday party, shopping, going to the theater, . . .). These tasks are comparatively transparent. The required organization either is purely a matter of routine or else can be arranged in a short time with the help of pencil, paper, telephone, and spouse. On the other hand, think of the organization required for the building of a house, factory, ship, or space capsule. This type of project requires very careful planning and timing in order to prevent bottlenecks, or at least to anticipate where they might occur.

The method which we shall discuss is a simplified version of the *critical-path method* (CPM). This is roughly the same as PERT, *program evalu-*

ation and review technique. Both these procedures were developed in the United States, more or less simultaneously. It is rumored that this new organizational device, CPM, speeded up the construction of the Polaris submarine by two years. This is a phenomenal success by all standards, especially by the standards of construction, which is so often behind schedule.

With both CPM and PERT, the first step consists of analyzing the various subtasks and determining their respective performance times. These data are then used for the construction of a network, the nodes of which are formed by the completed subtasks. Connected nodes are formed by subtasks which necessarily have to be completed in a certain order; other subtasks can be tackled simultaneously. Consider now, as an abstract example, a project which consists of nine subtasks, A, B, C, . . . , I, and which can be represented by the network in Fig. 2-1.

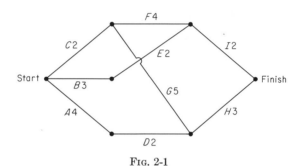

FIG. 2-1

This network shows that completion of A takes 4 days; and of H, 3 days. It also follows that C must be finished before starting F or G; however, the tasks F and G can proceed simultaneously, just as A, B, and C can. Before starting on H, both D and G have to be completed, and so on.

We now wish to determine the *critical path* of this network. This is a series of tasks so arranged that when a delay occurs in the performance of one of them, the completion of the whole project is delayed. On the other hand, if one of the subtasks on the critical path is finished more quickly than expected, the whole project is completed sooner. The critical path in such a network is the longest path (measured here in days) from start to finish. For example, it is evident from the network that one needs at least 7 days before starting on task H. This is true because the road CG requires 7 days and because one cannot start H before G is completed. The road to H via AD requires only 6 days. This means that tasks A and D are not critical: some delay in their completion is possible without influencing the total time required to complete the project. C and G, however, are critical tasks. The critical path is indicated in Fig. 2-2 by solid lines, and the noncritical tasks are shown as dashed lines.   In this simple case the critical path has been determined by observation.   In complicated cases the path can be determined— indeed, very simply and quickly—only with an electronic computer.[1]   A glance shows the possible bottlenecks—the tasks C, G, and H.   If A, B, D, E, F, or I takes a little longer than anticipated, the total time needed for the project is not influenced.   This situation changes, of course, when much more time than estimated is needed.   For example,

If A takes 6 days, the critical path becomes ADH.

If I takes 5 days, the critical path becomes CFI.

If E takes 5 days, both BEI and CGH are critical paths.

If G takes only 2 days, ADH becomes the critical path.

If G takes only 4 days, both CGH and ADH are critical paths.

The most obvious use of the critical-path method is to employ more men and/or machines for those subtasks which are on the critical path.

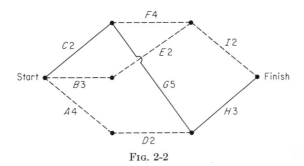

Fig. 2-2

The resulting economy often considerably outbalances the extra costs. In this respect the technique has proven its usefulness.   The extra men put to work on the critical tasks can sometimes be taken from uncritical tasks, which will then take a little longer.   This prevents long waiting times and idleness on the one hand, and tension and hurry on the other.

Moreover, the scheme is very clear.   The man in charge can keep a constant eye on the progress, and he can adapt the critical path when the latest information concerning delays becomes known.   In this simple way the appearance or disappearance of bottlenecks can be constantly checked and controlled.   The various departments connected with the project will have a better mutual understanding of each other's problems

---

[1] Moreover, a so-called Pert-o-graph can be obtained very inexpensively.   This is a disk-shaped pocket computer, like a ruler, constructed especially to solve critical-path problems.   It is a useful instrument for networks of moderate complexity.

because they have a better overall view. This will help curtail frictions and rivalry, an advantage which is not to be underestimated.

2-7. The Critical Path of This Book

Assume that you consider writing a book with a team of two others. The situation occurred when the publisher approached the Econometric Institute in Rotterdam in mid-January, 1963, about writing a book on econometrics and operations research. The preliminary question is whether or not to accept this proposal. The next question is how it should be accomplished, who should write what chapter, etc. The first draft had to be ready by mid-July, so that the summer, the quiet season in the academic world, could be used for the finishing touches. Moreover, during the summer there is more typing time available.

The first draft is our concern here. Below we give a list of chapters as originally envisaged, indicating at the left the author responsible for each chapter. The names have been changed to protect the innocent. (The problem of assigning chapters to the various authors is a problem in itself, closely related to the quiz problem.) Two chapters were divided into two parts each because they were to be written by different authors.

X 1. Linear Programming
X 2. The Optimum Path and Critical Path
X 3. Input-Output Analysis
Z 4. Macroeconomic Models
Y 5. Economic Predictions
Y 6. Entrepreneurial Gallup Polls
Y 7a. Uncertainty, Probability, and Simulation, Part I
X 7b. Uncertainty, Probability, and Simulation, Part II
Y 8. Mathematical Statistics
Z 9. The Consumer's Dollar
Z 10. Queueing
Y 11. Strategies
X 12. Game Theory and Management Decision Games
Z 13a. Production and Inventory Decisions, Part I
Y 13b. Production and Inventory Decisions, Part II

The time needed per chapter was determined largely by other duties, such as teaching, giving exams, research projects, and conferences. As a result of these considerations, a chapter by X was to take roughly 4 weeks, Y should require only 3, while Z was scheduled to require 6 weeks for a chapter. Chapters 7 and 13 are exceptions to this rule;

the times needed for 7*a*, 7*b*, 13*a*, 13*b* were estimated at 3, 1, 1, and 3 weeks, respectively.

Moreover, the chapters had to be written in a certain order, for three reasons. First, no author was to write two chapters simultaneously. Second, there is some connection between various chapters, and, third, it is preferable to write the chapters in the order indicated. This leads to the following constraints:

1, 2, and 3 are to be written in that order.
3 should precede 7*b* and 12.
5 can be written only when 3 and 4 are ready.
7*a* precedes 7*b*, 8, 10, and 11.
8 precedes 9.
11 precedes 12 and 13*b*.
13*a* precedes 13*b*.

The following chapters cannot be written simultaneously, because they are written by the same author: 5, 6, and 7*a*; 7*b* and 12; 4, 9, and 10.

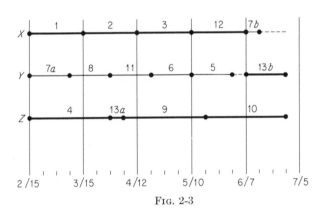

FIG. 2-3

The other undesired possibilities of simultaneity have already been excluded by the seven constraints given above.

Bearing in mind these constraints, we experimented with various schedules, all based on the assumption that the actual writing could start on February 15. The most convenient arrangement is given in Fig. 2-3. It is not in the form of a network with nodes, but is clearly of the critical-path type. It shows that the whole path of *Z* is critical and that the path 1, 2, 3, 12, 13*b* is a critical path. Y has an extra week for Chaps. 7*a*, 8, 11, 6, and 5. He can, if he so wishes, switch Chaps. 11 and 6, but this has the disadvantage that when a delay occurs, Chap. 12 has to wait, and 12 is on the critical path. Also, Y should start with

7*a* and 8, because otherwise Z cannot begin with 9; it is pleasant for Z—though not strictly necessary—to write 9 and 10 in that order. Y should hold up Chap. 5 until Chap. 3 is ready. Interestingly, it follows from this analysis that 7*a* should be written at the very beginning but that 7*b* should be added to this at the very end! A similar observation holds for parts 13*a* and 13*b*. Although X has two weeks to spare in the end, he forms an important part of the critical path in the beginning.

It is quite striking how easily it can be seen who will do what, when. Moreover, it could be concluded that even with some setbacks, the deadline of mid-July could be met.

Literature

Both the formulation and the solution of transportation problems preceded the more general linear programming problems. The problem is originally due to Hitchcock [1] and worked out in great detail by Koopmans [2]. The textbooks mentioned at the end of Chap. 1 all treat the problem in detail.

The solution presented in this chapter satisfies throughout all side conditions. In each step a new solution is found in which the total distance is less than that of the previously found solution. A different approach is possible. Ford and Fulkerson [3] describe a method in which not all side conditions are satisfied throughout, but in which—given the side conditions which are satisfied—the total distance is minimized throughout. In successive steps one then complies with more and more side conditions, until they are finally all satisfied.

The quiz problem admits an elegant solution procedure, which is discussed in detail by Kuhn [4]. Stilian and others [5] wrote an interesting and easy book on PERT and CPM. A short introduction is available in a *Fortune* article by Boehm [6].

[1] F. L. Hitchcock, "Distribution of a Product from Several Sources to Numerous Localities," *Journal of Mathematical Physics*, vol. 20 (1941), pp. 224–230.
[2] T. C. Koopmans, "Optimum Utilization of the Transportation System," *Econometrica*, supplement to vol. 17 (1949), pp. 136–145.
[3] L. R. Ford and D. R. Fulkerson, "Solving the Transportation Problem," *Management Science*, vol. 3 (1956), pp. 24–32.
[4] H. W. Kuhn, "The Hungarian Method for the Assignment Problem," *Naval Research Logistics Quarterly*, vol. 2 (1956), pp. 83–97.
[5] G. N. Stilian et al., *PERT, A New Management Planning and Control Technique*, American Management Association, New York, 1962.
[6] G. A. W. Boehm, "Helping the Executive to Make Up His Mind," *Fortune*, April, 1962.

3

Input-Output Analysis

3-1. Economic Interdependence

We take it for granted that railway systems function smoothly and according to the timetable. We also take it for granted that our complicated society functions smoothly, but without the use of a timetable. There are policemen, nurses, and teachers, although no one is told—let alone directed—to become a policeman, nurse, or teacher. There are steel and iron for the foundries, blast furnaces to produce that steel and iron, workers for those blast furnaces, eggs for those workers, chickens to lay the eggs, farmers to raise the chickens—and there are transportation services to transport all the goods from one producer to the next, to the merchants, to the consumer. In 1776, Adam Smith, the man generally recognized as the founder of economics, spoke in this context of an "invisible hand" ruling and organizing all this. Perhaps that hand has become a little more visible since the eighteenth century, and in particular since World War II, because the depression of the thirties led to the realization that the system did not always work as well as desired. If occasionally we are able to discern a visible hand, it is that of the government. Since the eighteenth century, however, our society has become vastly more complicated, and there remain, undoubtedly, sufficient grounds for astonishment.

The invisible-hand explanation is a little metaphysical, and more thorough investigation is warranted. We shall begin by describing the structure of the economy; that is, we shall describe the transactions among the different industries. Every firm produces its product and sells it to another firm, which in turn processes the goods and sells them, etc., until at the end the finished product is in the hands of the final consumer. Such transactions can be regarded as a kind of economic transportation system, the study of which is known as *input-output analysis*. The "father" of input-output analysis is Wassily W. Leontief of Harvard University. His standard work in this field was published in 1941.

The first step in input-output analysis consists of partitioning all the firms of a given country into a number of sectors. There are detailed schemes which distinguish as many as 250 different sectors and more concise schemes with not more than 30 or 40 sectors. The principles, however, can be equally well illustrated with an example in which one distinguishes only three sectors: agriculture, industry, and services. The services sector includes banking and insurance, trade, barbers, hotels and restaurants, government services (police, education, etc.), and transportation. Every firm must be classed in one and only one of these categories. There must be no misunderstanding here. Thus, a ruling must be made whether dairy processors belong to the industrial or the agricultural sector. (One usually ranks them under industries.) Each ruling has definite consequences, but here we shall assume that the classification problem has been settled.

The next step is the construction of a transaction scheme, showing how much each sector buys from each sector in a given year. This is in reality a very complicated job, but in theory it is quite simple. If a farmer buys a mowing machine, this is counted as a delivery from industry to agriculture. If a foundry buys iron from the steelworks, this is a delivery from industry to industry. It goes without saying, however, that not everything produced in the agricultural, industrial, or services sector is also consumed in one of these sectors. A substantial part of the production goes straight to the consumer, who buys his eggs from agriculture, his dishwasher from industry, and his stamps from services. As an example, consider the following input-output table, which shows transactions in billions of dollars per year.[1]

From sector	To sector			Consumers	Total
	Agriculture	Industry	Services		
Agriculture	1	2.25	0.2	1.55	5
Industry	2	6	1	16	25
Services	0.2	3	1.8	15	20

The input-output table specifies how much each of the sectors bought from the other sectors and how much they delivered to the various sectors

---

[1] When measured in billions of guilders, the table is a very rough representation of the Dutch economy in the fifties. (A guilder corresponds to 28 U.S. cents according to the official exchange rate; its purchasing power is larger.) If all numbers are multiplied by 1½ and are measured in units of $10 billion, the numbers roughly correspond to the situation in the United States during the fifties.

in a given year.   Thus, we see that the yearly value of the agricultural production was $5 billion and that $1 billion of the total, or 20 per cent, went from agriculture to agriculture, i.e., from farmer to farmer.   Nearly half of the total production ($2.25 billion) was delivered to the food-processing industries, and just about all the rest went directly to the consumers.   We also see that the industrial sector delivered goods worth $2 billion to agriculture; this is a little less than the amount sold by agriculture to industry, and so on.

The problems that arise in determining the transaction amounts must not be underestimated.   The most important source of information is provided by production statistics.   In principle there are two sets of data available for each transaction: the amount which the selling sector says it has sold and the amount which the buying sector says it has bought. If both sets of data are available and if they coincide, there are no problems.   Frequently, however, they do not coincide, in which case they must somehow be adapted so they will.   Sometimes only one of the two sets is available, sometimes neither is known, or they are both only partially known.   Then intuition and experience must be the guide.

It follows from the transaction scheme that consumers buy a total of $1.55 + 16 + 15 = \$32.55$ billion.   Where do the consumers get the money to buy foods, industrial products, and services for this total of $32.55 billion?   Some is obtained in the form of wages which the farmhand receives from agriculture, the foreman from industry, and the bank clerk from services.   Money is also received in the form of profit made by the independent shopkeeper and dividends payed out to the shareholder.   In short, the consumers pay with the income they receive from the respective sectors.   Take the agricultural sector: The total value of production here is $5 billion, of which $3.2 billion is accounted for by the sector's purchases of $1 billion from its own sector, $2 billion from industry, and $0.2 billion from services.   These are the numbers in the first column, and together they equal

$$1 + 2 + 0.2 = \$3.2 \text{ billion}$$

There remains $5 - 3.2 = \$1.8$ billion, the amount which the agricultural sector receives minus the amount spent on the products of the three sectors.   The $1.8 billion will be referred to as sector income and includes the remuneration of those who give their labor or capital to this sector: farmhand, farmer, and owner of the farm.[1]   With the addition of sector incomes, the transaction scheme now looks as follows:

---

[1] The technical term for sector income is *primary input*, which also includes items such as imports and depreciation.   We confine ourselves to a simplified exposition; cf. the beginning of Sec. 3-2.

From sector	To sector			Consumers	Total
	Agriculture	Industry	Services		
Agriculture	1	2.25	0.2	1.55	5
Industry	2	6	1	16	25
Services	0.2	3	1.8	15	20
Sector income	1.8	13.75	17		32.55
Total	5	25	20	32.55	

The second column shows that the industrial sector buys $2.25 billion from agriculture, $6 billion from industry, $3 billion from services, for a grand total of $11.25 billion. By deducting this from the total industrial production, which amounts to $25 billion (the second number in the last column), we get the income earned in industry, viz., $13.75 billion. The $17 billion income of the services sector has been similarly computed.

In this simplified scheme, therefore, total sector income equals 1.8 + 13.75 + 17 = $32.55 billion, precisely enough to pay for the total consumption. We also see that income in the services sector ($17 billion) is substantially larger than the total amount which the firms in that sector buy from the three sectors ($3 billion). Experience teaches us that this is so. A firm in the services sector (bank, insurance, government) is labor intensive; i.e., the wages are an important part of the total costs.

3-2. Input-Output Tables in Practice

To prevent misunderstanding, we repeat that the above scheme represents a very simplified structure. Thus, the economy is not usually closed, i.e., a system without contacts with the outside world. There are also exports and imports. In the Dutch economy about 50 per cent of the yearly GNP is exported; in the American economy, about 4 per cent. A second point which was totally disregarded is formed by savings. The income of $32.55 billion was completely spent. Also the government and taxes deserve more attention. All these refinements can be incorporated in the structure in a rather straightforward way. We shall not do so in this example, because it tends to be quite technical.

Before we further elaborate on input-output theory, we do want to show in some detail the Dutch input-output system. In the Netherlands an input-output table is constructed every year by the Central Bureau of Statistics in The Hague. An actual table may help to make the dis-

cussion more concrete. Thirty-five sectors are distinguished in the
Dutch economy:

1. Agriculture, forestry, and fishing
2. Coal mining
3. Crude petroleum and salt mining, etc.
4. Food manufacturing (animal products)
5. Food manufacturing (all other products)
6. Beverages and tobacco
7. Textiles
8. Footwear and clothing
9. Wood and furniture
10. Paper and paper products
11. Printing, publishing, and allied industries
12. Leather and rubber products (excluding footwear)
13. Chemicals; petroleum refineries
14. Earthenware, glass, lime, and stoneware
15. Basic metal industry
16. Metal products and machinery
17. Electrical machinery and apparatus
18. Transport equipment
19. Other metal products and diamonds
20. Construction
21. Electricity, gas, and water
22. Wholesale trade
23. Retail trade
24. Banks and other financial institutions
25. Insurance
26. Ownership of dwellings
27. Ocean and air transport
28. Other transport
29. Communication
30. Medical and health services
31. Business services, etc.
32. Recreation services
33. Hotels, cafés, and restaurants
34. Other personal services
35. Goods and services not elsewhere classified and correction items

As the above list shows, manufacturing, broadly defined, accounts
for roughly half of the sectors. All these sectors need to be defined in
greater detail. Sometimes the value of their services must be judged

by a rule of thumb.   For example, the services of the wholesale and retail trades, sectors 22 and 23, are valued at their gross profit margins.   Such technicalities will not be discussed, however, except in connection with sector 35—goods and services not elsewhere classified and correction items.   When a table is constructed and finally completed, the value of production must correspond to the value of sales—apart from inventory changes.   This is only the ideal situation, however; we have already mentioned that numerous entries are afflicted with errors, so that the totals do not correspond.   For this reason a remainder sector, here number 35, is added.   This sector is relatively unimportant, but an accounting necessity.

When 35 sectors are distinguished, the input-output table becomes much larger.   Nine (that is, 3×3) numbers sufficed to specify all intra- and intersector deliveries in the three-sector model.   Now we need $35 \times 35 = 1,225$ numbers.   To be a bit more concrete—without drowning in an ocean of numbers—we shall show a small part of the table, giving in millions of guilders the actual deliveries in sectors 6 to 10 for the year 1957:

Sector	6	7	8	9	10
6. Beverages and tobacco	12	0	0	0	0
7. Textiles	0	785	332	21	4
8. Footwear and clothing	0	2	53	0	0
9. Wood and furniture	18	5	4	78	4
10. Paper and paper products	16	17	8	5	249

In total there are $5 \times 5 = 25$ deliveries, of which 8 are zeros.   These zeros are not really zero, for the numbers have been rounded off to the nearest million.   The 12 million delivery from sector 6 to sector 6, therefore, means in principle a delivery of from $11\frac{1}{2}$ to $12\frac{1}{2}$ million guilders (in principle, because even without rounding off, the numbers are not completely accurate).   A zero consequently stands for a delivery of less than half a million a year.   It goes without saying that there are actually some deliveries from the beverages and tobacco sector to the other four sectors, if only the delivery of soft drinks to the canteen of the spinning mill (belonging to sector 7).

The intrasector deliveries tend to be high: 12 million for sector 6, 785 million for sector 7, 53 million for sector 8, etc.   (These form the so-called diagonal elements of the table.)   This is not as strange as it may seem.   In the textile industry, for example, raw cotton is the initial product.   According to the 1957 input-output table, nearly one billion guilders worth of imported raw cotton goes to the textile industry (not recorded in our small survey).   This goes to the spinning mills and is then moved on to the weaving mills, constituting a delivery from the textile sector to the textile sector.   From the weaving mills the textile goes to the finishing industries, where the cotton fabric is painted, dyed, printed, embroidered, etc.—again a delivery from the textile industry to the textile industry.   In more technical terminology, deliveries within the sector add to the diagonal values.   In this way the relatively large size of the diagonal numbers is explained.   Incidentally, the deliveries from the textile industry to the footwear and clothing industry (332 million) are not negligible either.

Were we to distinguish more sectors, the diagonal elements would decrease in value.   Suppose that we further split up the textile industry into spinning mills, weaving mills, and finishing industries as separate sectors.   Then the deliveries of the spinning mills to the weaving mills would fall outside the diagonal.   (Only deliveries from spinning mills to spinning mills, a presumably rather insignificant amount, would remain on the diagonal.)   Integrated industrial units also have the effect of decreasing the diagonal elements.   When the same company spins, weaves, and finishes the textile products, the deliveries from the spinning mill to the weaving mill take place within one firm, and such transactions are not recorded in the input-output tables.   Hence the diagonal values become smaller when the industrial units become larger by vertical integration.

3-3. The Purposes and Assumptions of Input-Output Analysis

Detailed input-output tables give a rather precise insight into the interdependencies of the various sectors of the economy.   However pleasant this may be, a more relevant question is whether this insight can help us in solving a number of important problems.   Specially, suppose that one is interested in the size of total production in the textile industry three years from now.   This is an important question not only for the textile manufacturers but also for the government (full employment policies, depressed areas policies) and perhaps for the unions.

The question is, therefore, whether an input-output table which includes the textile industry as a sector can help us to determine the production of textiles three years hence.   The answer is yes, provided we are willing to make a number of assumptions.   If the assumptions are approximately correct, we shall be able to determine the total production in the textile industry three years from now—approximately. What assumptions must be made?   How can we obtain the answer from the input-output table?

In this type of study the consumer expenditures on the commodities of the various sectors are assumed to be known.   We saw before that input-output tables focus attention on the intermediate deliveries from sector to sector.   What happens outside these sectors, in particular the amounts which consumers buy from the sectors, is assumed to be given.[1] This is the first assumption.   There is a second assumption of a rather different nature.   We shall illustrate it with our original example, reproduced here for convenience:

From sector	To sector			Consumers	Total
	Agriculture	Industry	Services		
Agriculture	1	2.25	0.2	1.55	5
Industry	2	6	1	16	25
Services	0.2	3	1.8	15	20

The question that corresponds to our textile problem for this compressed input-output table is: Given the consumer expenditures for the products of each of the three sectors, how can one determine the total production necessary in, for example, the agricultural sector three years from now?

The total production in the agricultural sector is $5 billion according to the table.   To produce that amount it was necessary to buy $1 billion worth of agricultural goods, $2 billion of industrial goods, and $0.2 billion of services.   How will this change when the total agricultural production rises from $5 billion to $6 billion, i.e., when production increases by 20 per cent?   It stands to reason that realization of this greater production will require a larger supply of goods from the other sectors.   The simplest assumption is the one of *proportionality*.   That is, if the total agricultural production increases by 20 per cent, the agricultural sector should receive 20 per cent more from each of the sectors.   Hence, 1.2 rather than 1 billion from the agricultural sector itself, 2.4 rather than 2 billion from the industrial sector, and 0.24 rather than 0.2 billion from the services sector.   Nobody really believes that this exact proportionality holds throughout—but it might well be a good approximation.   The theory of input-output indeed assumes that it is.

Let us continue the discussion of the 20 per cent increase in consumer demand for agricultural products.   Originally the agricultural sector

---

[1] In technical terms, the "final bill of goods" is assumed to be given.   This includes demand by all economic agents other than that by the specified sectors, such as consumer expenditure, exports, etc.

produced 5 billion and received deliveries of 1, 2, and 0.2 billion, respectively, from each of the three sectors. When we divide these three amounts by the total production of $5 billion, we get 0.2, 0.4, and 0.04, respectively. These numbers represent the deliveries of the three sectors to agriculture per billion dollars of agricultural production. After the 20 per cent increase, agricultural production amounts to $6 billion. When we now assume that the intersector deliveries also increase by 20 per cent, they will amount to 1.2, 2.4, and 0.24 billion, as we have seen. If we divide these increased deliveries by the total production of $6 billion, we obtain

$$\frac{1.2}{6} = 0.2 \qquad \frac{2.4}{6} = 0.4 \qquad \frac{0.24}{6} = 0.04$$

which are exactly the same ratios as we had before. Our assumption of equal percentage increases implies that the ratios between the deliveries of each of the sectors to agriculture and the total agricultural production are constant. To the extent that the ratios are not really constant, our assumption is wrong, but to the extent that they remain more or less constant, we shall obtain results which are more or less accurate.

Let us now briefly discuss the other two sectors. We have divided the deliveries to the agricultural sector by the total agricultural production. Analogously, we shall divide the deliveries to the industrial sector by the total industrial production and the deliveries to the services sector by the total production of services. Thus we obtain, for example, $2.25/25 = 0.09$ for the ratio between the deliveries of agriculture to industry and the total industrial production. If we again assume this ratio to be constant, it implies that 9 per cent of the total industrial production consists of input from the agricultural sector. Proceeding in this way, we get the following table:

From sector	To sector		
	Agriculture	Industry	Services
Agriculture	0.2	0.09	0.01
Industry	0.4	0.24	0.05
Services	0.04	0.12	0.09

The first column of this table has been determined from the input-output table by dividing the numbers of the first column (deliveries to the agriculture) by the first row total (total agricultural production). The other columns are similarly obtained.

The nine coefficients so obtained are known as the *technical coefficients*. This term suggest that a unit output of a sector technically requires a certain given and fixed percentage input from each of the sectors, which is admittedly an overstatement. The best we can hope for is that the technical coefficients remain reasonably constant through time.

3-4. The Method of Input-Output Analysis

Given the consumer demand, the total production in each sector still remains to be determined. The apparatus consists of the input-output table for a given year and the assumption that the technical coefficients computed from this table remain constant through time. Suppose now that for some reason or other the consumption of agricultural goods increases by half a billion, i.e., from 1.55 to 2.05 billion. We assume that the consumer demand for industrial goods and services remains at the old level ($16 billion and $15 billion, respectively). We shall now show how total production in the sectors changes as a result of this increase of half a billion in the consumer demand for agricultural goods.

It would be rash to conclude that the agricultural sector should produce half a billion more because consumer demand has increased by that amount. The technical coefficients show that to produce the extra half billion, the agricultural sector must obtain from its own sector an amount of $0.2 \times 0.5 = \$0.1$ billion. (In everyday language this means that if consumers want more bacon and hence more pigs, indirectly more grain will be needed to feed the extra pigs.) Hence, agricultural production should increase not by $0.5 billion, but by $0.6 billion. Indeed this is not the end, for the extra agricultural production also requires extra inputs from the industrial and services sectors. From the first column of the table of technical coefficients, we see that increasing agricultural production by half a billion requires increased deliveries of $0.4 \times 0.5 = \$0.2$ billion from the industrial sector and $0.04 \times 0.5 = \$0.02$ billion from the services sector. Even though there is no extra consumer demand for the latter two sectors, their production must increase to support the increased production of half a billion in agricultural goods. (After all, the extra pigs have to be processed by the meat packers, and the bacon has to be transported to the shops.) All combined, in addition to the half a billion increase in agricultural production, $0.1 billion of production is needed from agriculture, $0.2 billion from industry, and $0.02 billion from services.

Even this is not the end of the story, for these extra amounts of production (0.1, 0.2, and 0.02 billion) in their turn require extra production.

According to the table of technical coefficients, a \$0.1 billion increase in agricultural production requires

$$0.2 \times 0.1 = \$0.02 \text{ billion from the agricultural sector}$$
$$0.4 \times 0.1 = \$0.04 \text{ billion from the industrial sector}$$
$$0.04 \times 0.1 = \$0.004 \text{ billion from the services sector}$$

We must also produce \$0.2 billion worth of industrial goods. According to the second column of the table of technical coefficients, we see that this requires

$$0.09 \times 0.2 = \$0.018 \text{ billion from the agricultural sector}$$
$$0.24 \times 0.2 = \$0.048 \text{ billion from the industrial sector}$$
$$0.12 \times 0.2 = \$0.024 \text{ billion from the services sector}$$

Finally, the extra \$0.02 billion to be delivered from the services sector must be considered. The third column of the table of technical coefficients shows that this leads to the following extra deliveries:

$$0.01 \times 0.02 = \$0.0002 \text{ billion from the agricultural sector}$$
$$0.05 \times 0.02 = \$0.0010 \text{ billion from the industrial sector}$$
$$0.09 \times 0.02 = \$0.0018 \text{ billion from the services sector}$$

Thus, for each of the three sectors there are three amounts by which production needs to be increased. The total of this round is

$$0.02 + 0.018 + 0.0002 = \$0.0382 \text{ billion from the agricultural sector}$$
$$0.04 + 0.048 + 0.0010 = \$0.0890 \text{ billion from the industrial sector}$$
$$0.004 + 0.024 + 0.0018 = \$0.0298 \text{ billion from the services sector}$$

The total extra agricultural production needed has now increased from 0.6 to 0.6382 billion, the industrial production from 0.2 to 0.2890 billion, and the services production from 0.02 to 0.0498 billion.

This, of course, is not the end of the story, for the extra production of the previous round (0.0382, 0.0890, and 0.0298 billion in the three sectors, respectively) in its turn needs extra deliveries. And so it continues forever after. Complicated? Somewhat. Will it ever end? Yes and no. No, in the sense that the sequence of successive deliveries in principle continues forever. Yes, in the sense that there is a strictly finite upper limit to the extra amount needed in each sector. A small indication of this phenomenon has been obtained above. In the first round \$0.5 billion worth of increased agricultural production was needed.

In the second round—to support this production—we had to produce $0.1 billion more in agriculture, $0.2 billion in industry, and $0.02 billion in services—a total of $0.32 billion more or about 40 per cent less than in the first round.   In the third round, as can be easily verified, the total extra requirements add up to not quite half the amount of the second round.   In the end the sum of this infinite series of continually decreasing numbers remains strictly finite.

A simple example may clarify this apparent contradiction.   Suppose your son approaches you one week and asks for pocket money.   You give him a dollar.   The next day he is back and makes a similar request. After a little give and take, in the end he leaves with half a dollar.   This situation is repeated each day, and each day your son leaves with half the amount he received the previous day.   (You will not live quite long enough, and paying fractions of pennies is difficult in practice, but it can easily be imagined.)   We thus are concerned with an infinite series of payments, but the total amount involved never exceeds $2, for in the end your son has received in dollars:

$$1 + \tfrac{1}{2} = 1\tfrac{1}{2}$$
$$1 + \tfrac{1}{2} + \tfrac{1}{4} = 1\tfrac{3}{4}$$
$$1 + \tfrac{1}{2} + \tfrac{1}{4} + \tfrac{1}{8} = 1\tfrac{7}{8}$$
$$1 + \tfrac{1}{2} + \tfrac{1}{4} + \tfrac{1}{8} + \tfrac{1}{16} = 1\tfrac{15}{16}$$
$$\cdot \ \cdot \ \cdot \ \cdot \ \cdot \ \cdot \ \cdot \ \cdot \ \cdot \ \cdot \ \cdot \ \cdot \ \cdot \ \cdot \ \cdot \ \cdot \ \cdot \ \cdot$$

Hence the amount of $2 is gradually approached, but never quite reached. This amount of $2 is called the *limit* of the sum.

Exactly the same procedure applies in this case.   We want to find the limit of the sum of all successive deliveries needed to satisfy a $0.5 billion increase in the demand for agricultural products.   The computation of this limit need not be so cumbersome as the round-by-round approach above; we can proceed much more rapidly.

Let us denote the total agricultural production (in billions of dollars per year) by A, the total industrial production by I, and the total services production by S.   Reconsider the three-sector input-output table. The first row shows that A (there equal to 5) is the sum of four amounts, viz., the deliveries of agriculture to each of the three sectors plus the demand from consumers.   This last amount now equals 2.05 billion, since we are concerned with the effects of a half billion increase in consumer demand for agricultural goods.   For the first three components of A, the deliveries of agriculture to the various sectors, we return to the table of technical coefficients.   The first row specifies that agriculture must deliver to agriculture 0.2 of its total production, hence $0.2A$, since A is the total agricultural production; because I stands for the total industrial production, of which 0.09 must consist of agricultural inputs, agriculture delivers to industry an amount equal to $0.09I$; similarly, a total production of S in services requires a delivery of $0.01S$ from the agricultural sector.   Thus we obtain

$$A = 0.2A + 0.09I + 0.01S + 2.05$$

If we now deduct $0.2A + 0.09I + 0.01S$ from both sides, the result is

$$0.8A - 0.09I - 0.01S = 2.05 \tag{1}$$

The second row of the input-output table concerns the industrial sector. The total production I again consists of four components.   The demand from consumers is \$16 billion, since we agreed to leave this unchanged. The three other components indicate what industry must deliver to the three sectors, given that total production in these sectors equals A, I, and S, respectively.   The table of technical coefficients then shows that industry should deliver $0.4A$ to agriculture, $0.24I$ to industry, and $0.05S$ to services.   Thus we obtain

$$I = 0.4A + 0.24I + 0.05S + 16$$

or, after deducting $0.4A + 0.24I + 0.05S$ from both sides,

$$-0.4A + 0.76I - 0.05S = 16 \tag{2}$$

Similarly, the services sector gives

$$S = 0.04A + 0.12I + 0.09S + 15$$

or $$-0.04A - 0.12I + 0.91S = 15 \tag{3}$$

Formulas (1), (2), and (3) are three linear equations in the three unknowns A, I, and S.   From Chap. 1 we know that such a system allows for a unique solution—barring exceptional cases.   In our case the solution is

$$A = 5.6659$$
$$I = 25.3555$$
$$S = 20.0762$$

as can be easily verified by substitution.[1] When we recall that in the original situation the production in each of the sectors was 5, 25, and 20 billion, respectively, the conclusion is that eventually

> 665.9 million in agriculture
> 355.5 million in industry
> 76.2 million in services

are needed to support the half billion increase in the demand for agricultural goods. The problem is now solved. The step-by-step, or iterative, procedure showed that the following increases were required after three rounds:

> 638.2 million in agriculture
> 289.0 million in industry
> 49.8 million in services

We were well on the way, but still far from the final results.

3-5. Some Further Details

The method sketched above, which leads to three linear equations in three unknowns, is vastly simpler than the original iterative procedure which required us to find step by step the consequences of the sectors' interdependence. We can, however, further improve the present procedure. That is very important, because it is quite possible that one is interested in many alternative specifications of consumer expenditure. Obviously, given any other specification, one *can* proceed along exactly the same lines. All that is required is to solve another system of three linear equations in three unknowns. This is not difficult when there are only three sectors, but it becomes rather a nuisance when 35 sectors are distinguished—leading to 35 linear equations in 35 unknowns. Even an electronic computer requires some time to solve such systems. For this reason it is of considerable importance to have a method which quickly gives the solution for all conceivable demand specifications.

To indicate how this method proceeds, refer to equations (1), (2), and

---

[1] Substitution of these values for A, I, and S in (1) gives

$0.8 \times 5.6659 - 0.09 \times 25.3555 - 0.01 \times 20.0762$
$$= 4.5327 - 2.2820 - 0.2008 = 2.0499$$

Allowing for rounding off, this is equal to 2.05, the right-hand side of (1). For (2) and (3) the check is equally straightforward.

(3). Notice that the consumer expenditures all appear to the right of the equality sign: 2.05 in the agricultural equation (1), 16 in the industrial equation (2), and 15 in the services equation (3). At the left are the three unknowns A, I, and S, each multiplied by certain coefficients which have been derived from the technical coefficients. We assume that these technical coefficients remain unchanged, so the conclusion is that whatever specification we give to consumer demand, the coefficients at the left-hand side remain unchanged. Those at the right-hand side depend, of course, upon the chosen specification for which we shall write C_A, C_I, and C_S. (The symbol C_S, for example, stands for the consumer demand for services.) The equations (1), (2), and (3) now look as follows:

$$0.8A - 0.09I - 0.01S = C_A$$
$$-0.4A + 0.76I - 0.05S = C_I \qquad (4)$$
$$-0.04A - 0.12I + 0.91S = C_S$$

We can solve this set of equations, which gives

$$A = 1.3319C_A + 0.1614C_I + 0.0235C_S$$
$$I = 0.7110C_A + 1.4135C_I + 0.0855C_S \qquad (5)$$
$$S = 0.1523C_A + 0.1935C_I + 1.1112C_S$$

Given those equations, for any specification of C_A, C_I, and C_S we can immediately determine how much should be produced in each of the sectors. The problem has been reduced to an exercise in substitution. Suppose we specify $C_A = 1.55$, $C_I = 16$, and $C_S = 15$. Then we obtain

$$A = 1.3319 \times 1.55 + 0.1614 \times 16 + 0.0235 \times 15 = 5.00$$
$$I = 0.7110 \times 1.55 + 1.4135 \times 16 + 0.0855 \times 15 = 25.00$$
$$S = 0.1523 \times 1.55 + 0.1935 \times 16 + 1.1112 \times 15 = 20.00$$

This result should not be surprising—it is already known from our original input-output table. Given any set of values C_A, C_I, and C_S, all that remains is a matter of simple substitution.

Meanwhile, it is evident that in this model only the required *total* industrial output can be determined. We cannot determine the required production in the textile industry and the paper industry separately. The Dutch input-output table, which is more detailed, can do precisely this. Let us return to the question of what the total textile production should be three years from now, given the Dutch input-output table for 1957. To that end, consider as given the consumer expenditures three years from now in each of the 35 sectors: C_1, C_2, . . . , C_{35}. According to the list of sectors given at the beginning of Sec. 3-2, C_7 stands for the total consumer demand (in three years time or in 1960) for textiles, C_8 for the total consumer demand (in 1960) for footwear and clothing, etc.   In addition to assuming as given these demands in three years time, we assume that the technical coefficients are known.   These coefficients are determined from the 1957 input-output table as indicated above.   That is, each figure in the first column is divided by the total production of sector 1, and so on for the 34 remaining sectors.   Thus we obtain $35 \times 35 = 1,225$ technical coefficients.   Reproduced below are the 25 technical coefficients (multiplied by 100) for sectors 6 through 10:

Sector	6	7	8	9	10
6. Beverages and tobacco	0.90	0	0	0	0
7. Textiles	0	27.30	19.73	2.28	0.37
8. Footwear and clothing	0	0.07	3.15	0	0
9. Wood and furniture	1.35	0.17	0.24	8.46	0.37
10. Paper, paper products	1.20	0.59	0.48	0.54	23.08

Let us give an example of the derivation of the above coefficients.   The numbers in the last column (applying to sector 10, the paper industry) have been obtained by dividing each of the deliveries to sector 10 (0, 4, 0, 4, 249; cf. Sec. 3-2) by the total production of sector 10 (1,079)[1] and multiplying by 100.   (The actual technical coefficients, therefore, are 0, 0.0037, 0, 0.0037, and 0.2308.)   The other technical coefficients have been similarly determined.   As they are all multiplied by 100, the technical coefficients are expressed as percentages.

It follows from the numbers in the first column (under 6) that a production of 100 guilders worth of beverages and tobacco requires 0.90 per cent or 90 cents of inputs of beverages and tobacco, 1.35 per cent or 135 cents worth of wood products (cases for beer bottles), and 1.20 per cent or 120 cents worth of paper products (cigarette packs and cartons); no textiles or footwear is required, at least not directly.   These percentages are assumed to be constant.   It is interesting to compare them with the numbers in the input-output table.   If there are no deliveries between two sectors, the technical coefficients are automatically zero.   This is the case for deliveries from the textiles to the beverages and tobacco sector as indicated by the zero in the second row, first column of the input-output table.

---

[1] This was the total value of Dutch paper production in 1957 in millions of guilders.

Armed with all these data—the technical coefficients and the consumer expenditures C_1, C_2, ..., C_{35} three years hence—we can determine how much the textile industry should produce three years hence. All that is needed is to solve a system of 35 linear equations in 35 unknowns, just as a system of three linear equations in three unknowns previously was solved. Fortunately, the Dutch Central Bureau of Statistics has carried out the necessary computations. If T represents the total value of production in the textile industry needed to realize the desired pattern of consumption, it can be found from the relevant table that

$$100T = 0.53C_1 + \cdots + 0.11C_6 + 137.67C_7 + 28.65C_8 + 3.56C_9$$
$$+ 0.81C_{10} + \cdots + 0.32C_{35}$$

If $C_1 = 100$, i.e., if consumers spend 100 guilders on the products of sector 1, the textile industry should produce 53 cents of value to support this demand. If the consumers buy 100 guilders worth of products from sector 6, the textile sector should produce a value of 11 cents. If the consumers spend 100 guilders for products of sector 7, the textile industry itself, that sector should produce a value of 137.67 guilders, and so on for consumer expenditures in the remaining sectors. Similarly, when the amounts consumed total any value other than 100 guilders, the necessary production in the textile industry is proportionally changed. Further, when consumers spend not only in one sector but in all sectors, as always happens in reality, the necessary textile production equals the sum of the individual components.

Perhaps it is surprising to find a coefficient of 0.11 for C_6. This implies, as we just explained, that to consume 100 guilders of beverages and tobacco one needs to produce 11 cents of textile industry products. This seems remarkable, for the production of beverages and tobacco does not directly require any production of textiles: The corresponding coefficient is zero. Indirectly, however, a certain amount of textiles is required. This, too, can be derived from the table. For example, 100 guilders worth of beverages and tobacco requires 1.35 guilders worth of wood and furniture. But 1.35 guilders worth of wood and furniture (sector 9) contains about 2.28 per cent or 3 cents worth of textiles. Analogously, 100 guilders worth of production in sector 6 requires 1.20 guilders worth of production in sector 10, which in turn requires 0.37 per cent or nearly half a cent from sector 7, the textile industry. All these indirect requirements, which may well be even more indirect and complicated, add up to 11 cents.

Let us take an even more general approach by assuming that one wishes to consume a value of 100 guilders in each of the sectors 6 through 10: $C_6 = C_7 = C_8 = C_9 = C_{10} = 100$ guilders. The textile production needed for this consumption has a value in guilders of

$$0.11 \ \text{(for } C_6)$$
$$137.67 \ \text{(for } C_7)$$
$$28.65 \ \text{(for } C_8)$$
$$3.56 \ \text{(for } C_9)$$
$$0.81 \ \text{(for } C_{10})$$

hence, a grand total of 170.80 guilders. Of this total production only 100 guilders worth is consumed. The balance, 70.80 guilders, is used for interindustry deliveries. It is of some interest to compare the components of this value for interindustry deliveries with the corresponding technical coefficients. They are, respectively,

$$0 \quad \text{(for } C_6)$$
$$27.30 \ \text{(for } C_7)$$
$$19.73 \ \text{(for } C_8)$$
$$2.28 \ \text{(for } C_9)$$
$$0.37 \ \text{(for } C_{10})$$

These last values indicate that if one produces goods valued at 100 guilders in each of the sectors 6 through 10, the textile industry needs to produce $0 + 27.30 + \cdots + 0.37$ guilders for direct interindustry deliveries to these five sectors. However, there are indirect interindustry deliveries as well (some of which involve sectors outside these five). And what the textile industry eventually delivers to these five sectors is substantially more, to wit, $0.11 + 37.67 + \cdots + 0.81$ guilders as given above.

3-6. Bottlenecks

So far we have assumed a particular interest, for one reason or another, in the future production of the textile industry. Input-output tables can also be used, however, for far more important problems, such as the spotting and avoiding of bottlenecks. For example, at the onset of World War II the United States had to convert quite rapidly from a peacetime to a wartime economy, where labor and machines were used to capacity. In such a situation bottlenecks can easily arise. To prevent these, the problem must be studied. Stopgap measures which solve one problem but create others are not of much value. If, at a certain moment, a shipyard has sufficient labor available to build a ship, one might decide to build one. But such a ship requires, apart from labor, a lot of iron, iron requires coal, and labor is required to get the coal. If the mines are short of labor, a much better approach might well be to send some of the shipyard employees to the mines. The huge advantage of input-output tables is their clear indication of the indirect effects of certain measures and decisions.

As a final example, consider the following simple illustration. Return to the three-sector model of agriculture, industry, services. The following consumption pattern is proposed: $C_A = 6$, $C_I = 50$, $C_S = 60$, all in billions of dollars a year. In such a program the amounts of consumption are three or four times as large as in the original table. Such a veritable cornucopia would give everybody ample and excellent food, nobody would be without a car, and enough doctors would be available. The corresponding production program [as seen by simple substitution of these values into equation (5) of Sec. 3-5] requires

$$A = 17.4714$$
$$I = 80.0710$$
$$S = 77.2608$$

This is a sizable program, but why not? There is a simple answer: It cannot be realized. As we have seen, a production of agricultural goods of 5 billion gives a sector income of 1.8 billion or 36 per cent. For the industrial and services sectors this percentage is substantially higher. That income consists for a considerable part of remuneration for labor: wages for the glassblower, salary for the bookkeeper, 10 per cent for the waiter. If we want to increase the total production as drastically as proposed here, the required labor also increases sharply (in fact, proportionally). Some increase from year to year is possible, because more people can be employed and/or greater productivity achieved. But the change needed for *this* program is so immense that it cannot conceivably be realized in the short run. The program $C_A = 1.6$, $C_I = 17$, and $C_S = 16.5$ is far more realistic. It implies an increase in total sector income from 32.55 to 35.1 billion, i.e., an increase of 7 per cent. Such an increase might be accomplished by a combination of 5 per cent greater productivity and 2 per cent more laborers.

In this example we discussed a case where labor is the bottleneck which keeps a check on the possible growth. This may indeed be the case in a full-employment economy, but there can be other bottlenecks, such as limited availability of machines or imported goods (balance of payments). These too can be dealt with in the framework of input-output analysis; for examples we refer the reader to the literature.

Literature

There is extensive literature on input-output analysis. The original work in this field is due to Leontief [1], who further elaborated on the topic in [2], which he co-authored with many others.   An excellent treatment can be found in Chenery and Clark [3].   A very interesting appraisal of input-output analysis is given by Hatanaka [4].

[1] W. W. Leontief, *The Structure of American Economy, 1919–1939*, 2d ed., Oxford University Press, Fair Lawn, N.J., 1951.   (The first edition appeared in 1941.)
[2] W. W. Leontief et al., *Studies in the Structure of the American Economy*, Oxford University Press, Fair Lawn, N.J., 1953.
[3] H. B. Chenery and P. G. Clark, *Interindustry Economics*, John Wiley & Sons, Inc., New York, 1959.
[4] M. Hatanaka, *The Workability of Input-Output Analysis*, Fachverlag für Wirtschaftstheorie und Ökonometrie, Ludwigshafen am Rhein, 1960.

4

Econometric Macromodels

4-1. Some Further Thoughts on Economic Interdependence

In the previous chapter we considered economic interdependence of a very special nature. We were concerned mainly with intra- and inter-industry deliveries. Such concepts as unemployment, balance-of-payments equilibrium, the national income (and its distribution) were not given explicit attention. Nevertheless, they are important, and thus we shall devote the present chapter to a discussion of these so-called macro-economic variables. *Macroeconomics* deals with the economic process of a country as a whole. It is not concerned with such problems as the sales of hot dogs in Menasha, Wisconsin, or the unemployment in Beverly Hills, California, or the explanation of why children buy Beatle records. Such problems—however important they may be for the hot dog sellers, unemployed people, and record manufacturers concerned—are of minor interest to the nation as a whole. They are, at best, microeconomic problems. For our present interest in macroeconomics, we work with variables such as total investments, price indices, total exports. This interest is partly motivated by our scientific curiosity: we should like to understand the economic process and the relations which govern that process. It will clearly be impossible to explain every single action or phenomenon—such as the price of cream puffs in some specific store and why Mrs. Close buys these cream puffs at that price. It is evidently more feasible, rather, to describe the economic process in terms of relationships in aggregated economic variables.

Apart from curiosity there is another, more practical interest in the achievements of macroeconomics. It is evident that the variables mentioned in the previous paragraph, such as unemployment and balance of payments, cannot really be influenced by individual persons or firms; it is up to the government to tamper with questions of such magnitude. For example, when unemployment rises, everyone expects the government to do something about it.   The days when government interference was unthought of are past.

Let us consider in a little more detail the example of rising unemployment.   What can the government do about it?   The easiest solution is perhaps to employ the unemployed in government service and have them build roads, for example.   This is not a very attractive solution, however, if only because most of the unemployed are not trained to build roads. Unemployment is the result of stagnation in the economic development, and the government should try to get the economy moving again rather than employ stopgap measures to make the unemployment invisible. This might be accomplished by a tax reduction.   The people will then have more to spend, they will buy more, production will increase to satisfy the increased demand, and more people will be needed for this increased production.   The government will also need to ponder on the possible side effects of the measure, however, such as increasing imports which lead to an increasing balance-of-payments deficit and an increasing budgetary deficit.   We could spin out this line of reasoning, but for our purposes the following conclusions suffice:

1. A sensible government policy demands awareness of the consequences of the measures under consideration.   One should realize, for example, that the reduction of taxes leads to higher consumption, decreasing unemployment, and presumably increasing budgetary deficits and balance-of-payments difficulties.   One should also realize that, due to the economic interdependence, there may be many indirect consequences. For example, the increase in consumption may lead to increased profits, which in turn may lead to an increased willingness of entrepreneurs to invest in buildings, machinery, etc.

2. It is also important to know, or at least to have an inkling about, the quantitative effect.   For example, one would like to know by what percentage the unemployment decreases when the taxes are reduced by 1 per cent.

3. It is also important to have an idea about the time delay before the measures become effective.   This may take a few days, but often it will be much longer before the effects are noticeable.   Such lags are important. Here, too, the question is quantitative: *How* large will the effects be after *how* long a period?

We wish to answer the above three queries, but we cannot promise that the present chapter will be the Santa Claus satisfying all our wishes. With the present state of the art, exact, foolproof answers to all these relevant questions cannot be given.   We shall have to be satisfied with approximate results, as in the discussion of input-output analysis. We intend to form a number of mathematical equations which purport to describe the economic process. A system of such equations, when numerically specified, is called an *econometric model*.

The purpose of this chapter is to show what these models look like. We shall begin with two models where realism is sacrificed on the altar of simplicity. The models do serve, however, to illustrate the fundamental concepts. Thereafter, we shall discuss a more detailed model of the Dutch economy. We shall not discuss the construction of such models; suffice it to say that models are usually constructed on the bases of theoretical economical considerations (for the general form of the model) and empirical statistical observations (for the numerical specification of the model). The latter topic is discussed further in Chap. 12.

4-2. A Very Elementary Model

We shall at first be occupied with a very simplified economy, in which only total consumption C, total investment I, and national income Y perform a role. The country concerned has no contacts with the outside world; i.e., there are no imports and exports.

If income increases, consumption increases. We assume that the situation in the country is such that 80 per cent of the income is consumed. Thus

$$C = 0.8Y$$

This is a consumption function, although admittedly a very simple one. It is not very difficult to construct more complicated consumption functions, but we shall not undertake that here and now.

National income and national product are identical concepts. (Taxes and depreciation are disregarded.) This national product Y must serve some purpose; it will be either consumed (C) or invested (I) in buildings, factories, etc. Thus

$$Y = C + I$$

These are the only two equations of the model. We have two equations in three variables C, I, and Y. It is wise to be skeptical about this model. The primitive wisdom embodied in it will not be of any help in concrete, realistic situations and problems, but it does serve the purpose of clarifying some concepts. Let us first consider the investments I. Suppose that these investments are determined by psychological influences or perhaps wild expectations which are not even remotely based on any economic reality.   This would imply that the magnitude of the investments is wholly independent of the economic process depicted in our model. In such a case we call the investments an *exogenous variable* with respect to this model.   It is, like the weather, a variable whose value is determined by outside influences.   The variables C and Y are, however, determined by the model; they are *endogenous variables*.   The consumption function determines C as a function of Y, and Y is determined in turn as the sum of C and I.

Thus our model consists of two equations in two endogenous variables and one exogenous variable.   The value of the exogenous variable is, by definition, determined from outside; given its value, the values of C and Y can be computed with the help of the model.   We then have two linear equations in two unknowns and hence (barring exceptional situations) a unique solution for both.   Hereby we have indicated the main purpose of econometric models: whether large or small, complicated or simple, the purpose of the model is to determine the values of the endogenous variables from the (given) values of the exogenous variables.   When the number of equations is equal to the number of endogenous variables, the model leads to unique answers, in which case we call the model *complete*.   We shall confine our attention to complete models.

The two equations of our model fulfil the purpose just mentioned in a rather indirect manner.   The consumption function, for example, does not express the endogenous consumption directly as a function of the exogenous investments, but as a function of the national income which is equally endogenous.   The other equation $Y = C + I$ only partly expresses the endogenous income in terms of the exogenous investments; partly it is expressed in terms of the endogenous consumption.   We should like to change this by expressing each endogenous variable explicitly as a function of only the exogenous variable.   This can be easily accomplished: we simply substitute the consumption function $C = 0.8Y$ into the equation $Y = C + I$ to get

$$Y = 0.8Y + I \quad \text{or} \quad 0.2Y = I \quad \text{thus } Y = 5I$$

And since consumption is 80 per cent of the national income we also have

$$C = 4I$$

Thus we have found two alternative ways to describe the same economic model.   The first consists (in our case) of a consumption function and the equation which states that national income equals the sum of investment and consumption.   This is the so-called *structural model*, and the equations which form it are called the *structural equations*. This terminology is appropriate because these equations purport to give the structure of a specific part of the economic process; thus, the consumption function deals with the consumption sector of the economy. The second consists of two equations, $Y = 5I$ and $C = 4I$, obtained by reducing the structural form to the form in which all endogenous variables are expressed as functions of the exogenous variables. Such a system of equations is called the *reduced form* of the model.

Both the structural and the reduced forms serve their purpose. The structural form is handier when we are primarily interested in the relations and connections—the interdependencies—of the sectors of the economy. The reduced form is more suitable when we are given the values of the exogenous variables and want to determine the values of the endogenous variables. Further, if the values of the exogenous variables are changed, the reduced form shows to what extent the endogenous variables change in value. In our simple model the changes in consumption and national income are, respectively, four and five times as large as the changes in investment.[1]

4-3. A Small Model of the United States

Our next model, due to the American econometrician L. R. Klein, is a little more realistic. It contains six equations, based on statistics from the years between the two world wars. The fact that such statistical evidence forms the basis of this model is an important reason to consider it with a little more respect.

Let us first take consumption. It is assumed that the consumption habits of families of employees on the one hand and of self-employed persons (such as a shopowner or a dentist) on the other hand are different. The independent group will presumably have a greater opportunity to invest (expand the shop, buy more modern equipment), and hence their inclination to save will be greater. Also, to a considerable extent, their income often consists of dividends, which are available in cash only after the profit has been made. The consumption will then be delayed. The equation reads

$$C = 16.8 + 0.02P + 0.23P_{-1} + 0.80(W_1 + W_2) \tag{1}$$

and should be interpreted as follows: The total yearly consumption C (in

---

[1] Note that we proceeded in exactly the same way with the input-output model of the previous chapter. That model consists of as many equations as there are sectors. The total production of each sector is an endogenous variable; the total consumption of each sector is an exogenous variable. For the three-sector model, the structural equations are given in equation (4) and the reduced form in equation (5) of Sec. 3-5.

billions of dollars per year[1]) includes a hard core of \$16.8 billion. Furthermore, consumption depends on profits P and on wages $W_1 + W_2$. W_1 is the wage income earned in the private sector; W_2 stands for the wage income earned in the public sector (government). This distinction of wage incomes has been made in view of the third equation, to be discussed below. In the present equation the distinction is irrelevant. The coefficient of the wage income is 0.80, which means that every extra dollar in wage income leads to an extra consumption of 80 cents. Hence, the wage earners save 20 cents of every extra dollar received.

Let us next consider the terms involving profits P. If we disregard the difference between P and P_{-1}, we have $0.02P + 0.23P = 0.25P$. This implies that each extra dollar profit leads to an increase in consumption of only 25 cents. The people receiving their income in nonwage form do *indeed* save considerably more. Actually, however, we do not have $0.25P$ but $0.02P + 0.23P_{-1}$. This P_{-1} stands for the profits made one year ago. If in any year the profit increases by \$1, the increase in consumption during *that* year only equals 2 cents, but in the *next* year consumption will increase by 23 cents. There is a rather substantial lag between the making and the spending of the profit, to the extent that it *is* spent; we saw above that fully 75 cents is saved.

The second equation is an investment equation. In our very primitive model of the previous section we considered the investments as exogenous, but that is no longer the case here. The basic idea is that increasing profits will make the entrepreneurs optimistic regarding the profitability of new investments. Furthermore, the investments must be financed in some way or other, and that is easier when there is a large stream of profits. Hence, the investments I are related to the profits P. Another aspect is how many buildings, machines, etc. (for short, capital goods), the entrepreneurs already have. It will be clear that the more there are, the smaller the inducement to add to them. The investment equation is

$$I = 17.8 + 0.23P + 0.55P_{-1} - 0.15K_{-1} \qquad (2)$$

The K stands for the stock of capital goods at the end of the year. Hence, K_{-1} stands for the stock of capital goods at the end of the previous year or, what amounts to the same, at the beginning of the current year. The negative coefficient (-0.15) shows that a larger stock at the beginning of the year leads to smaller investments during the year, just as we should expect. The coefficient of P (0.23) is substantially larger than the cor-

---

[1] All variables are expressed in dollars of constant purchasing power, which is accomplished by division by a price index.

responding coefficient in the consumption function (0.02). Also, as before, we have a substantial lag; the coefficient of P_{-1} is 0.55, again much larger than the corresponding coefficient in the consumption equation (0.23). Apparently investments are more sensitive than consumption with respect to profits.

The third equation attempts to explain the wage income W_1 which is paid out by trade, industry, and agriculture. (The government wage bill W_2 will be considered as an exogenous variable; we shall come back to this point in Sec. 4-4.) When the total production X of the private sector increases, more employees will be needed, and hence the wages W_1 will increase. Conversely, the wage bill W_1 will decrease when production X decreases. Quite often these effects work with a certain delay, so that here again we have a lagged variable X_{-1}, the production during the previous year. The resulting equation is

$$W_1 = 1.6 + 0.42X + 0.16X_{-1} + 0.13(t - 1931) \qquad (3)$$

The last term, $t - 1931$, may need some further explanation. In the years between the two world wars the position of the unions became increasingly stronger, resulting in a trend of wage increases wholly independent of the increasing production as represented by X and X_{-1}. According to Klein's computations, the growing union movement accounted for a wage increase of \$130 million per year. This is represented by the last term, in which the variable t stands for time measured in calendar years. In 1935 we have $t - 1931 = 1935 - 1931 = 4$, and the term therefore adds \$0.52 billion. The next year we have $t - 1931 = 5$, and hence in that year $0.13 \times 5 = \$0.65$ billion is added. The difference is $0.65 - 0.52 = \$0.13$ billion or \$130 million.

The three equations discussed so far are so-called *behavioral equations*. They describe the behavior of certain groups of households: the consumption behavior of the families, the investment behavior of the entrepreneurs, and the personnel policy (measured by the wage bill) of the entrepreneurs. The remaining equations are, so to speak, accounting identities that must be true by definition; they are called *definitional equations*. The equation $Y = C + I$ of the previous section is an example of such a definitional equation. In this model there are three such equations. The first states that the aggregate production X is destined for consumption C, or for investment I, or for government G. Specifically, if G stands for the government purchases from trade and industry, we have

$$X = C + I + G \qquad (4)$$

The second defines profits P as the value of the total production X minus the wages W_1 minus the business taxes T:

$$P = X - W_1 - T \tag{5}$$

The third states that the capital stock at the end of the year is equal to the capital stock at the beginning of the year plus the net investment I added during the year:

$$K = K_{-1} + I \tag{6}$$

These are the six structural equations of the model.

4-4. Further Discussion of Klein's Model of the United States

We still have a host of questions about the model described above. We must determine, for example, which variables are endogenous, which variables are exogenous, whether the model is complete, what the additional difficulties due to the lagged variables are, what the reduced form looks like. We shall answer these questions more or less systematically. As we have seen, the variables that play a role are the following ten:

C consumption
P^* profits (nonwage income)
I (net) investment
K^* stock of capital goods (at the end of the year)
X^* production in the private sector
W_1 wage bill of the private sector
W_2 wage bill of the public sector
T business taxes
G government purchases from the private sector
t time (in calendar years)

The variables which occur with a one-year lag are starred. For example, C appears in current form in equations (1) and (4) and is nowhere lagged. P, however, appears in current form in equations (1), (2), and (5) and also in lagged form in equations (1) and (2).

What variables are exogenous? In the first place, of course, calendar time (t). The time passes independently of anything, hence certainly independently of the economic process of the United States which we try to describe with our model. Next consider the three government variables W_2, T, and G. If the government really wants to influence the state of the economy—and this is the prime reason for constructing such models—then it would indeed be very surprising if the values of the government variables were to be determined by the economic process. The purpose is precisely to influence the economic process with the help of these government variables. This implies that W_2, T, and G are determined by the government rather than by the economic process in a direct sense; hence, they are exogenous. In total we thus have four exogenous variables: t, W_2, T, and G. The remaining six variables are considered endogenous. We have also six equations; hence, the model is complete.

In order to understand the interdependence of the variables, it is useful to consider a number of so-called *arrow schemes*. Consider Fig. 4-1, which represents the structure of the consumption function. In the large shaded

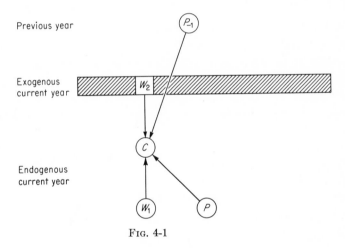

FIG. 4-1

bar we have the current exogenous variables, in this case, W_2. Above the bar we indicate the lagged variables, in this case, P_{-1}. Below the bar we indicate the current endogenous variables: C, W_1, and P. These variables are then connected with arrows in accordance with the structure given by equation (1), which we reproduce here for convenience:

$$C = 16.8 + 0.02P + 0.23P_{-1} + 0.80(W_1 + W_2) \qquad (1)$$

Thus, four arrows point to C, since C is determined by P_{-1}, W_2, W_1, and P.

We can draw such an arrow scheme for each of the equations. The investment equation (2) contains only endogenous variables. Arrows in this case come in at I (a current endogenous variable and hence below the bar) from P, P_{-1}, and K_{-1}; the latter two are above the bar since they are lagged. Together the two equations make up the scheme shown in Fig.

4-2.   And so we continue.   When all six equations are taken into account, we obtain the rather intricate arrow scheme of Fig. 4-3.

What can we infer from this illustration?   Primarily, we can now see clearly how the variables influence each other, at least qualitatively. Thus, W_1 influences C [the upward-pointing arrow; cf. equation (1)], C

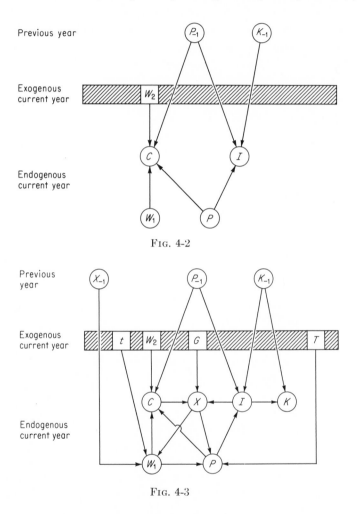

Fɪɢ. 4-2

Fɪɢ. 4-3

influences X [the arrow pointing to the right; cf. equation (4)], and X in turn influences W_1 [the arrow pointing in the southwest direction; cf. equation (3)].   That cycle is now complete.   There are more such cycles: P influences I, I influences X, X influences P.   We cannot see from the illustration how important these influences are.   We could solve this difficulty by attaching the relevant coefficients to the arrows, but that would decrease the clarity.

The arrow scheme teaches us another important point. It shows that there are actually two sorts of variables. On the one hand there are the variables where arrows arrive and depart; these are the current endogenous variables drawn below the bar. On the other hand there are variables from which arrows only depart; these are the exogenous variables in the bar and the lagged variables above the bar. If arrows were to *arrive* at the exogenous variables, this would imply that the economic process is described by a model in which exogenous variables depended on other variables, so that the exogenous variables would no longer be exogenous. It is also difficult to think of arrows pointing toward the lagged variables, for that would imply that values assumed by these variables in the past are determined by what happens today.

The model is essentially concerned with the way in which the *current endogenous variables* are determined. The model specifies (1) relations between those current endogenous variables themselves, as indicated by the arrows arriving at and departing from variables under the bar, and (2) the dependence of the current endogenous variables on all other variables, i.e., the lagged and exogenous variables. In the last instance, the current endogenous variables are fully determined by the exogenous and lagged variables. The arrow scheme itself presents only the *direct* interdependence. If one goes to the root, that is, the reduced form, it turns out that everything is ruled by the exogenous and lagged variables only. This term "ruled by" should, of course, be taken somewhat skeptically; there will certainly be deviations between reality and the model, as we shall see in the next chapter.

How does the reduced form of the model look? We have six linear structural equations in six current endogenous variables. If we solve this system of equations, we find for consumption

$$C = 41.8 + 0.74P_{-1} - 0.10K_{-1} + 0.19X_{-1} \\ + 1.34W_2 - 0.19T + 0.67G + 0.16(t - 1931)$$

The terms on the lower line are concerned with exogenous variables, those on the top line with the lagged variables.

It is of considerable interest to compare this reduced-form consumption equation with the structural consumption equation

$$C = 16.8 + 0.02P + 0.23P_{-1} + 0.80(W_1 + W_2) \tag{1}$$

Both equations have C to the left of the equality sign, but that is all they have in common. Suppose the Secretary of the Treasury would like to increase the national consumption. If he confines his attention to the structural equation (1), he could conceivably reason: "The freedom of private industry cannot be tampered with lest this administration be called antibusiness. I can therefore not influence P or W_1. Obviously, I cannot influence yesteryear's profit P_{-1} anymore. What I can do is to increase the government wages W_2, and apparently consumption increases by 80 per cent of the value of the increase of W_2." If the Secretary reasons in this way, however, he doesn't see past the end of his nose. There is more to the economy than a consumption function. When we also take into consideration the other sectors of the economy (as described by the other equations of the model), we can easily pinpoint mistakes in the argument. In the first place—cf. the reduced-form equation—the increase in the national consumption is not 80 per cent but 134 per cent of the increase of the government wage bill W_2. Furthermore, there are other ways open to the Secretary: he could decrease business taxes or purchase more from industry, i.e., decrease T or increase G. Both measures would increase consumption. This can be inferred from the reduced-form equation which, contrary to the structural equation, does take account of the interdependencies of the economy and the indirect effects of the measures.

One can proceed in exactly the same way with the other current endogenous variables. One simply solves the six linear structural equations by explicitly expressing the current endogenous variables in the exogenous and lagged variables. All resulting expressions are linear; their coefficients are the only matter of importance. These coefficients are given in the following table. The numbers in the first row are the coefficients of the reduced-form consumption equation, which we discussed before.

Current endogenous variables	Constant term	Lagged and exogenous variables						
		P_{-1}	K_{-1}	X_{-1}	W_2	T	G	$t-1931$
C	41.8	0.74	−0.10	0.19	1.34	−0.19	0.67	0.16
P	38.1	0.86	−0.16	−0.06	0.90	−1.28	1.12	−0.05
I	26.6	0.75	−0.18	−0.01	0.21	−0.30	0.26	−0.01
K	26.6	0.75	0.82	−0.01	0.21	−0.30	0.26	−0.01
X	68.4	1.49	−0.28	0.17	1.54	−0.48	1.93	0.14
W_1	30.3	0.63	−0.12	0.24	0.65	−0.20	0.81	0.20

Thus we see that when the government decides to spend a billion dollars more on purchases from industry (i.e., it raises G by \$1 billion), the consumption C increases by \$0.67 billion, the profits P by \$1.12 billion, the investments I by \$0.26 billion, etc. For the other government variables (W_2 and T) the argument proceeds in the same way.

4-5. The Long-run Consequences

We have introduced a Secretary of the Treasury and convinced him to consider the reduced-form equations rather than the structural equations if he wants to study the effects of certain measures. Suppose he trusts our advice but wonders about the long-run effects. Specifically, he has understood by now that an increase of G by one billion increases consumption by \$0.67 billion, profits by \$1.12 billion, etc., but what will be the consequences in the future?

There will be substantial consequences in the future as well. This is contrary to what one might think at first glance, because the reduced form does not explicitly specify that current endogenous variables (such as C) are dependent on lagged exogenous variables (such as G_{-1}). The appearance is deceptive, however, for implicitly G_{-1} does play an important role. Let us explain this with an example. Suppose the Secretary is interested in the production X. We then consider the reduced-form equation of X,

$$X = 68.4 + 1.49P_{-1} - 0.28K_{-1} + 0.17X_{-1}$$
$$+ 1.54W_2 - 0.48T + 1.93G + 0.14(t - 1931)$$

the coefficients of which are taken from the fifth row of the above table. To the right of the equality sign we first have three lagged endogenous variables, which *a year ago* were *current* endogenous variables. If we assume that the structure of the model remains unchanged through time, we have

$$P_{-1} = 38.1 + 0.86P_{-2} - 0.16K_{-2} - 0.06X_{-2}$$
$$+ 0.90(W_2)_{-1} - 1.28T_{-1} + 1.12G_{-1} - 0.05(t - 1932)$$

This is the reduced-form equation for P (given in the second row of the table) "pushed back one year." Hence P becomes P_{-1}, P_{-1} becomes P_{-2}, K_{-1} becomes K_{-2}, etc. If we substitute this expression for P_{-1} into the reduced-form equation of X and if we substitute similarly for the other two lagged endogenous variables K_{-1} and X_{-1}, we find after some arithmetic

$$X = 129.4 + 1.33P_{-2} - 0.52K_{-2} - 0.06X_{-2}$$
$$+ 1.54W_2 - 0.48T + 1.93G$$
$$+ 1.54(W_2)_{-1} - 1.91T_{-1} + 1.93G_{-1}$$

disregarding a term in t (the time) which is not very interesting for our purposes. We have now expressed X as a function of the endogenous variables lagged two years and the exogenous variables lagged one year. We have, so to speak, pushed back the dependence.   The interpretation is evident.   If, for example, the taxes T are increased by one billion, the production X decreases by \$0.48 billion the same year, but by \$1.91 billion the following year.[1]

We can proceed in this way.   We can get rid of P_{-2}, K_{-2}, and X_{-2} by expressing them in P_{-3}, K_{-3}, and X_{-3}, etc., and the result shows us the whole path of the effects through time.   In principle such a path extends ad infinitum, but in practice the coefficients decrease after a number of years to levels where they are no longer important.   For the variable X the path through time is as follows:

	W_2	T	G
In the same year	1.54	−0.48	1.93
After 1 year	1.54	−1.91	1.93
After 2 years	0.99	−1.52	1.24
After 3 years	0.34	−0.63	0.42
After 4 years	−0.22	0.23	−0.27
After 5 years	−0.57	0.82	−0.72
After 6 years	−0.72	1.11	−0.90
After 7 years	−0.70	1.11	−0.87
After 8 years	−0.55	0.91	−0.69
After 9 years	−0.35	0.60	−0.44

It clearly takes a long while before the effects of the measures are worked out.   Moreover, in the fourth year the signs change; an increase in taxes now increases production.   This is an unexpected result, albeit the positive influence in later years is considerably smaller than the negative influence during the first years.   Perhaps the model exaggerates a bit; it is, after all, a very small model with little pretense!

4-6. Large Models

Models which are to be taken seriously have about 10 to 50 equations. To date there are few operative models, i.e., models which governments actually use in mapping out a course of action.   The Netherlands is an exception; the Central Planning Bureau in The Hague has been using such models for many years, in particular, for the preparation of the annual Central Economic Plans.   Preparing such a plan is prescribed by law, which speaks in lofty terms about "a balanced structure of estimates and

---

[1] It is a pure coincidence that the coefficients of W_2 and $(W_2)_{-1}$ are both equal (to 1.54).   In fact, they are not equal, because the third decimal figures are different. The same holds for the coefficients of G and G_{-1}.

guide lines with respect to the country's household." Those who have scruples about government planning should not be overly wary, as it is not planning in the socialist, let alone communist, sense of the word. It does not tell the government what to do, but only shows the consequences that can be expected from alternative government measures.[1] No entrepreneurs are called on the carpet when there turns out to be a large deviation between the predicted and the actual investments.

As a description of all the equations (about 35) does not make a thrilling story, we shall discuss only one equation in some detail. We choose the import equation because the international sector has so far been treated in a stepmotherly fashion. We are concerned, then, with the import of goods (not of services), which are of varied natures. They may, on the one hand, be goods which go straight from the importer to the consumer, such as fountain pens, washing machines, or potato chips. The goods may, on the other hand, be half-finished, to be assembled or further processed domestically before going to the consumer. The largest component of imports, however, consists of basic materials such as agricultural staples (cotton, grains) or sources of energy (coal, oil). Some of the imported goods will eventually be consumed, others will go to the government or will serve as investments (machines), a part will be exported again, and, finally, a part will be stored for later use (additions to inventories).

Thus it can be explained that the import of goods (M) is dependent on consumption (C), government purchases (G), investments (I), inventories (n), and exports, subdivided into exports of goods (E_g) and services (E_s). The latter consists of the transportation services of the Holland-America Line and the KLM, for example, or dredging in the harbor of Bombay. The equation looks as follows:

$$M = 0.38C + 0.39G + 0.71I + 0.63E_g + 0.28E_s + 0.79n$$

The variables have all been measured as changes from year to year. Thus, M stands for the change from the previous year in imports of goods, C stands for the change from the previous year in consumption, etc., all in billions of guilders. The coefficients exhibit rather substantial differences. A large coefficient (0.71) is associated with investments I. This implies that investments have a large *import content;* for each extra guilder invested in machines, buildings, etc., 71 cents worth of imports are required. The coefficient of goods exported E_g is almost as high,

---

[1] Such as raising the consumption price of milk, raising the (government-controlled) rents, paying out higher old-age benefits, devaluing the Dutch guilder, reducing income tax rates.

but the one of exported services E_s is much lower.   This stands to reason, for services require a large use of manpower, which does not usually need to be imported.   For the coefficient of inventories n (0.79) the situation is a little different, because n is not measured in billions of guilders.   The term $0.79n$ means that an increase in inventories by 1 per cent leads to an increase of imports equal to 1 per cent of 0.79 billion guilders, hence 7.9 million guilders.

This, then, is one of the equations.   Together with all others, it forms a complete model of structural equations from which the reduced form can be determined.   From this reduced form one can compute the effects of changes in the exogenous variables on the endogenous variables.   Here, too, the model contains lags, and the effects are noticeable over a number of years.   For example, it turns out that the effect of an increase in government expenditures of one billion guilders on the balance of payments is

In the same year	-0.96
After 1 year	-0.43
After 2 years	-0.27

This means that such an extra expenditure of one billion guilders decreases the surplus (or increases the deficit) by 0.96 billion guilders in the same year, 0.43 in the next year, etc.   The conclusion is self-evident: If the balance of payments does not show a large surplus, the government should be cautious in its expenditures.

Next we shall briefly trace the effects on the cost-of-living index of changes in the import price index and of changes in the wage level. The price index of imports is not perceptibly influenced by the Dutch economy and is thus regarded as exogenous.   Moreover, during the fifties the wage level was subject to government control and hence was also exogenous.   If the values of these exogenous variables change, the resulting change in the cost-of-living index is as follows:

	Price index of imports	Wage level
In the same year	0.24	0.75
After 1 year	0.08	0.10
After 2 years	-0.01	0.02

Thus, if the price level of imported goods increases from the previous year by 1 per cent, the result is an increase in the cost-of-living index of 0.24 per cent in the same year, 0.08 per cent in the next year, and a negligible decrease of 0.01 per cent during the third year. In total, the effect equals about 0.3 per cent. Wage increases are seen to influence the cost-of-living index about three times as much. In both cases the total effect is spread over a number of years, but this so-called dynamic aspect is far less pronounced than in the small model of the United States.

Such a table showing the long-run effects of changes in exogenous variables on endogenous variables is a sort of timetable. To what extent it is accurate, as a good timetable should be, is one of the topics of our next chapter, where we shall consider the accuracy of various prediction devices.

Literature

The first econometric macromodel is due to Tinbergen. His pioneering article has been translated into English and can be found in [1]. His study for the League of Nations [2], which contains a model for the economy of the United States, is better known. Other models for the United States are due to Klein [3] and Klein and Goldberger [4]; the six-equation model discussed in this chapter can be found in [3]. For the reduced-form coefficients of this model and the long-run effects we refer to Theil and Boot [5]. The Central Planning Bureau model discussed in this chapter is given in the Appendix of [6]; a new, revised model is available in [7]. The coefficients given at the very end of this chapter—relating to the lagged effects of certain policy measures—have been taken from a recent book by Theil [8].

[1] J. Tinbergen, *Selected Papers*, North Holland Publishing Company, Amsterdam, 1959, pp. 37–84.
[2] J. Tinbergen, *Statistical Testing of Business Cycle Theories*, vol. 1, *A Method and Its Application to Investment Activity;* vol. 2, *Business Cycles in the United States, 1919–1932;* League of Nations, Geneva, 1939.
[3] L. R. Klein, *Economic Fluctuations in the United States, 1921–1941*, John Wiley & Sons, Inc., New York, 1950.
[4] L. R. Klein and A. S. Goldberger, *An Econometric Model of the United States, 1929–1952*, North Holland Publishing Company, Amsterdam, 1955.
[5] H. Theil and J. C. G. Boot, "The Final Form of Econometric Equation Systems," *Review of the International Statistical Institute*, vol. 30 (1962), pp. 136–152.
[6] Central Planning Bureau, *Central Economic Plan 1955*, The Hague, 1955.
[7] Central Planning Bureau, *Central Economic Plan 1961*, The Hague, 1961.
[8] H. Theil, *Optimal Decision Rules for Government and Industry*, North Holland Publishing Company, Amsterdam, and Rand McNally & Company, Chicago, 1964.

5

Economic Forecasts

5-1. Forecasting: Art or Science?

The need for predicting the consequences of economic measures is self-evident. Occasionally, these consequences are clear-cut, but more often the results of the measures taken are rather uncertain, so that a prediction must be made. Take the example of the rather sizable and consistent unemployment in the United States since 1955. The government is rightly concerned about this phenomenon and tries to make measures to improve the situation, such as the Depressed Areas Bill or, as a more drastic decision, the major tax cut effectuated in 1964. The relevant question is what effect such a tax cut will have on unemployment. Roughly the chain of consequences is that when people pay less taxes, they have more money to spend; thus, they will buy more, more must be produced, and hence more people will be employed. Exactly how many more people, however, needs to be estimated or predicted. Quite apart from this, the measure has side effects that must also be considered. The Treasury will get less funds, the deficit will grow, and again the question is by how much. Another question that must be considered is the effect on the balance of payments. This must also be predicted, or, at least, one should have a rough idea about the size of the effect.

All these predictions are *conditional predictions*, for we are concerned with the decrease in unemployment, the increase in the deficit, the effects on the balance of payments, etc., under the *condition* of a specific decrease in the tax rates. Another example of a conditional prediction is that the Common Market GNP in 1970 will be 50 per cent above its 1964 level provided England is admitted before 1967. There are also *unconditional predictions*, for example, the statement that the GNP in the United States in 1970 will be 50 per cent above the GNP level of 1964.

When should we take these predictions seriously? When can they be given the weighty adjective "scientific"? Or are they always at best educated guesses based on intuition or experience and at worst just off-the-cuff statements, such as our GNP predictions above? The latter attitude is a bit too pessimistic. Since World War II a great deal of work has been done to improve the quality of economic predictions and to make them more reliable. Indeed, good predictions are an important test for the state of economic science. What, then, are the requirements for a *scientific* prediction?

The basic requirement for a prediction is that it should be verifiable (or falsifiable). It must be possible to verify whether the prediction eventually does come true or not, and *both* results must be possible. This excludes trivial predictions of the type "Tomorrow it might rain, but then again it might not," because this cannot possibly be falsified. Also excluded is the prediction "The U.S. GNP in 1970 will be ten times as large as in 1964," because that cannot conceivably be correct. It also excludes conditional predictions based on an unrealistic condition, such as "If the U.S. GNP in 1970 is ten times as large as in 1964, the import volume will be doubled." The most important implication of verifiability is that the prediction should be well defined. "We shall get to the moon some day" can never be falsified because there is no time limit. And the famous prediction of the Oracle of Delphi, "If King Croesus crosses the Halys, a powerful empire will be defeated," is not well defined unless it is specified which empire will be defeated. There are more tricky examples as well, such as "By 1970 there will be no more poverty in the U.S." What, then, is poverty? This is obviously very difficult to define, and anyone making such a bland statement should be called upon to define poverty. As it stands, the remark has no content and cannot, therefore, be verified or falsified.

Quite apart from the fact that the prediction must be verifiable or falsifiable, the forecaster must specify something about the prediction error. In this context, we must distinguish so-called *point predictions* and *interval predictions*. A point prediction gives a specific numerical value or date, such as "The U.S. GNP will be $832,760,000,000.00 in 1970" or "The Americans will get to the moon at noon, October 23, 1970." An interval prediction gives a certain range within which the predicted phenomenon will fall. The predictions "The U.S. GNP will be between $800 billion and $850 billion in 1970" and "The Americans will get to the moon during 1970" are examples of interval predictions. A point prediction will always be false and is therefore not a scientific prediction unless it is amended to have more meaning, as will be done below. With interval predictions the case is different as there are two realistic possibilities: Either the realization is within the limits indicated, in which case the prediction is correct, or it lies outside these limits, in which case the prediction is wrong.

Apparently the case for point predictions is not so simple. What is their value if they are—for all practical purposes—certain to be proved false? Indeed, when that is the only thing that is known about a forecast, it is better not to speak about a scientific prediction. But sometimes we do know more. There are cases in which the prediction procedure is such that statements on forecast errors can be made before data on realizations are available. These are not, of course, statements with certainty, such as "The forecast will turn out to exceed the actual value by 3 per cent." If that were the case, we would subtract the 3 per cent! The statements which we have in mind are of the probabilistic type, for example, "The chance that the realization will exceed the prediction is 60 per cent." In other words, we require that a point prediction be accompanied by such a probability statement in order that it can be regarded as scientific (i.e., verifiable, provided we have a sufficiently long series of such predictions). However, the calculus of probabilities will not be considered before the next chapter, so that we prefer not to go into details.

So far we have been concerned with the verifiability of the predictions themselves, but the prediction *procedure* should also be verifiable. Take again the point prediction "The U.S. GNP in 1970 will be $832,760,000,000.00." Suppose that all requirements have been met; that is, GNP is measured in a precisely defined way, and there is some probability statement attached to the prediction. Even then it is not necessarily a scientific prediction, because all statements could be a product of fantasy (as, in fact, is the case here).

Thus, not only the prediction but also the prediction procedure must be verifiable. Is it possible to make any general remarks on prediction procedures? Yes, indeed. Predictions are based on two sources of information. On the one hand, there are certain theoretical considerations, which may be very simple but also quite sophisticated. On the other hand, there are empirical observations, however few they may be and however poor their quality. A very simple prediction theory rests on the assumption that nothing will change. If the sales of a paint factory during 1965 were 50,000 tons, one predicts the same for 1966. The theory is that the sales volume will not change; the empirical observation consists of the sales volume in 1965. Slightly more sophisticated is the method of *linear extrapolation*. The theory in this case is that the difference in sales volume from year to year remains constant. The empirical observations consist of actual sales during a number of past years. For example, if sales in 1964 were 45,000 tons and in 1965 amounted to 50,000, the 1966 prediction would be 55,000 tons. A vastly more complicated procedure predicts with the help of an econometric model—a system of equations purporting to describe how the economy works. Such models were discussed in the previous chapters. As an example, recall the procedure of forecasting the total textile production three years hence based on input-output analysis, discussed in detail in Chap. 3. Here we have as observations the input-output table of some year and as theory that the technical coefficients computed from this table remain unchanged through time. It will be observed that the theoretical considerations invariably assume that "something or other" remains constant: the sales themselves, the difference in sales from year to year, the technical coefficients, etc. This constancy should not be taken too literally. For example, there might be solid grounds for changing some technical coefficients as time proceeds. As long as these changes are made systematically for clearly explained reasons, however, the constancy remains. In that case it is not the coefficients themselves which remain constant, but rather the procedure by which they are adapted.

By insisting that the prediction procedure be verifiable, one tries to increase its objectivity. An element of subjectivity, if only the choice itself of a prediction procedure, will always remain and forms the "art" aspect of forecasting. The scientific part consists of grinding out the results according to the strictly specified rules of the chosen procedure.

It is often thought that economic predictions are frustrated by the difficulty that the phenomenon predicted (sales, GNP, etc.) is always the result of the free actions of millions of people. This is indeed one of the reasons why the prediction errors in economics are frequently greater than in astronomy. There are also certain advantages, however, in dealing with human beings rather than stars. For one thing, one can ask humans questions and get answers, while even such a simple question as "Moon, are you made of green cheese?" is left unanswered. Of course, it is still quite a problem to get honest answers to relevant questions. The interview technique is indeed an art in itself. Yet, it is perfectly feasible and certainly valuable to ask entrepreneurs about their investment plans for the next year; this is a kind of economic Gallup poll. It will not lead to a scientific prediction in the sense given above, but it might well lead to a more or less correct prediction. After all, the investment plans for next year have already partly been prepared; that is, the entrepreneurs are already partly committed. Also, it is conceivable that scientific procedures can be found to reduce the prediction errors. We shall devote the next section to such an entrepreneurial Gallup poll.

5-2. An Example of an Investment Poll

Shortly after World War II the Dutch Central Bureau of Statistics organized its annual investment poll. It was primarily interested in investments in fixed assets, such as buildings and machinery. Investments in inventories were excluded. The procedure is quite simple. Each January the Central Bureau of Statistics sends a questionnaire to a large number of firms, asking about the realized investments in the past year and the planned investments for the coming year. For each firm that answers, there are two figures (in guilders): the recent realization and the plan for the near future. Next, all participating firms are classified according to the industry to which they belong, and thus investment predictions and realizations can be made for each industry. Were all firms to participate, it would simply be a matter of addition, but this is not the case. The investments per industry are then estimated under the assumption that within the same industry the investment per employee is the same in participating as in nonparticipating firms. Since the number of employees in each firm is known to the Bureau of Statistics, it is an elementary exercise to compute the total investment predictions and realizations for each industry. These numbers are thus based on the assumption —which need not necessarily be true—of equal investments per employee in participating and nonparticipating firms. Quite apart from the errors in the individual plans, this leads to a second source of error, the incomplete data.

The whole of the economy is divided into 13 different industries, such as the metal industry, the chemical industry, and public utilities. For each of those industries the prediction and corresponding realization over a number of years are available. By comparing the prediction made for the year 1957 with the corresponding realization data received in the January, 1958, poll, one can determine the quality of the forecast. This can be very elegantly represented graphically. For that purpose we express both the predicted and the realized investments per industry as a percentage of the previous year's realization. For example, assume that the predicted investment for 1957 in some industry was 50 million guilders and the realized investment in 1957 (which becomes available in the 1958 poll) was 60 million guilders. Furthermore, assume that the realized investment in 1956 (as given in the 1957 poll) was 40 million guilders. Then, expressed in percentages, the prediction is $^{50}\!/_{40} \times 100 = 125$ and the realization $^{60}\!/_{40} \times 100 = 150$. Graphically we measure the forecast along the horizontal axis and the realization along the vertical axis. The numerical example above is represented in Fig. 5-1 by point A. Had the prediction been correct, it would have been 150 rather than 125.

This is given by point B, which lies on the dashed line through the origin. This line, which bisects the right angle at the origin, is the line of *perfect forecasts*. For each point on this line the realization coincides with the prediction; it can be called a bull's-eye. For all points to the left and above this line (such as point A) the prediction is *below* the realization, and hence the investments are *under*estimated. For all points to the right and below the line of perfect forecasts the prediction lies *above* the realization, and hence investments are *over*estimated. This is the case in point C; the realization there is 130 (investments are 30 per cent higher than the previous year), but the prediction was 150 (investments were expected to be 50 per cent higher).

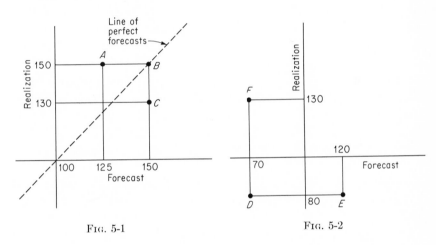

FIG. 5-1   FIG. 5-2

So far we have discussed cases where both the prediction and the realization of investments are above 100 per cent; i.e., in a given year both are larger than the realized value of the previous year. The *direction* is thus predicted correctly: an increase has been predicted; an increase has been realized. There is, of course, one other situation in which at least the direction is correctly predicted, namely, when both forecast and realization are smaller than the previous year's realization. An example is the point D in Fig. 5-2, where the realization of 80 per cent has been predicted as 70 per cent. If the realization had been 80 per cent while 120 per cent was predicted, the prediction direction would clearly have been wrong: an increase would have been predicted, but a decrease realized. This is the case in point E to the right of and below the origin. In the upper left-hand section (point F) the direction is also wrongly predicted, for the prediction is 70 per cent (a decrease), but the realization is 130 per cent (an increase). Incorrect predictions of the direction of change are, of course, thoroughly annoying. Such errors can be wholly avoided by systematically predicting that there will be no change at all. All points will then lie on the vertical axis, but such an artificial procedure has no merit whatsoever if changes in investments are to be predicted.

What are the concrete results of the investment predictions of the 13 industries? Figures 5-3 and 5-4 give an impression of this. (The axes have been scaled logarithmically to give a neater figure.) Figure 5-3 deals with the four years 1953 through 1956; thus there are about 50 points. One sees immediately that the points certainly do not all lie on the line of perfect forecasts. Nevertheless, the result is much better than that of no-change predictions, in which case all points would have been on the vertical axis. In fact, the points are more or less scattered around the line of perfect forecasts. A more careful observation shows that the points are more often than not (about 60 per cent of the time) to the left of and above the perfect-forecasts line. This implies that during the period considered, the entrepreneurs had the tendency to underestimate realizations. In Fig. 5-4, which is concerned with the period 1958 through 1961, this effect is far more pronounced. About 90 per cent of the points are situated to the left of and above the line of perfect forecasts. About half the points lie in the upper left-hand corner, indicating that the direction of change was incorrectly predicted.

The striking difference in the two figures is due to the change in the definition of the concept "investments." Before 1957 the question concerned the cost of the buildings and machines installed during the past twelve months. In this case, the entrepreneur had to predict the actual expenditures on fixed assets to be *installed* during the coming year. Since 1957 the question is how much has been *ordered* during the past year and how much one intends to *order* in the coming year. The new definition incorporates an important difference in timing. What will be installed in the coming year is frequently ordered a long time in advance. Thus the fixed assets to be added during the next year will largely be known; the deviations will tend to be rather small. This is evident from Fig. 5-3. However, the prediction of investments that remain to be ordered is far more difficult and the results far less exact, as seen in Fig. 5-4. Clearly, the investment predictions here are systematically too low. The Central Bureau of Statistics made the change in definition to be able to look further ahead, but this can only be done at the price of a far lower quality of predictions.

Can we repair some of the damage? Well, there is a very simple procedure. The points in Fig. 5-4 are scattered more nicely around the dashed line parallel to the line of perfect forecasts than they are around the perfect-forecasts line itself. The dashed line intersects the horizontal axis at the point where the prediction is 70. Thus, if we mul-

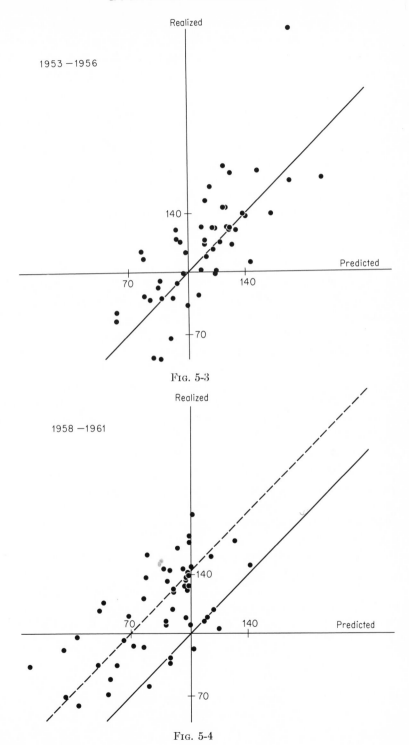

FIG. 5-3

FIG. 5-4

tiply all predictions by $^{100}/_{70} = 1.43$, that is, if we increase them all by 43 per cent, we move all points of the figure parallel to the horizontal axis to the right in such a way that they are now scattered nicely around the line of perfect forecasts.   This is an elegant, simple correction procedure: Keep the present investment definition (*orders* rather than *installations*), wait till the forms return, compute the answer, and increase the resulting forecast by 43 per cent.   The points so obtained give a better result than the original forecasts themselves.   Apparently, the typical manager "forgets" about 30 per cent of his forthcoming investments ($^{43}/_{143}$ is about 30 per cent).

Does this procedure make sense?   Does it work?   To a certain extent, yes, at least during the period concerned.   It works as long as we are interested in the individual industries without worrying about the differences in the level of investments among the various industries.   When we do take these differences into account, the correction of 43 per cent is far too great.   We should not forget that the Figs. 5-3 and 5-4 have the advantage of clarity, but they are wholly based on percentage changes; hence they disregard the absolute magnitude of the investments.   This absolute magnitude is important, however, for economic policy makers are usually interested in total investment, which is found by adding the investments of the various industries.   Suppose now that in Fig. 5-4 the points associated with large industries are close to the line of perfect forecasts and that the small industries are the culprits mainly responsible for the bad underestimation.   In that case, the underestimation of the investment level involves small absolute amounts, so that the underestimation of the total investment amount is less than 43 per cent.

It can be easily verified whether this is indeed the case.   We are concerned with the years 1958 to 1961.   The total predicted and realized investments, as well as the realization as a percentage of the prediction, are given below in millions of guilders:

Year	Realization	Prediction	Realization as a percentage of the prediction
1958	1,990	1,799	111
1959	2,688	2,190	123
1960	3,388	2,664	127
1961	3,771	3,073	123

One immediately sees that the underestimation of the total investment amount is not so very large.   It varies from 11 to 27 per cent.   That is only half of the 43 per cent suggested by Fig. 5-4.

Is it then indeed true that the large industries underestimate relatively less than the small ones? This, too, can be verified. We give below the results for each of the 13 industries, ranked in order of size; the amounts in the first two columns are the averages per year, computed on the basis of the years 1958 to 1961, in millions of guilders.

Industry	Realization	Prediction	Realization as a percentage of the prediction
Metal and metal products	703.7	545.6	129
Utilities	614.2	628.0	98
Chemicals	466.8	438.1	107
Food	330.1	244.6	135
Textiles	198.2	133.6	148
Construction	152.6	93.1	164
Paper and paper products	113.8	76.8	148
Printing and allied products	85.9	49.4	174
Pottery, glass, and related products	84.7	59.9	141
Mining	81.7	79.4	103
Clothing	45.1	27.8	162
Leather and rubber	44.4	28.0	158
Timber and allied products	38.2	26.6	144

The result shows that in the public utilities, chemical industry, and mining, there is little or no underestimation (98, 107, and 103 per cent). The metal industry and the food industry (129 and 135 per cent) also perform relatively well. Of these five industries, four are on top of the list. Thus we observe that there is a clear tendency for the largest industries to estimate their investments most accurately. If we wish to correct the predictions by some simple, automatic device, we could proceed more accurately by considering each industry separately. Then it would be good to verify in advance, however, whether the proportion of underestimation is indeed reasonably constant through time.

5-3. Predictions Based on Econometric Macromodels

Predictions based on econometric models approach the scientific ideal much more closely than those based on entrepreneurial polls. We recall that the purpose of such a model is to predict the values of certain endogenous variables on the basis of the values of exogenous and lagged variables. Hence, once the model has been built, the procedure is straightforward: Determine the values taken by the relevant exogenous and lagged variables, substitute these into the model, and compute the result.

There is an important difference between conditional and unconditional econometric model predictions.   To explain this difference we consider the model consisting of the structural equations, $C = 0.8Y$ and $Y = C + I$, and the associated reduced-form equations, $Y = 5I$ and $C = 4I$.   Suppose now that today is January 1, 1966, and we wish to predict consumption during 1966 with the help of this model.   We know that $C = 4I$, but the exogenous investment I during the coming year 1966 is as yet unknown.   If we now wait until the end of 1966 so that the I value of 1966 is known, our model predicts $C = 4I$.   This is a *conditional* econometric-model prediction, the condition being that the value of I is the actually realized value of I during 1966.   The *unconditional* prediction first predicts I and on the basis of that prediction gives a forecast for C.   If the conditional C prediction is wrong, it is due to a faulty model.   If an unconditional C prediction is wrong, it may be caused by the fact that the model is wrong, but it may also be caused by an incorrect forecast of the exogenous variable I.   Thus, there are two sources of error (model errors and incorrectly specified exogenous variables) in the case of unconditional predictions and only one type of error (model errors) in the case of conditional predictions.   In the present section we shall be concerned with conditional predictions, in the next section with unconditional predictions.

The quality of conditional predictions based on one of the models of the Dutch Central Planning Bureau has been investigated by J. Lips and D. B. J. Schouten for 14 endogenous variables.[1]   The conditional predictions based on this model were compared with their realizations in each of the six years 1949 to 1954.   Thus in total there were $6 \times 14 = 84$ pairs of observations.   For each of these 84 cases the observed percentage change from the previous year was compared with the predicted percentage change.   The results are given in Fig. 5-5, which shows that the points are clustered rather snugly around the line of perfect forecasts and that the number of wrongly predicted directions of change is small indeed.   This picture compares favorably with Figs. 5-3 and 5-4 of the investment predictions based on questionnaires.   To be sure, not all individual predictions are of good quality.   Take, for example, the point N, indicated in the figure, representing the import volume in 1949.   A 26 per cent increase was predicted (compared with the 1948 level), but only an 11 per cent increase materialized, which is not a very pretty result.   The total picture, however, is not bad.

It is only a matter of honesty to admit that the results are not always so

---

[1] The variables are the following: imports of commodities, consumption, gross investment, national product, employment, indirect taxes, nonwage income, income tax paid by wage earners, income tax paid by nonwage earners, and price indices of commodity exports, of consumption, of investment goods, of inventories, and of government commodity purchases.

pleasing. A number of years ago a similar study was made for an econometric model of the United States, of which the coefficients were fitted to statistical data from the years between the world wars. The predictive value of this model for a postwar year was then investigated, and it gave poor results. It is possible, of course, that the structure of the American economy changed after the war, and it is also conceivable that the American economy is more difficult to predict with an econometric

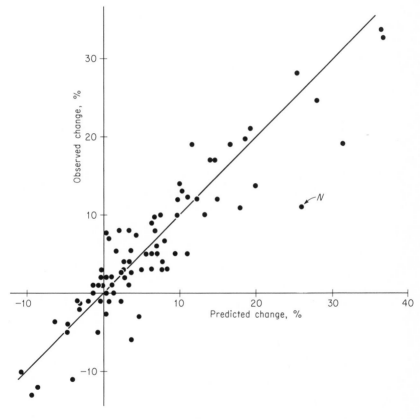

FIG. 5-5

model than the Dutch economy. We do not want to discuss this in great detail, but we want to make one exception. As stated above, both in the Dutch model and in the United States model we are concerned with *conditional* predictions, the condition being that the exogenous variables are given their true value as observed later. Then the question immediately arises of how important these exogenous variables are in the economic process. Take the exports, for example. In the prediction analysis of the Dutch model, exports have been considered as exogenous; moreover, exports are an important variable since they equal roughly half the yearly GNP. It goes without saying that when so important a factor is taken as given, in fact *correctly* given, we are a long way on the road to correctly predicting the endogenous variables of the model. In the United States, on the other hand, exports are relatively unimportant (not even 5 per cent of GNP), and then the knowledge of their value means far less for the prediction of the endogenous variables.

5-4. The Predictive Value of the Dutch Central Economic Plans

So far we have assumed that the exogenous variables were correctly specified. In practice, however, the values taken by these exogenous variables have to be predicted as well, because they are not known in advance. To predict the endogenous variables one first predicts the exogenous variables and then substitutes these into the model. The quality of the endogenous predictions (which are then unconditional) will probably diminish, because apart from errors in the model there are also mistakes in the values predicted for the exogenous variables. There is one marginal note, however. When discussing exogenous variables in the previous section, we mentioned a variable subject to foreign influence, viz., exports. There is another important group of exogenous variables: the government variables, such as taxes and government investments, i.e., the instruments with which the government can try to direct the economy. These government variables are subject to government control, and hence if the government carries through its intentions, the values are correctly and exactly known in advance. Therefore, to the extent that the exogenous variables fall under this category, the rather favorable picture of the conditional forecasts remains relevant.

Now we shall consider the Planning Bureau's predictions as they are actually made. Their quality has been studied by C. van de Panne, who compared predictions and realizations of 23 variables for the period 1949 to 1956.[1] In total, $7 \times 23 = 161$ pairs of observations are available.

---

[1] The year 1952 had to be left out of consideration because that year's Central Economic Plan consisted of several alternative sets of forecasts. The 23 variables are the following: consumption volume, consumption value, volume and value of commodity imports, volume and value of commodity exports, value of imports of services, value of exports of services, surplus on the balance of services, net investment, value added in the private sector, wage bill paid by the government, government commodity purchases, indirect taxes, industrial production, production by the construction sector, labor force, labor productivity, employment in the private sector, employment in the government sector, and price of consumption, of commodity imports, and of commodity exports.

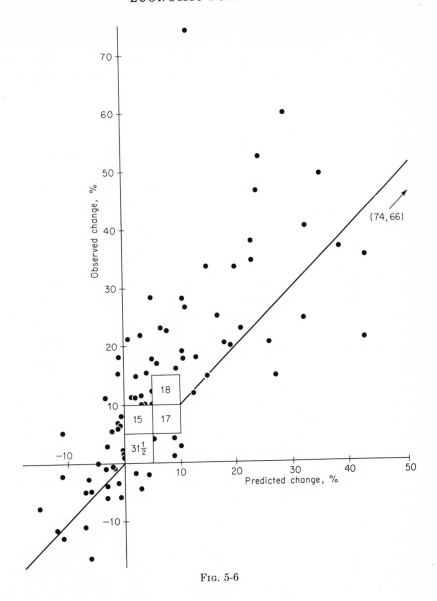

Fig. 5-6

Again, the observations are expressed as percentage changes from year to
year.   The 161 points are depicted in Fig. 5-6.[1]

Our conclusions are twofold.   The first conclusion is that the unconditional predictions are less accurate than those depicted in Fig. 5-5.   This

----

[1] One point is outside the chart and is indicated by an arrow.   The four numbers
($31\frac{1}{2}$, 15, 17, and 18) represent the number of points in the corresponding squares,
the numbers being too large to permit the indication of the points individually.   The
$\frac{1}{2}$ of $31\frac{1}{2}$ refers to a point on the edge of the square.

need not surprise us, because faulty predictions of the exogenous variables now play their role as we anticipated. It nevertheless remains true that there is a clear association between predicted and realized changes. If "no change" had been predicted throughout, there would have been no such association. Of course, a no-change prediction for the postwar development of the Dutch economy would have been vastly unrealistic. Most variables increased, as evidenced by the fact that in the great majority of cases the points are above the horizontal axis. However, even if we had taken this growth into consideration by predicting, for example, a constant yearly percentage increase for all variables, the results would be inferior to those actually obtained. In summary we conclude that the unconditional predictions have certain merits, but that they are clearly less accurate than the corresponding conditional predictions.

The second conclusion is that the unconditional predictions exhibit a systematic error. Consider the points in the upper right-hand corner of Fig. 5-6, corresponding to an increase both in predicted and realized value. These points for the most part lie *above* the line of perfect forecasts, which implies that the predicted changes are smaller than the realized changes. In short, changes have been underestimated. There is no such evidence for negative changes, since the underestimation cases (here below the line of perfect forecasts) are about as numerous as the overestimation cases. However, the number of negative changes is rather small, so that as a whole underestimation of changes dominates on a large scale. Overestimation occurs occasionally, but it is the exception rather than the rule. When we also bring into consideration the third possible kind of error, i.e., incorrectly predicted directions of change, the distribution per year is as follows:[1]

	1949	1950	1951	1953	1954	1955	1956	Total
Change underestimated	18½	17½	12	12	17	17½	17	111½
Change overestimated	3½	4½	8	9	3½	1	5	34½
Incorrect direction	1	1	3	2	2½	4½	1	15
Total	23	23	23	23	23	23	23	161

In total there are 23 cases each year, because 23 variables have been analyzed. We see that each year a majority of changes is underestimated,

[1] The halves result from points exactly on the line of perfect forecasts, which are split and then considered as one half overestimation and one half underestimation. There are also some points located on the axes, which are counted as halfway "incorrect direction."

often a huge majority. A minority (often small) of changes is over-estimated. Finally, there are invariably a few cases of an incorrectly predicted direction of change.

Why is there a tendency to underestimate changes? The immediate cause can be easily given. The culprits must be the incorrectly predicted exogenous variables. In Fig. 5-5, where the actual values of the exoge-nous variables were used, there was no noticeable tendency to under-estimate changes. Then the real question is why we tend to underestimate the changes in the exogenous variables. To answer this question we should note that, in fact, underestimation of change is a well-known and widespread phenomenon. The increase of the Dutch population since World War II exceeded all expectations. The number of cars grew much faster than anticipated. Upsets in sports are the result of changing levels of performance, which are invariably underestimated by sportswriters. Their predictions are usually based on past results, and although there certainly is a correlation between past and present performance, the rela-tionship is not as strict as journalists think. Ultimately, the systematic error is caused by the prediction technique itself. As we discussed before, when the chips are down, the predictions depend on the assumption that "something or other" remains constant. If the "something or other" is the phenomenon to be predicted itself, we have underestimation of changes in its extreme form. By delving more deeply into the fundamental causality explaining the phenomenon, we may hope that the bias becomes less evident. This section to some extent suggests that this hope is justified, for we saw that the conditional predictions based on an intricate econometric model of the Netherlands exhibited no tendency toward change underestimation, whereas the much less sophisticated exogenous forecasts exhibit a sizable tendency in this direction.

5-5. Predictions Based on Input-Output Tables

As a last illustration, we shall consider the quality of predictions based on input-output analysis. This section heavily relies on the work which C. B. Tilanus and G. Rey have done in this area.

We are again concerned with conditional predictions, because input-output analysis purports to predict the total production per sector, given the amount the consumers spend on products of each sector. We there-fore proceed in precisely the same way as we did with the econometric-model predictions of endogenous variables. We substitute the actually observed consumption in the input-output equations[1] and compute the resulting total production per sector. We then compare the prediction

---

[1] For example, the set of equations (5) of Sec. 3-5.

thus obtained with the realized total production in that sector. Note, however, that this total production consists partly of production which goes straight to the consumer. These amounts, as we just explained, are substituted in the input-output equations and are without error. Thus it will be clear that we get a far too optimistic view of the quality of the predictions, as they contain a substantial part which is without error. For example, suppose that the total production in a sector is 100 and the consumption from that sector is 80. Then the total interindustry deliveries of that sector are 20. Suppose now that the prediction of total production is 102, so that an error of only 2 per cent is made. But of those 102 there is a component 80 which is immediately substituted and without error. The difference, 22, is the production for interindustry deliveries. This is the only "real" prediction, and the error, when compared with the realization of 20, is 10 per cent. We should therefore consider input-output analysis as a method of predicting the values of interindustry deliveries per sector (and not of the value of the total production per sector).

Now that we have established what we want to do, let us do it. A major difficulty, then, is that we nearly drown in numbers. We have input-output tables for each of the years 1948 to 1957, 10 in total. We can use *each* of these tables to forecast the total of interindustry deliveries for *each* of the sectors for *each* of these years. Actually, we shall work with 27 sectors instead of all 35 because a number of sectors have hardly any interindustry deliveries and hence are not very interesting.[1] Also, we shall confine ourselves to *fore*casts; this means we shall use the 1950 input-output table for predictions only in the years *after* 1950. Thus, the 1948 table is used for the 10 years 1949 through 1958, whereas the 1957 table can be used only for 1958. We then have a total of $27 \times (10 + 9 + \cdots + 1) = 27 \times 55 = 1{,}485$ pairs of predictions and realizations. We can list all these pairs in a large table, but it then becomes an immense mess. The sensible approach is to order the data in groups and compute certain key numbers which summarize the most relevant aspects.

Let us begin with an example. Take sector 13 (the chemical industry) and the 1948 table. By substituting the consumption per sector in 1949 in the input-output equations associated with the 1948 table, we obtain for each sector the conditional prediction of the total interindustry deliveries. For sector 13 we then find a prediction which, when confronted with the realization in 1949, turns out to be 1.5 per cent too high. So we

---

[1] The disregarded sectors are the numbers 23, 26, 27, 30, and 32 through 35 of the list given in Sec. 3-2.

have an error of $+1.5$ per cent.   We can repeat this procedure for the year
1950, again using the input-output equations based on the 1948 table; we
then find a prediction error of 1.4 per cent.   With the 1948 table, we thus
continue to calculate the predicted interindustry deliveries in sector 13
for each of the successive years until 1958.   The calculations result in the
following prediction errors (in per cent):

1949	1950	1951	1952	1953	1954	1955	1956	1957	1958
1.5	1.4	-11.2	-11.5	-10.7	-7.6	-9.0	-8.3	-9.7	-11.4

The minus signs indicate that the prediction lies below the realization.
    The results are rather irregular, but there is some evidence that the
prediction errors are less in the first years than in later years.   That
stands to reason, for we are using the 1948 table based on the production
structure of that year.   This structure will gradually change.   For the
year 1949 this change will not be very significant, but the changes will
become more important as we proceed.   Accordingly we can, within
reason, expect that the prediction errors will become larger as we predict
further ahead.
    This argument suggests that we should distinguish between predictions
made different lengths of time in advance.   A one-year-ahead prediction
uses the 1948 table to predict the interindustry deliveries for 1949, for
example, or the 1953 table to predict deliveries for 1954.   Given the
available data, we can use predictions made up to 10 years in advance (the
limit being that of the 1948 table used for 1958 predictions).   Let us now
first consider the 10 possible one-year-ahead predictions for sector 13:
the predictions for 1949 based on the 1948 table through those for 1958
based on the 1957 table.   The successive prediction errors are (in per cent)

1.5	0.4	-12.5	-0.7	0.2	3.9	-1.6	0	-2.2	-1.9

Let us consider this group of predictions as more or less homogeneous,
because they are all concerned with the same sector and are all predictions for one year in advance.   The question then arises of how we can
express the quality of these predictions by one single number.   One of
the many ways in which this can be accomplished is to take the average of
the 10 prediction errors.   This has the disadvantage, however, that errors
in opposite directions cancel each other.   Thus, if an error of 3 per cent is
averaged with a following error of -3 per cent, the result is the same as if
there were no prediction errors, which is obviously misleading.   This
difficulty can be overcome by considering the *mean-square prediction error*,

obtained by taking the mean of the squares of all prediction errors. In our case

$$\frac{1.5^2 + 0.4^2 + \cdots + 1.9^2}{10} = 19$$

The basic principle underlying the mean-square prediction error is that the seriousness of a prediction error is proportional to its square. An error twice as large is considered four times as serious. Whether this is realistic depends upon the use that is made of the predictions, but that is another story which we will not go into. What we do notice is that equally large errors are regarded as equally serious irrespective of the direction of the error. An error of $+3$ per cent and an error of -3 per cent both add 9 to the sum of squares.

One can now continue by determining for each sector the mean-square prediction error for all predictions made 1, 2, . . . , 10 years in advance. If we do this for sector 13 we obtain

Years predicted ahead	Mean-square error
1	19
2	38
3	58
4	55
5	50
6	60
7	69
8	108
9	118
10	131

Clearly the mean-square error increases—and hence the predictions according to this criterion deteriorate in quality—the further ahead we predict.

We have now succeeded in characterizing the quality of the predictions in one sector with only 10 numbers. We can do this for each of the 27 sectors and get a total of 270 numbers. This is a vast reduction from the original 1,485 numbers, but still a sizable number. We shall, therefore, try to compress it even more, not only to make the data easier to survey, but to obtain an additional advantage. To see this, one should realize that some mean-square prediction errors were based on precious few observations. For example, there is only one prediction for each sector made 10 years in advance, the 1958 prediction obtained with the 1948 input-output table. The mean-square error ordinarily obtained by squaring all prediction errors, adding these squares, and dividing the sum by the number of observations amounts in this extreme case to squaring the single prediction error.[1] Again, for predictions made 9 years ahead, we have only two observations for each sector. Whenever there are few observations, our results of the mean-square error will be very uncertain and unreliable. By combining observations into greater groups, we can eliminate some of this unstability. This is the additional advantage of compressing the data, which can easily be done by averaging over the sectors. This gives us an indication of the quality of the predictions of the data as a whole (rather than sector by sector).

Thus, for each of the 27 sectors we have the mean-square error of predictions 1 year ahead. If we compute the average of these 27 values, we get the mean-square prediction error of all predictions made 1 year ahead for all 27 sectors. We can repeat this procedure for predictions 2 years ahead, etc. The result is

Years predicted ahead	Mean-square error
1	62
2	131
3	189
4	241
5	294
6	361
7	399
8	473
9	560
10	611

The increase in value is very systematic; for each extra year in advance the predictions are made, the mean-square prediction error increases by about 60. If we compare these results with those for sector 13, we notice that this particular sector has lower values and hence better predictions than the average of all 27 sectors. Indeed, there is a considerable difference between the various sectors in prediction achievements. In general the predictions for the sectors with relatively large interindustry deliveries are better. The coal mining industry is an exception because of the substantial adoption of other sources of energy during the period concerned.

The quality of input-output predictions has now been measured in a nutshell with 10 numbers, corresponding to predictions made from 1 to 10 years ahead. It stands to reason that we now ask ourselves whether

[1] We saw above that the prediction error for 1958 based on the 1948 table for sector 13 is -11.4. The mean-square error for sector 13, if one predicts ten years ahead, equals 131. The statement of the text implies that 131 is $(-11.4)^2$.

the same accuracy can be obtained with simpler techniques.   After all, the construction of input-output tables is a time-consuming and expensive affair.   Therefore, to be worthwhile, it should give substantially better results than more elementary methods.   Let us therefore briefly compare it with a very simple prediction technique.   Assume that in 1948, 60 per cent of the total production of a certain sector was used for inter-industry deliveries and only 40 per cent for consumption.   The inter-industry deliveries for that particular sector are thus $^{60}/_{40} = 1.5$ times as large as the consumption of products from that sector.   The naïve pre-diction procedure which we shall now compare with the input-output prediction procedure assumes that this ratio will remain constant in the future.   We assume that for this sector the interindustry deliveries each year are $1\frac{1}{2}$ times as large as the consumption.   This is a very cheap and easy procedure of prediction, requiring no complete table.

The question is whether this naïve prediction technique gives accurate results.   This question can be answered by computing the mean-square prediction error and comparing the results with those obtained with input-output tables.   It turns out that the input-output method is better as long as the tables are not too old.   To mention an example: Predictions based on the 1948 table are clearly better (at least when averaged over all sectors) than those based on our naïve prediction procedure.   However, suppose we are concerned with the prediction of interindustry deliveries in 1953 and the most recent input-output table available is dated 1948, whereas the 1951 ratios of interindustry deliveries to deliveries for con-sumption are available.   The naïve method can, in that case, be based on more recent figures than the input-output method.   It turns out that the input-output prediction loses its superiority when the available input-output tables are two to three years less recent than the interindustry-consumption ratios.   This is an interesting result which provides a guide line for the degree to which input-output tables can afford to be obsolete.

Literature

A more elaborate discussion on the criteria which a prediction has to satisfy in order to be scientific can be found in Theil [1].   The Central Bureau of Statistics publishes each year the results of the investment poll [2] in Dutch; further details about the quality of the predictions based on these polls can be found in an article by Mouchart and others [3].   In this chapter we have freely borrowed results from others on the quality of predictions based on econometric macromodels and input-output tables; cf. [4], [5], [6], [7], and [8].   This last article by Christ discusses the less successful predictions based on the United States model.

[1] H. Theil, *Economic Forecasts and Policy*, 2d ed., North Holland Publishing Com-pany, Amsterdam, 1961.
[2] Centraal Bureau voor de Statistiek, *Investeringen in vaste activa*, a yearly publica-tion by the W. de Haan Publishing Company, Zeist.

[3] M. Mouchart, H. Theil, and J. I. Vorst, "On the Predictive Value of Investment Surveys," *Statistica Neerlandica*, vol. 17 (1963), pp. 287–297.

[4] J. Lips and D. B. J. Schouten, "The Reliability of the Policy Model Used by the Central Planning Bureau of the Netherlands," chap. 2, in M. Gilbert and R. Stone (eds.), *Income and Wealth*, ser. 6, Bowes & Bowes, London, 1957.

[5] C. van de Panne, "De voorspellingskwaliteit van de Centrale Economische Plannen, 1949–1956," *De Economist*, vol. 107 (1959), pp. 91–123.

[6] G. Rey and C. B. Tilanus, "Input-Output Forecasts for the Netherlands, 1949–1958," *Econometrica*, vol. 31 (1963), pp. 454–463.

[7] C. B. Tilanus and G. Rey, "Input-Output Volume and Value Predictions for the Netherlands, 1948–1958," *International Economic Review*, vol. 5 (1964), pp. 34–45.

[8] C. F. Christ, "A Test for an Econometric Model of the United States, 1921–1947," in National Bureau of Economic Research, *Conference on Business Cycles*, New York, 1951, pp. 35–107.

6

Uncertainty and Probability

6-1. Uncertainty: A Universal Phenomenon

In the previous chapters we repeatedly assumed that certain facts were known, when this was not necessarily the case. For example, in a linear programming problem we came across an entrepreneur whose future sales per quarter were assumed to be known exactly. Or again, in the discussion of the critical path we estimated the time needed for the several subtasks and then proceeded as if these estimates were correct. However, the future is intrinsically uncertain. There is also uncertainty in the construction of econometric models. What is the best model to describe an economy? This depends on the nature of the economy, the purpose of the model, the availability of data, the mathematical convenience, and so on. It is well-nigh impossible to give a clear-cut answer. In fact, we just saw in the previous chapter that there will always be deviations between the model and reality so that the criterion of perfection will never be met.

This is nothing very new. Even in the "exact" sciences we are confronted with deviations between model-predictions and observations. If we take an iron bar and uniformly heat it, the model says that each additional degree of heat results in the same expansion. If we measure the expansion to verify this, we shall find deviations. This imperfection will be due partly to measurement errors, partly to the fact that we did not succeed in really uniformly heating the bar, and partly to more fundamental causes. Thus even in the exact sciences there are deviations between the mathematical model on the one hand and the empirical observations on the other, but they tend to be smaller deviations than in economics. Moreover, in the sciences it is usually possible to experiment and to repeat the experiment time and again. Unfortunately, in economics such repeated experiments are not often feasible. Of course, one can try to copy the idea of repeated experiments by using a large number of similar data observed in the past. For example, our entrepreneur who has to predict future sales can determine for a number of years in the past the ratios between sales in the second and first quarters and then compute the average of these ratios. The sales in the second quarter of the current year can then be predicted once the first quarter sales are known (by applying that average ratio). This all seems quite reasonable, but one should not be too optimisitic about the results of such a method. If the entrepreneur tries to determine the optimum production schedule based on such predictions, it is far from certain that the linear programming solution will lead to the optimum answer.

6-2. The Philosophy of Classical Probability Theory

Given the universality and the importance of the uncertainty phenomenon, we are well advised to treat it seriously. We shall certainly do so, despite the fact that our examples will be of a somewhat flippant nature, such as rolling dice. The origin of *probability theory* is at the gambling tables in seventeenth-century France. Opponents of gambling will be relieved to know that nowadays, however, probability theory is used for such weighty problems as observing the life-span of a radioactive atom and crossing two species of plants and observing the phenotypes of the offspring. It is concerned with phenomena such as the sex of a newborn baby, the number of busy trunklines in a telephone exchange, random noise in an electrical communication system, routine quality control of a production process, frequency of accidents, the number of double stars in a region of the skies, the position of a particle under diffusion. (These examples have been quoted from Feller's time-honored book *An Introduction to Probability Theory and Its Applications.*)

The elements of classical probability theory are best explained with a simple example. Suppose we have an unbiased, or fully symmetrical, coin; suppose further that we flip this coin 10 times. The result will be something like 4 tails and 6 heads. We express this more formally by saying that the relative frequency of tails is 4 out of 10, hence 0.4. Let us continue to throw until we have flipped the coin 100 times. If the result is 54 tails and 46 heads, the relative frequency of tails equals 0.54. Finally, suppose that we are persistent enough to throw 10,000 times, which gives us 5,060 tails and 4,940 heads. The relative frequency of tails is then 0.506.

Frankly, we have not actually performed these experiments, but the results correspond with what one might expect should the experiment be made (and the coin in fact be unbiased). The crux of the matter is that the relative frequency of tails approaches the value $\frac{1}{2}$ as one throws more and more often. To be sure, the road toward $\frac{1}{2}$ is certainly neither gradual nor regular. It is quite conceivable that after a first set of 10 throws with a result 4 tails and 6 heads—relative frequency 0.4—we flip a second set of 10 resulting in 3 tails and 7 heads.   For the first 20 throws we then have 7 tails in total, hence a relative frequency of 0.35, which is even further from $\frac{1}{2}$ than the 0.4 obtained with the first set of 10 throws.   But

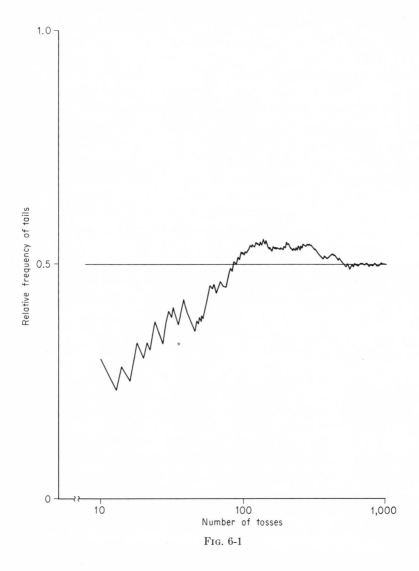

FIG. 6-1

eventually, however irregular the path may be, one can be certain of coming arbitrarily close to $\frac{1}{2}$.   Figure 6-1 with a logarithmic scale along the horizontal axis is more or less typical of the way the path looks.   It is based on numerical results obtained with a computer (by means of a method called *simulation*, which will be considered in Chap. 10).

This imperfect regularity is the basis of the classical probability theory. There are irregular ups and downs in the path, but there is regularity in the sense that eventually the value converges to $\frac{1}{2}$. This latter aspect is expressed by stating that the *probability* of tails equals $\frac{1}{2}$. The probability of an event is always a number between 0 and 1, inclusive. If an event is certain to occur, its probability is by definition equal to 1; if it is certain that the event will not occur, its probability is 0.

Probability theory is in fact geodesy in the territory of uncertainty. If an event is certain, the probability theorist measures 1. If the event is nearly certain, he measures something close to 1, such as 0.98. If the event is very unlikely, the measurement will be 0.05 or something of that order of magnitude. There is some freedom with respect to the values the probability theorist ascribes to the events, but there are limitations to this freedom. For one thing, he should not stretch the truth as observed by postulating probabilities far away from the observed relative frequencies. As an example, it is not necessarily true that the coin is unbiased. It is quite conceivable that the probability of tails will turn out to be 0.52; this will become evident when the coin is tossed many, many times.

There are more stringent limitations to the freedom. Certain rules should be satisfied independently of the specific application. These are the so-called *axioms*, to be compared with the geometric axiom "through two points there is one and only one straight line." There are three axioms of which the first two have been discussed above:

1. The probability of an event is a number between 0 and 1 inclusive.
2. The probability of a certain event is 1.
3. If two (or more) events are mutually exclusive—that is, if they cannot occur together—the probability that one of these events will happen equals the sum of the separate probabilities of occurrence of the individual events.

This last axiom may be clarified as follows. Let us throw a die a great many times. We will then observe—if the die is unbiased, not loaded, "honest"—that the relative frequencies of throwing 1, 2, 3, 4, 5, and 6 are all equal to $\frac{1}{6}$. Consider then the events "throwing 5" and "throwing 6." These events are mutually exclusive because one cannot simultaneously throw a 5 and a 6 with the same die. If we throw 60 times, the result may be: 13 times "5" and 9 times "6," so that the relative frequencies are $\frac{13}{60} = 0.217$ and $\frac{9}{60} = 0.150$, respectively. We have "5 or 6" in $13 + 9 = 22$ cases, so that the relative frequency of "5 or 6" is found by adding the separate relative frequencies of "5" and "6":

$$\frac{13}{60} + \frac{9}{60} = 0.367$$

Obviously, this addition rule for relative frequencies holds whenever the two events (like "5" and "6") cannot occur at the same time. We know, however, that probabilities are defined as the limits which the relative frequencies approach when the number of experiments increases more and more. It is therefore fairly obvious to impose the same rule on probabilities. That is what the third axiom amounts to.

The situation is different when the two events are not mutually exclusive. For example, let A be the event of a throw of 1, 2, or 3. Then event A has a probability of $\frac{1}{6} + \frac{1}{6} + \frac{1}{6} = \frac{1}{2}$ in view of the third axiom, because the results "throwing 1," "throwing 2," and "throwing 3" are mutually exclusive. Let event B be the throwing of an even number, 2, 4, or 6. Again, the probability of event B equals $\frac{1}{2}$. Notice, however, that event A and event B are not mutually exclusive. In fact, both occur simultaneously when 2 shows up as the result. The event "A or B," which occurs when a 1, 2, 3, 4, or 6 turns up, has a probability which is equal to $\frac{1}{6} + \frac{1}{6} + \frac{1}{6} + \frac{1}{6} + \frac{1}{6} = \frac{5}{6}$, again according to the third axiom. But the probability of event A is $\frac{1}{2}$, and that of event B is also $\frac{1}{2}$. Their sum 1 is thus larger than $\frac{5}{6}$, i.e., larger than the probability of "A or B." This also holds quite generally: If two events A and B can occur simultaneously, the probability of "A or B" is smaller than the sum of the individual probabilities of A and B.

6-3. Discrete Distributions

The quotations from Feller's book have shown that probability theory is concerned with a vast variety of phenomena. Some of these are qualitative in nature, which means that they are not measured by a number, for example, the sex of a newborn baby. (One might be interested to know that the probability of the birth of a boy is about 0.51.) However, we shall confine ourselves to quantitative chance events which can be numerically measured, such as the result of a throw of a die. This example also has the property that only certain specified possibilities can be realized (1, 2, 3, 4, 5, 6). Whenever this is the case, we speak of a *discrete distribution*, which will be our main concern for the time being. For our die example, the distribution is illustrated in Fig. 6-2. On the horizontal axis we indicate the values of the phenomenon with which we are concerned, in this case the possible outcomes of the throws. On the vertical axis we measure the probability with which these outcomes occur. Thus we obtain the picture of 6 vertical bars, each with a height $\frac{1}{6}$.

The die example is of course only one out of many possible examples. Probability theory—like other parts of mathematics—derives its importance from the fact that it can be applied to so many different problems. It is therefore important to introduce a terminology independent of the concrete example at hand.   We shall agree to call the variable on the horizontal axis the *random variable*.   The random variable is here the outcome of the roll of a die, but it can also be the number of births in Massachusetts per day, the sales of automobile tires in Atlanta, Georgia, per month, or the number of rejected radios leaving a conveyor belt per week.   Incidentally, it is an exception when the probabilities of the values assumed by the random variable are all equal, as in the die example.   In general, the heights of the bars will differ as illustrated in Fig. 6-3.   Such

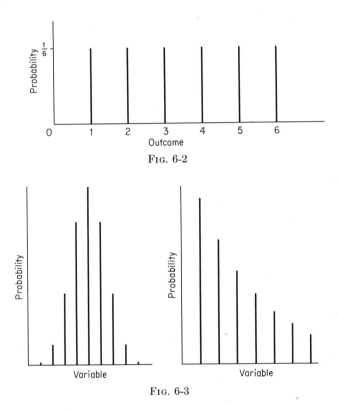

FIG. 6-2

FIG. 6-3

figures are known as *probability mass functions* or *distributions* of a random variable.   Probability mass functions specify the probabilities with which the values of the random variable occur.

6-4. Expectation and Variance

The discrete probability mass function is specified by indicating (1) the values which the random variable can assume and (2) the associated probabilities.   Such a specification becomes very cumbersome when the random variable can assume a great number of values, in particular when the associated probabilities are not all equal, as in our die example.   So we are tempted to search for measures which describe in a nutshell the most important characteristics of the distribution. The best known of these measures is the *mathematical expectation* or the *expected value* or the *mean value* of the distribution. It is a measure of what one might expect, on the average, as a result. Assume that we have a random variable which can take on the n values

$$x_1, x_2, x_3, x_4, \ldots, x_n$$

and let the associated probabilities be

$$p_1, p_2, p_3, p_4, \ldots, p_n$$

The mathematical expectation is defined as

$$\mu = p_1 x_1 + p_2 x_2 + p_3 x_3 + p_4 x_4 + \cdots + p_n x_n$$

At the left-hand side we write μ, the Greek letter mu, which is conventionally used to denote the expected value. According to the definition, the expected value is found by taking all values which the random variable can assume, multiplying these values by their probabilities, and adding the results. In more formal language, μ is said to be a weighted average of the values $x_1, x_2, x_3, \ldots, x_n$ with weights equal to the probabilities $p_1, p_2, p_3, \ldots, p_n$. The expected value in our die example is

$$\mu = \tfrac{1}{6} \times 1 + \tfrac{1}{6} \times 2 + \tfrac{1}{6} \times 3 + \tfrac{1}{6} \times 4 + \tfrac{1}{6} \times 5 + \tfrac{1}{6} \times 6 = 3\tfrac{1}{2}$$

In view of our first axiom, all the p's just introduced must be zero or positive, because they stand for probabilities. In view of our second and third axiom, their sum must be 1:

$$p_1 + p_2 + p_3 + \cdots + p_n = 1$$

because the outcomes $x_1, x_2, \ldots, x_n$ are mutually exclusive and it is certain that one of them will be realized. The die example satisfies this requirement; the sum of the p's is found by adding six $\tfrac{1}{6}$s.

The expectation of a distribution is a reasonable measurement with which to characterize the central tendency, i.e., the average result. The actually realized outcome, of course, may differ substantially from the expectation. The die example again provides an easy illustration. The expected value is $3\tfrac{1}{2}$, and when we throw a 3 or a 4, we are reasonably close.[1] But we can also throw 1, which happens with a probability of $\frac{1}{6}$ and hence is a far from negligible possibility. It therefore stands to reason that we want to have a measure for the degree to which the actual values may differ from the expected value. The most common measure is known as the *variance* of a distribution. It is written as σ^2, σ being the Greek letter sigma, and is therefore sometimes called "sigma squared." This is a measure of the dispersion around the expectation, defined as follows: The variance is a weighted average of the squared differences between the realized values and the expected value, with weights equal to the probabilities.

In the die example, the expected value is $3\frac{1}{2}$. The differences between realized and expected values are

$$1 - 3\tfrac{1}{2} = -2\tfrac{1}{2} \qquad 2 - 3\tfrac{1}{2} = -1\tfrac{1}{2} \qquad \cdots \qquad 6 - 3\tfrac{1}{2} = 2\tfrac{1}{2}$$

We square these differences, multiply each by the probability weight $\frac{1}{6}$, and consider the weighted sum:

$$\sigma^2 = \tfrac{1}{6}(-2\tfrac{1}{2})^2 + \tfrac{1}{6}(-1\tfrac{1}{2})^2 + \cdots + \tfrac{1}{6}(2\tfrac{1}{2})^2 = 2\tfrac{11}{12}$$

In general terms: If the possible values of the random variable are x_1, x_2, . . . , x_n and the associated probabilities are p_1, p_2, . . . , p_n, the variance equals

$$\sigma^2 = p_1(x_1 - \mu)^2 + p_2(x_2 - \mu)^2 + \cdots + p_n(x_n - \mu)^2$$

where $\mu = p_1 x_1 + p_2 x_2 + \cdots + p_n x_n$ is the expected value. The variance can never be negative, for neither squares nor probabilities are ever negative. The variance is 0 if and only if all possible values x_1, x_2, . . . , x_n coincide with μ; this happens when the random variable takes on only one value.

The square root of the variance, σ, is known as the *standard deviation* of the distribution. The standard deviation is also often used as a measure of the dispersion. In the die example its value is 1.71, because $\sqrt{2\tfrac{11}{12}} = 1.71$ (in two decimal places). In summary we conclude that if an unbiased die is thrown, the outcome is distributed around an expected value of $3\frac{1}{2}$ with a standard deviation equal to 1.71.

6-5. Continuous Distributions

Until now we have confined our attention to the discrete case, in which the random variable can assume only specific values (usually integer values

---

[1] In this case the expectation cannot possibly coincide with the result, for one cannot throw $3\frac{1}{2}$. This is comparable to the statement that the average American family has $2\frac{1}{2}$ children.

0, 1, 2, . . .).   There are numerous examples of such variables: the number shown on a die, the number of deadly accidents in California per day, the number of baseballs lost per game, the number of cars waiting for the Holland Tunnel at 5.30 P.M.   Nevertheless, there are other situations in which the variable can take on all values, or all values within a certain interval, such as all positive values.   In that case we speak of *continuous random variables;* for example, the height of soldiers, the time a car spends in the Holland Tunnel if it enters between 5.15 and 5.30 P.M., the amount of rainfall per month in Pierre, South Dakota.   We can, of course, reduce these examples again to the discrete type if we round off the numbers. For example, if we measure the height of soldiers in inches, we have a discrete variable which (apart from negligible exceptions) will assume values of 60, 61, . . . , 85 with certain probabilities.   But this is a stop-gap measure that does not go to the root of the problem.

We shall discuss continuous random variables using the following example.   Suppose we have randomly chosen 50 American families for a budget survey.   All families consist of husband and wife and two children, and all have a monthly income of $1,000.   We are interested in the total monthly expenditures of these families.   Obviously, although all these families are of the same size and earn the same amount of money, their expenditures will not all be identical.   Tastes differ, as do other circumstances such as hospital bills, vacation trips, attitudes toward saving.   These monthly expenditures are considered as random variables. If we list the families alphabetically, we have the following picture (measured in dollars spent per month):

1. 716	14. 797	27. 768	40. 827
2. 937	15. 759	28. 818	41. 939
3. 782	16. 862	29. 808	42. 786
4. 835	17. 883	30. 998	43. 724
5. 1082	18. 722	31. 891	44. 837
6. 1012	19. 803	32. 768	45. 572
7. 701	20. 570	33. 623	46. 836
8. 834	21. 878	34. 816	47. 937
9. 864	22. 866	35. 879	48. 904
10. 811	23. 766	36. 820	49. 733
11. 798	24. 916	37. 931	50. 839
12. 714	25. 876	38. 835	
13. 801	26. 700	39. 874	

Results of this nature appear to be the same as those obtained by throwing a die 50 times and recording the results.   The difference is that the result of throwing a die can assume only one of six alternative values, whereas the monthly consumption expenditures can, in principle, take on any value.[1]

There are some problems when we want to present these outcomes graphically. When a probability distribution is of the continuous type, we no longer use a mass function to specify the shape of the distribution, because the probability of finding a family with an expenditure of exactly $784.39 is extremely small, if not zero. Therefore, we count the frequency of families per interval (for instance the interval of $600–$700) and divide not only by the total number of families (50) but also by the width of the interval (in this case $100). The resulting numbers are

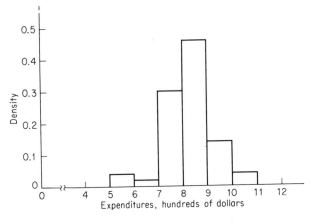

Fig. 6-4

called *probability densities* or just *densities*. The resulting figure is called a *probability density function* (as distinguished from a probability mass function). Let us apply this to our specific example. We notice that there are no families that spend less than $500, two families with expenditures between $500 and $600, only one with expenditures between $600 and $700, etc. The relative frequency of families with expenditures below $500 is therefore 0; between $500 and $600, $\frac{2}{50} = 0.04$; between $600 and $700, $\frac{1}{50} = 0.02$; etc. We now make a diagram with the expenditures measured horizontally and the density vertically. The

---

[1] The quibbling reader may object that it must always be a multiple of a penny, and hence a discrete variable. That may be true, but the convention is to disregard the discrete nature of the random variable if the steps are very small compared with the variability of the phenomenon. A penny is very small compared with the observed differences between expenditures which can be hundreds of dollars. (For simplification, we have recorded the expenditures in dollars without bothering about the pennies.)

resulting probability density function is depicted in Fig. 6-4.   One can see that the majority of families spends about $800; the balance is saved.

Suppose now that we have 150 rather than 50 families, each with a husband, wife, and two children and each earning the same income. Then we can apply exactly the same procedure.   The results—which are not reproduced here—can again be compiled in a diagram.   Because we have more observations, we shall distinguish more classes.   Instead of counting the number of families with expenditures between $500 and $600, $600 and $700, . . . , we shall now count the number with expenditures between $500 and $550, $550 and $600, ...   The width of the interval is hence reduced from $100 to $50.   We obtain Fig. 6-5, which looks roughly the same as but perhaps a little more regular than Fig. 6-4.

Actually, we are doing the same thing as we did at the outset of this chapter when we flipped more and more coins.   There we studied the relative frequency of tails, and the result was 0.4 when we threw 10 times, 0.54 when we threw 100 times, 0.506 when we threw 10,000 times.   We concluded that the relative frequency converged to the value $\frac{1}{2}$, which we subsequently called the probability of tails.   The case here is analogous. We study the distribution of expenditures of families of a certain type (husband, wife, two children, and an income of $1,000 a month) by considering more and more families.   Here, also, we find an increasing regularity which in fact converges to a limit that is depicted in Fig. 6-6.   This curve is again a probability density function; in particular it is the density function of the so-called *normal distribution*.   The mathematical form of this function is

$$f(x) = \frac{1}{\sigma \sqrt{2\pi}} e^{-\frac{1}{2}(x-\mu)^2/\sigma^2}$$

a rather complicated formula indeed.   There are 5 symbols, x, π, e, μ, and σ.   The x stands for the values which the random variable (the expenditures) can assume.   The π and the e are just numbers; $\pi = 3.14159$ . . . , and $e = 2.71828$ . . . .[1]   The use of the symbols μ and σ suggests that they represent the expected value and the standard deviation of the distribution.   That this is true can be verified with the mathematical technique of integration, but we shall not derive it here.

It is interesting to compare discrete with continuous probability distributions.   In the discrete case there is only a certain number of values which the variable can assume; there is a positive probability that the

---

[1] The number e can be defined as a limit.   Take any positive number n and determine the nth power of $1 + 1/n$; then let n approach infinity.   For $n = 1$, we find 2; for $n = 2$, we get 2.25; for $n = 3$, we obtain 2.37; etc.   As n increases, we approach 2.71828 . . . .

variable will indeed assume each of these possible values. All other values have a probability of 0: they cannot possibly occur. The graph of a discrete probability function consists of a number of vertical bars. The sum of the heights of these bars equals 1 because it is certain that one of the possible values will be realized. In the continuous case the

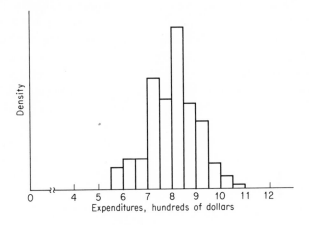

FIG. 6-5

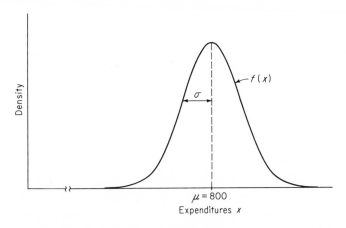

FIG. 6-6

random variable can, in principle, take on an infinite number of values. The probability that the random variable in our continuous example will take on a value between 750 and 800 is given by the shaded area in Fig. 6-7. The *total* area under the curve equals 1, which follows from the fact that some value will be realized with certainty.

Let us return to Fig. 6-6. The density function of the normal distribution is bell-shaped and symmetric. If we start at the left of the figure (corresponding with low values of the random variable) and move to the right, the curve at first increases.   In fact, it increases more and more rapidly.   Then we reach a point where, although the curve continues to increase, the rate of increase becomes smaller and smaller.   This point corresponds to the point $\mu - \sigma$ on the horizontal axis.   The curve increases until it reaches its maximum at the expected value μ; then it decreases at an ever increasing rate until it reaches the point corresponding with $\mu + \sigma$ on the horizontal axis.   From then on the curve decreases at an ever slower rate.   The curve always remains above the horizontal axis.   The zero value is reached only at "infinity," that is, never.   One might resent the fact that, in principle, the expenditures of families can therefore be infinitely large or, even more absurd, negative.   This objection, though theoretically correct, has no relevance in practice.   The

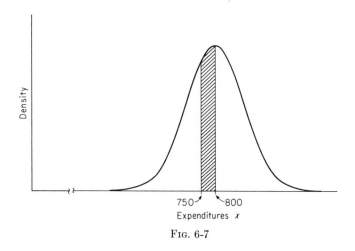

Fig. 6-7

normal curve used here has an average of $800 per month and a standard deviation of $100 per month.   With the help of a table of the normal distribution, one then finds that the probability of actually coming across a negative value is about 6×10^{-16} (0.000,000,000,000,000,6).   In other words, if we investigate daily the expenditures of one million (10^6) families and if we do this for a billion (10^9) days, i.e., about 30,000 centuries, we might find a family with negative expenditures.   If our models do not give rise to difficulties more often than this, we may be extremely satisfied. To be honest about it, there *are* more difficulties, but they are of a different nature.

A minute ago we referred to a table of the normal distribution.   Indeed, this distribution has been very carefully tabulated in great detail.   We shall not discuss this extensively, but might mention one feature which is illustrated in Fig. 6-8.   It answers the following question: What is the probability that the variable assumes a value which is more than two standard deviations away from its mean? We are then on the horizontal axis to the left of $\mu - 2\sigma$ or to the right of $\mu + 2\sigma$, and the probability is given by the sum of the two shaded areas. Numerically, the probability is 0.0455 (a little less than 1 in 20). This is true for *all* normal distributions whatever value their mean and standard deviation may have. To repeat, whenever a random variable is normally distributed, slightly less than once in 20 times will one find an observation which deviates from the expected value by more than 2 standard deviations. Statements of this nature are frequently used in statistics.

The only continuous distribution we have discussed is the normal distribution. This can be justified not only because the normal distribution often snugly fits the empirical observations but also because the

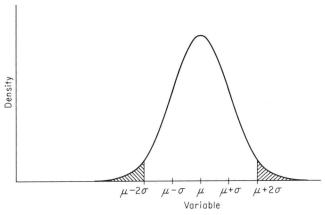

Fig. 6-8

normal distribution is of great importance in mathematical statistical theory. This is formulated in the central limit theorem, which states that if we add a number of random variables, their sum will be approximately normally distributed if the number of variables is sufficiently large. This holds only under certain conditions, the most important of which is that there should be no systematic connection between the separate random variables. This requirement is violated when we are concerned with the height and the waist line of the same woman. Indeed, a tall woman, more often than not, has a greater waist line than a small woman. Hence there is a certain connection between the variables, height and waist line of the same woman.

Yet the importance of the normal distribution is sometimes overestimated. It has been jocularly said that statisticians believe that the normal distribution is based on a mathematical law, while mathematicians believe that the normal distribution is based on empirical statistical observations. This would then explain its popularity in mathematical statistics. Obviously, other continuous probability density functions exist besides the normal one. In Chap. 9 on queueing problems we shall meet another kind of continuous distribution.

Literature

There are a great many textbooks on probability theory and statistics, though most of them require a substantial working knowledge of mathematics. This is true for Feller's book [1] which we quoted in the text. A good elementary (and inexpensive) book is that of Gnedenko and Khinchin [2]. A competently written book by Moroney [3] will require some effort from the reader, but presupposes no mathematics; it emphasizes statistics rather than probability theory.

[1] W. Feller, *An Introduction to Probability Theory and Its Applications*, vol. 1, 2d ed., John Wiley & Sons, Inc., New York, 1957.
[2] B. V. Gnedenko and A. Ya. Khinchin, *An Elementary Introduction to the Theory of Probability*, translated from the 5th Russian ed., Dover Publications, Inc., New York, 1962.
[3] M. J. Moroney, *Facts from Figures*, 3d rev. ed., Pelican Books, Penguin Books, Inc., Baltimore, 1956.

7

The Concept of a Strategy

7-1. Strategy and Tactics

"He is a competent tactician, but not a great strategist." This means, of course, that the person concerned meets rather well the little crises as they occur from day to day, but that he does not think enough about future planning and the consequences of his actions in the long run. He has no strategy.

The game of chess provides a convenient example to introduce the concept of a strategy. Take an arbitrary position, and assume that White must make the next move. If White is a halfway decent chess player, he will consider a number of alternative possibilities, he will try to anticipate Black's answer, he will then think about his answer to Black's possible answers, etc. If White in this way thinks a number of moves ahead, he makes what is technically called a combination. A strategy is such a combination; it is an absolutely full-fledged and complete combination from the very beginning to the very end of the game.

To understand the situation in which we are about to be involved, let us make a slight detour, and consider two different types of behavior which are met in practice, though seldom in their extreme form. One attitude is: Let us cross the bridge when we reach it. The other is the attitude of the person who thinks of all conceivable eventualities that no normal living soul would ever consider. Neither attitude is ideal. The happy-go-lucky person who solves problems as they arise does not look ahead and never considers how the problem might have been avoided in the first place. The other type tends to find a problem for every solution rather than a solution for every problem and gets so mixed up in thinking that no time is left to act. Suppose, however, that thinking and considering take place sufficiently quickly and effortlessly. Then, clearly, this attitude is not at all that objectionable; in fact, we shall return to the chess game under the assumption that White is superhumanly smart.

127

He can then perceive all possible contingencies that might occur and can have his answer ready. His answer will preferably lead him to a victory in the end, or at least to a draw. With this object in mind, White determines his best opening. As soon as Black makes his move, White replies. This can be done quickly, since White has prepared his answer to each possible move Black might make. This, then, is a *strategy* or a *decision rule*. The strategy specifies, for all successive stages, a decision dependent on the information which will be available at the moment the decision has to be made. In our example, White's strategy enables him to move immediately when it is his turn; his move is dependent on the previous course of the game, including Black's last move. In short, a strategy has its answer ready, whatever the circumstances may be.

7-2. Examples of Strategies

A strategy, as we saw, is a decision rule which prescribes what one will do in every conceivable situation that may arise. For example, President Kennedy made a statement in August, 1963: "Whatever will happen, the gold value of the dollar will remain unchanged." This is a nearly trivial example of a strategy, but it *is* a strategy, for it is a decision rule that prescribes what to do with the gold value of the dollar in every conceivable situation that may arise. A somewhat more interesting example is provided by a thermostat. Such an instrument can be instructed, for example, to turn the heater off if the room temperature reaches 73°F, but to turn it on again when the temperature drops to 67°F. This is a decision rule instructing the thermostat what to do in every (heating and temperature) situation that may arise. Hence, it is a strategy.

The first conclusion is that once a strategy has been formulated, a machine properly constructed and instructed can do the work. This is nicely illustrated in the thermostat example and follows from the concept of a strategy. If indeed the answers have been formulated for all situations that can conceivably arise, there is no reason why a clever technician could not construct an instrument which automatically gives the answer according to the specified rule. The second conclusion is that it is not really necessary to mention or sum up explicitly "every conceivable situation that may arise." Indeed, that would frequently be impossible. However, because one is interested only in the decisions to be made, *all those situations which lead to the same decision can be lumped together.* In the gold-value example, this means literally lumping all situations together, since the decision is the same in all situations. In the thermostat example, there are only three different decisions, so three different (sets of) situations are distinguished:

1. *Situation:* The heat is on, and the temperature reaches 73°F.   The *decision* is to turn the heat off.

2. *Situation:* The heat is off, and the temperature drops to 67°F.   The *decision* is to turn the heat on.

3. In *all other situations* the *decision* is to keep the state of heating (on or off) unchanged.

This happy result, however, does not help us in the game of chess discussed in the previous section.   There the difficulty is that the number of different situations and the number of different answers required in practice are too large to sum up.   In chess a strategy is conceptually possible, but practically not feasible.   We shall now discuss the easier game of ticktacktoe (zeros and crosses), which has exactly the same structure as chess—two players moving in turn and seeing each other's moves—but which is so simple that a very good strategy can indeed be formulated.

7-3. Ticktacktoe

The game of ticktacktoe is played on nine squares as illustrated below:

1	2	3
4	5	6
7	8	9

There are two players, A and B, who in turn occupy one (not previously occupied) square.   For example, A fills in 5, then B occupies 1, next A occupies 8, etc.   The object of the game is to be the first to occupy a complete row, a complete column, or a complete diagonal (1, 5, 9 or 3, 5, 7). The game ends in a draw if after all nine squares have been occupied (that is, after nine moves, five by A and four by B), neither player has completed one whole row, column, or diagonal, in short, a whole line.

Obviously, it is quite possible to play this game the happy-go-lucky way. Just make your move, light a cigarette while awaiting your opponent's answer, and, having seen his move, start to think about your strongest next move.   It is also possible, however, to play the game like our sophisticated chess player, that is, to anticipate all possible moves of your opponent and prepare your answer in advance.   This leads to the strategic way of playing.   Suppose that player A is a strategist.   He can then, for example, formulate the following rules:

(i) To start, I shall occupy center field 5.

(ii-*a*) If *B* now occupies a corner, I shall occupy the opposite corner.

(ii-*b*) If *B* occupies a middle field (2, 4, 6, or 8), I shall occupy the first corner field clockwise from B's choice.

The answer in all possible situations that may arise (after *one* move by *B*) is thus specified.   Expressed numerically,

(1) *A* occupies				5				
(2) *B* occupies	1	2	3	4	6	7	8	9
(3) *A* occupies	9	3	7	1	9	3	7	1

Is this, then, a strategy?   No, not quite, for *A* must anticipate all conceivable situations that may arise and *B* will surely make another move. Thus there is no reason for complacent relaxation.   Before *A* can really speak of a strategy, he must anticipate *B*'s successive moves and *prepare his answers*.   In the case (ii-*b*), where *B* occupied a middle field in his first move, *A* can continue by formulating his next moves as follows:

(iii-*ba*) If possible, I shall complete the diagonal and claim victory.

(iii-*bb*) Otherwise, I shall occupy the first corner field counterclockwise from *B*'s last choice.

Using numbers, suppose *B* has filled in square 2 in his first move.   Then if *A* applies the specified rules, the following sequence of moves is made:

(1) *A* occupies			5			
(2) *B* occupies			2			
(3) *A* occupies			3			
(4) *B* occupies	1	4	6	7	8	9
(5) *A* occupies	7*w*	7*w*	7*w*	9	7*w*	7*w*

The suffix *w* indicates that *A* has won the game.   In fact, even in the one remaining case *A* wins, as shown by the next sequence: After (1) *A*5 (i.e., *A* occupies field 5), (2) *B*2, (3) *A*3, (4) *B*7, (5) *A*9, we consider

(6) *B* occupies	1	4	6	8
(7) *A* occupies	6*w*	6*w*	1*w*	6*w*

Hence, *A* can claim victory no matter what *B* does; it thus follows that *A* can always win the game if *B* occupies a middle field on his first move.[1]

---

[1] Strictly speaking, we proved this only for the special case in which *B* occupies the middle field 2.   However, it follows easily from symmetry considerations that the general statement is correct.

Moreover, A knows *how* to win because he has just formulated a winning strategy. All he needs to do is pursue it mechanically. In fact, A need not even play himself, but can instruct a computer to perform the moves instead.

Similarly, we could have formulated a good strategy for A in case B occupies a corner field on his first move. This good strategy leads to a gain for A unless B occupies a corner field on both of his first two moves and continues to play well afterwards; in that case the game will end in a draw. Thus, it follows that the beginning player A can always play to obtain at least a draw. This result has been obtained by formulating a specific, good strategy. One would be wrong, however, to assume that a strategy necessarily must be good. We repeat that *all* a strategy needs to do is to specify what one will do in every situation that may arise. It is perfectly possible to play ticktacktoe with the strategy: *Whenever it is my turn I shall occupy the lowest numbered field not occupied before.* This strategy will yield disappointing results, however. The object is, of course, to find a *good* strategy, not just *a* strategy. Preferably, one wants to find an *optimum* strategy. In the game of ticktacktoe this is not too difficult, but it is doubtful that the strategy of keeping the gold value of the dollar constant *whatever may happen* is optimal; yet, it is a strategy. The difference between a strategy, a good strategy, and an optimum strategy spells the difference between failure, mediocrity, and success.

Once an optimum strategy has been formulated, the game as such is finished; it is no fun to play. In fact, a machine can be instructed to play the game instead. One can even die and yet, having properly instructed the machine, become posthumously the world ticktacktoe champion. It is fortunate that the game of chess is so vastly more complicated that no winning strategy is known or is likely to become known. Yet chess-playing machines have been constructed which consistently beat opponents of mediocre quality, so that some progress has been made.

7-4. Why One Should Use Strategies

One might argue that in the cases we have been discussing, chess and ticktacktoe, too much fuss has been made about a strategy. It turned out that in chess no winning strategy could be formulated, while the game of ticktacktoe is so simple that even without the use of strategies reasonable results can be obtained. Therefore, we shall now discuss an example taken from everyday life which will show how the use of a strategy can help to prevent frustration. For the down-to-earth mind whose main concern is money and profits, we shall also discuss an example taken from the business world. The latter example will show how one can make the wrong decision by not properly recognizing and formulating a strategy.

Suppose, then, that you are at the railway station of Palo Alto, California, on your way to a party in San Francisco.   A round-trip ticket to San Francisco costs $3, a one-way ticket only $2.   You intend to return by train, but there is a small chance (one in five) that you will meet a friend at the party who will go back by car, and, of course, you prefer the car to the train.   So here you are:

	Buy round-trip ticket	Buy one-way tickets	
		Friend shows up (chance 0.2)	Friend does not show up (chance 0.8)
Costs ($)	3	2	4

Suppose now that you base your decision on the simple criterion of minimizing expected costs.   You are then advised to buy a round-trip ticket for $3 rather than a one-way ticket, for the expected costs of the latter alternative is $0.2 \times 2 + 0.8 \times 4 = \$3.60$.   Thus you find yourself at the party with a return ticket.   Once there, lo and behold, your friend turns up to offer you a ride back.   You laugh rather sheepishly, thank him for the offer, and accept it with the suggestion that he pass by the San Francisco railway terminal to get your money refunded.   But (as you anticipated) your friend, however nice he may be, thinks that is too much trouble and too far out of the way, so he says: Take it or leave it.   In this situation many people would take the train because they had paid for it, even though they prefer the car as a means of transportation.   Many others, probably including you, would indeed go back by car, but would feel that it was a painful decision and somehow think that it cost them $1 to go by car.

Compare this frustrating experience with a similar situation in which you have formulated the various possibilities explicitly in advance.   In particular, you should realize that once you decide to buy a round-trip ticket for $3 on the perfectly sensible criterion of minimizing expected costs, the two possibilities are that you will go back by train or by car. You prefer the second possibility.   Thus, you should be pleased that your friend turns up and should stop fretting about the fact that you might have bought a one-way ticket and thereby saved $1.

You may wonder what you *did* pay the $1 for.   The answer is, of course, that you paid that dollar to insure yourself against the 0.8 probability of having to pay a total of $4 rather than $3.   It is, to some extent, comparable to insuring your house against fire.   The premium insures you against the possibility of losing a large amount at the cost of paying a relatively small amount.   Indeed, when it turns out that you paid the premium for nothing because the house did *not* burn down, you feel pleased rather than annoyed.   By the same token, you should be pleased to meet your friend.

7-5. A Choice between Investments

Now, as a final example, consider the case of a manager who has to choose between two investment projects.   On the one hand, he can invest in a machine.   This costs $100,000 during the first year, but will yield savings of $35,000 during the next three years and $20,000 during the following year.   On the other hand, the manager can incur research expenditures of $13,500 the first year and $100,000 the next.   Then there will be four years to reap the harvest, which may be very substantial if the research is successful.   As of today, the probability of success is 0.4.   *After one year* (after $13,500 has been spent) *it will be known for certain whether or not the research will pay off*.   The financial data are summarized in dollars in the following table:

Year	Machine	Research	
		If successful (chance 0.4)	If not (chance 0.6)
1	-100,000	-13,500	-13,500
2	35,000	-100,000	-100,000
3	35,000	50,000	30,000
4	35,000	50,000	30,000
5	20,000	50,000	30,000
6	0	20,000	27,000
Discount rate	10%	20%	1%

The bottom row of this table gives the discount rate which makes the present value of these expenditures and returns equal to zero.   The discount is based on the very elementary fact that $1 today is not the same as $1 next year—because by bringing the dollar to the bank you can get $1.03 next year if the interest rate is 3 per cent.   Or, the other way around, if you want to have $1 next year, you need only about 97 cents today.   If you bring those 97 cents to the bank, they will pay you $1 next year.   Thus, $1 next year, when the interest rate is 3 per cent, is worth only 97 cents today.

In determining the relevant discount rate as given in the above table, we ask ourselves what interest rate makes the present value of the expenditures and returns equal to zero.   As we see from the table, the discount rate is in the case of the machine 10 per cent.   Roughly, this can be verified as follows.   The $100,000 we have to pay today for the machine is worth $100,000 today.   The $35,000 next year when the interest rate is 10 per cent is only worth about $35,000 − 3,500 = $31,500 today.   The next year's $35,000 is only worth approximately 31,500 − 3,150 = $28,350, and the following $35,000 is only worth about 28,350 − 2,835 = $25,515. Finally, the $20,000 four years from now is worth about $13,150.   The sum total of these amounts is approximately $100,000, which confirms the discount rate of 10 per cent.   (The simplified computations described here give only approximate results.)   The other discount rates are similarly computed and can be similarly checked.   Actually, they are found with the help of available discount tables.

We now assume that the manager bases his decision on the simple criterion of maximizing the expected discount rate, because the higher the discount rate, the more profitable the investment.   On the basis of the above evidence, then, he may decide to buy the machine, because its discount rate is 10 per cent, whereas the expected discount rate of research is $0.4 \times 20 + 0.6 \times 1 = 8.6$ per cent.   However, this decision would be *wrong*.   The manager has not used the information that after one year of research with an expenditure of $13,500 he would *know* whether the research would prove successful or not.   At that time, if it proved unsuccessful, he could switch to the machine.   This would lead to an expenditure of $13,500 during the single year of research, $100,000 for the machine during the second year, and then four years during which savings amount to $35,000, $35,000, $35,000 and $20,000, respectively.   The corresponding discount rate turns out to be 4 per cent.   Therefore, if the manager decides to go into research but to *switch* to the machine if the research is not successful, the expected discount rate is $0.4 \times 20 + 0.6 \times 4 = 10.4$ per cent.   This is more than 10 per cent, hence—according to his decision criterion—he should go into research.   By not accounting for the possibility of switching over to the machine, by not using a strategy, by not having an answer ready for each situation that might arise, the manager made the wrong decision.

This, it may be said, was a case of bad luck for the manager.   We found a numerical example by juggling with numbers and using such a simple, automatic decision criterion as maximizing the expected discount rate to prove that a decision not based on a strategy may be wrong.   Let us suppose then that our figures are modified so that research, if successful, pays off so handsomely that the discount rate is 30 per cent rather than 20 per cent.   The correct decision in that case, even when no strategy is used, is to go into research, for $0.4 \times 30 + 0.6 \times 1$ is more than 10 per cent. Thus the correct decision is made, even if the manager does not realize *one year in advance* the possibilities of switching. Now one year later the manager has discovered to his regret that the research was not successful. Will he then recognize that he can switch to the machine? The decision is now of immediate relevance: $100,000 more in unsuccessful research (paying $30,000, $30,000, $30,000, and $27,000) or in the machine (paying $35,000, $35,000, $35,000, and $20,000). Put in this way, he will obviously choose the machine. Or will he? The actual facts of life show that he will probably *not* do so. "Wouldn't it be just foolish to stop now that $35,000 has been spent on research?" "I can't back down; I have made too many commitments." "How can I explain to my Board of Directors why I didn't buy the machine in the first place?" In short, the manager has lost the flexibility to change the decision which was originally correct, given the available information and his decision criterion, but which turned out wrong. This situation, brought about because one does not properly understand what sunk costs are, or because one is blackmailed by vested interests, or because one will not confess that a decision turned out wrong, must be avoided. It *can* be avoided by using strategies.

7-6. Three Conditions for Strategies

We will sum up the discussion on strategies with a concise survey of the conditions which should be satisfied if the application of a strategy is to be relevant. There are three such conditions:

1. It is necessary that decisions have to be made (actions have to be taken) *at successive moments of time.* A once-and-for-all decision which cannot later be amended or further built upon does not permit the formulation of a strategy. For example, the question whether to take a coat with you when you leave your house in the morning asks for a single decision, not a strategy.

2. This "dynamic" decision problem should be characterized by uncertainty about what will happen in the future. The uncertainty may be due to the fact that one does not know in advance what an opponent will do; it may also be due to the fact that, for example, the outcome of research is dubious. If it were *certain* what would happen, we would not need a strategy—an answer to all situations which could *conceivably* arise—but it would be sufficient to have just a decision—an answer to the specific situation which will certainly arise.

3. The uncertainty should diminish in the course of time. That is, one should after some time receive *information* on the things that were uncertain before. For example, at the beginning of a chess game White does

not know Black's opening move, but he is informed about that move before he himself has to make the second move. Moreover, it should be possible to *react* to the information received. This is self-evident in the case of chess, because White can make his second and later moves depending on Black's first move. It is also true for the manager of Sec. 7-5, because at the end of the first year he can switch to the machine if the research turns out to be unsuccessful. However, if switching were impossible—for whatever reason—it would not be possible to *answer* all situations that could conceivably arise, which is tantamount to saying that it is impossible to formulate a strategy in the real sense.

It will be realized that these three conditions are often met in practice, so that a strategy is an important concept. Its main limitation is that designing a full-fledged strategy is usually a very complicated matter unless the problem is simple.

Literature

The concept of a strategy is an essential ingredient in the theory of games. The standard work in this field was written by Von Neumann and Morgenstern [1]; for further literature in this field we refer to the list of books at the end of the next chapter (which is devoted to game theory). The examples mentioned in the text are taken from Boot [2]; a more elaborate example can be found in Theil [3].

[1] J. von Neumann and O. Morgenstern, *Theory of Games and Economic Behavior*, 3d ed., Princeton University Press, Princeton, N.J., 1953.
[2] J. C. G. Boot, "Strategy: The Concept," *De Economist*, vol. 112 (1964), pp. 190–205.
[3] H. Theil, *Economic Forecasts and Policy*, 2d ed., North Holland Publishing Company, Amsterdam, 1961.

The decision criterion in this chapter invariably amounted to maximizing the expected value of the return (or minimizing the expected value of the costs). This expected-value criterion need not necessarily be realistic, as anyone who compares the following two situations will realize: (1) One is offered a fifty-fifty chance of either winning \$2 or losing \$1, and (2) one is offered a fifty-fifty chance of either winning \$200,000 or losing \$100,000. The first possibility has an expected value of 50 cents, and will usually be accepted. The second alternative has an expected value of no less than \$50,000, but will usually be refused. It can be shown, however, that under some rather plausible assumptions the expected-value criterion is quite generally appropriate, provided it is not applied to the outcomes themselves, but to a function of the outcomes, such as the logarithmic function.

8

Game Theory

8-1. Two Airlines

Two airlines, A and B, serve the same St. Louis–Oklahoma City route. Both companies strive for as large a market share as possible. The total number of passengers per year is constant; hence, what the one company gains is lost by the other. Let us now suppose that each company can

1. Do nothing special to attract passengers
2. Show cartoons during the flight
3. Advertise in the daily papers

For example, it is possible that A will do nothing special, but B will show cartoons. For convenience, we shall assume that a company cannot both show cartoons and advertise. There is then a total of $3 \times 3 = 9$ different combinations of possibilities, all with certain effects on the market share. If both companies just fly but do nothing special, the division of passengers remains stable. If A advertises but B does nothing, the yearly number of passengers of A will increase by 350 at the expense of B. If, on the contrary, B advertises while A does nothing, A loses 300 passengers to B. This effect is slightly smaller than in the opposite case (300 against 350); apparently A has a better advertising agency.

For each of the nine combinations we can determine the passenger gains for A, which are the passenger losses for B, as shown in the following table. Such a table will be referred to as a *payoff matrix;* in this case the payoff is

Company A	Company B		
	Does nothing	Shows cartoons	Advertises
Does nothing	0	-100	-300
Shows cartoons	100	0	-100
Advertises	350	125	50

measured in extra passengers per year for company A. If the payoff is negative, of course, it means that A loses passengers to B. The question is now what policy is best for A and, likewise, what policy is best for B. In this example the answer can be found rather easily. If the companies are interested only in winning passengers, disregarding the costs associated with the various policies, A is well advised to advertise. Whatever B does, the policy of advertising invariably gives A an advantage: 350 compared with 0 or 100 if B does nothing, 125 compared with -100 or 0 if B shows cartoons, and 50 compared with -300 or -100 if B advertises. The decision to advertise is also the best for B, for whatever A does, B has the greatest gain or the smallest loss of passengers by advertising. If B advertises, he has a profit of 300 if A does nothing, 100 if A shows cartoons, and he loses only 50 if A also advertises. (These are the numbers given in the last column, but with different signs because the profit of B is the same as the negative profit of A.) The conclusion is that A and B should both advertise. This pair of policies leads to a gain of 50 passengers a year for A and the loss of those passengers for B.

In most cases there is, unfortunately, no policy which is "dominant" over all others as advertising is here. That is, there is no policy which leads to a better result *irrespective of what the opponent does*, and the best policy is then much more difficult to determine. This is the topic of game theory, which was developed during World War II by the mathematician John von Neumann and the economist Oskar Morgenstern. A number of aspects of game theory have already been shown in our airlines example. There are a number of players (not necessarily only two); the players have alternative actions from which they must choose (not necessarily the same alternatives for both players). There is also a specified result for each of the players, given the alternatives they have chosen; i.e., the payoff matrix is fully specified numerically. We shall be mainly concerned with *two-person zero-sum games*. As the name implies, these are games played by two opposing persons or, more generally, parties or interests. Also, the sum total of the profits and losses equals 0; hence, what the one wins is necessarily lost by the other and vice versa. The players are therefore antagonistic; they have diametrically opposed aims; they cannot gain by forming a cartel or combination. The airlines were playing such a two-person zero-sum game.

It is good to realize that such two-person zero-sum games are indeed of a very special nature and are of limited interest in the practical reality of day-to-day life. In reality, games usually involve more than two players, and it is not usually true that gains and losses exactly offset each other. (In fact, if the airlines example is made more realistic by assuming that advertising can influence the total number of passengers, it is no longer a zero-sum game.)   Such zero-sum restrictions are made, however, because the more general theory is much more difficult and in an early stage of development.   In the last section of this chapter we shall come back to that.

8-2. Game, Move, Strategy

The very simple game of heads or tails suffices to show that there are not always dominant policies.   Two players, A and B, each have a quarter which they can place with either tails or heads up without showing the other what they do.   Each then simultaneously shows his opponent what he has done.   If it turns out that both did the same (both put up tails or heads), A receives the quarter from B.   Otherwise, B receives the quarter from A.

This is clearly a two-person zero-sum game.   The payoff matrix, giving the number of quarters which A wins, is as follows:

A shows	B shows	
	Tails	Heads
Tails	1	-1
Heads	-1	1

Apparently it is preferable for A to put heads up if B does so, but to show tails if B shows tails.   Thus, there is no dominating strategy.   The best policy for A very much depends upon what B actually does.   Unfortunately, A does not know what B will do at the moment A has to decide.

A more complicated example is provided by the game of *morra*, which is played by little Italian boys in the alleys of Genoa.   For outsiders there is nothing much to see—only two little Italians, shouting, waving arms, every now and then exchanging marbles.   Yet, they are not playing marbles, but morra.   The game is played as follows.   Simultaneously, players A and B show either 1 or 2 fingers; furthermore, and at the same time, each says either 1 or 2 as a *prediction* of the number of fingers that will be shown by the opponent.   Thus, A has four possibilities:

Show 1 finger and say 1
Show 1 finger and say 2
Show 2 fingers and say 1
Show 2 fingers and say 2

B has the same four possibilities.   In total, there are $4 \times 4 = 16$ possible combinations.   The rules further determine that if both players correctly predict the number of fingers shown by the opponent, neither gains or loses. The game ends in a draw. The game also ends in a draw when both players predict incorrectly. When one predicts correctly and the other does not, however, the successful player receives from his opponent a number of marbles equal to the total number of fingers shown.

All in all, this is a fairly complicated game, which those little Italians play with remarkable speed and a great deal of temperament (which tends to flare up rather fast, because there is a tendency to accuse the opponent of saying 1 or 2 too late, of "predicting" what is already shown; the game that results has little to do with morra). As can be seen, the payoff matrix is not overly complicated. The zeros without an asterisk are cases where both players predict correctly. The zero in the upper left-hand

A	B			
	Says 1, shows 1	Says 1, shows 2	Says 2, shows 1	Says 2, shows 2
Says 1, shows 1	0	−3	2	0*
Says 1, shows 2	3	0*	0	−4
Says 2, shows 1	−2	0	0*	3
Says 2, shows 2	0*	4	−3	0

corner, for example, indicates that both players show 1 and say 1: both predict correctly, and no marbles change hands. The asterisked zeros represent cases where both players are wrong in their prediction. In all other cases, A wins or loses some marbles. The −3 in the first row, for example, stands for the case where A is wrong because he says 1, whereas B shows 2; B is right, for A shows 1 and B says 1. A total of 2 + 1 = 3 fingers are shown, so B wins 3. Thus, A loses 3, and we enter −3 in the payoff matrix.

Again, there is no dominant policy in this game. If B, for example, had said 1 and shown 1, A should have said 1 (thereby predicting correctly) but shown 2 (making B's prediction wrong). A's policy "say 1, show 2" earns him in that case 3 marbles. The same policy would result in A's losing 4 marbles, however, if B were to say 2 and show 2. The best strategy for A vitally depends on what B does. A has no dominating strategy; neither, of course, has B. It follows from the complete symmetry of the game that what is true for the one must also be true for the other.

For games with coins and marbles, we have shown that there are not necessarily dominating policies. These examples also serve to introduce some important concepts—in the first place, the concept of a *game*. This consists of a specification of the alternatives open to the players and of the payoffs in each of the situations that can arise. A game consists of *moves*. The game of heads or tails and the game of morra both consist of one move only. (It may seem that the players of morra have two moves each, since they say something and show something, but since they do so simultaneously, this effectively amounts to one move.) More complicated games, such as chess or ticktacktoe, have more moves. However, these games are formally equivalent to games with one move, because all that needs to be specified is the *strategy* the players will use. Instead of the various possible moves, all conceivable strategies can be written down, and the resulting payoff can be determined. Hence, for more complicated games with a succession of moves the formal framework of game theory can be preserved by choosing between the various alternative strategies rather than moves. In what follows, we shall always speak about the strategies which A and B choose, although in games with only one move the concept of a strategy is reduced to that of a simple move.

8-3. Minimax and Saddle Point

Let us now consider a game which is defined by the following payoff matrix:

Strategies of A	Strategies of B	
	B_1	B_2
A_1	9	2
A_2	4	3

A must choose between two strategies, A_1 and A_2, and B also has two strategies, B_1 and B_2. Further, A will always receive some amount, at least 2 and at most 9, dollars, marbles, points, anything. He wants to receive as much as possible. The opposite holds for B; he must always pay and prefers to pay as little as possible. The game is to B's disadvantage, but that is not important for us since we are not B.

What, then, should A do? Obviously he is fascinated by the possibility of obtaining 9, and to get that he should pick strategy A_1 and then hope that B chooses B_1. If B, however, through espionage, telepathy, intuition, or what have you, has discovered that A plays A_1, he will be wiser than to pick B_1 and lose 9. Instead, he will pick B_2, which costs him only 2. When B chooses B_2, then, it is profitable for A to pick A_2 rather than A_1; this increases his gain from 2 to 3. We have now reached a remarkable situation: Neither A nor B has reason to change his position.

A does not want to change because when B plays B_2, he is better off playing A_2 than A_1. B does not want to change because when A plays A_2, he is better off playing B_2 than B_1 (because B_1 costs him 4 and B_2 only 3). We apparently have reached an equilibrium situation.

Let us reconsider the game from a slightly different angle. A can reason: If I choose strategy A_1, the *worst* that can happen is that I get only 2, the *minimum* of the first *row* of the payoff matrix. By choosing A_2, I might have to be satisfied with 3, the minimum of the second row of the payoff matrix. B reasons: By choosing B_1, I run the risk of having to pay 9, the *maximum* of the first *column*, and if I choose B_2, I run the risk of having to pay 3, the maximum of the second column. We can indicate these row minima and column maxima in the margin of the payoff matrix:

Strategies of A	Strategies of B		Row minimum
	B_1	B_2	
A_1	9	2	2
A_2	4	3	3*
Column maximum	9	3*	

Player A strives for as high a payoff as possible, assuming that his opponent plays as well as possible. In particular, he wants to maximize the payoff under the somewhat suspicious assumption that his own choice will be discovered by B. Then A is well advised to maximize the row minima, and we speak of a *minimax solution*. In this case, that leads to playing A_2, which has a minimum payoff of 3. This value 3 is starred in the right-hand column as the maximum row minimum. In his turn B reasons similarly. Since every choice means a loss for B, he will choose the strategy with which the maximum possible loss is as small as possible; this is strategy B_2, the maximum possible loss being 3 (starred in the bottom row). The two starred 3s correspond to the same 3 in the payoff matrix, the minimax solution which is obtained by A's playing A_2 and B's playing B_2. By playing A_2, A receives a payoff of at least 3 (it may be as much as 4 when B plays B_1). By playing B_2, B loses at most 3 (it may be only 2 in case A plays A_1). The amount which A receives from B when both play according to the minimax criterion is called *the value of the game*. In this case the value of the game is 3.

The minimax solution is known as the *saddle point* of the payoff matrix, because it is the minimum of its row and the maximum of its column. The reason for this terminology becomes more evident when we add a third strategy for A and B. The highest row minimum remains 3, and

Strategies of A	Strategies of B			Row minimum
	B_1	B_2	B_3	
A_1	9	2	1	1
A_2	4	3	5	3*
A_3	0	1	7	0
Column maximum	9	3*	7	

the lowest column maximum also remains 3, corresponding to the strategies A_2 and B_2. The minimax solution, therefore, does not change. Now suppose A chooses A_2; his payoff will be (in order B_1, B_2, B_3) 4, 3, 5. The payoff decreases from 4 to 3 and then increases from 3 to 5. In case B's choice is B_2, A will receive 2, 3, or 1 depending on whether his choice is A_1, A_2, or A_3. First the payoff increases from 2 to 3; next it decreases from 3 to 1. The number 3 in the middle has a somewhat asymmetric role: it forms a trough when we look at the second row; it forms a ridge when we consider the second column. That is exactly like a saddle and hence the term saddle point, for the center of the saddle is both a ridge and a trough depending on the side from which one looks at it. We have the same phenomenon at a mountain pass. If we follow the road, we climb until we reach the pass and descend afterwards. Seen from another point on the road, the pass is a maximum. However, if we look left and right when we are at the pass, we see the rising mountains on both sides; considered in this way the pass is a minimum.

The solution for the airlines, too, was a minimax solution. We can complete the payoff matrix by adding a bottom row giving the column maxima and a right-hand-side column giving the row minima. Clearly, the highest row minimum corresponds again with the lowest column

Strategies of A	Strategies of B			Row minimum
	Do nothing	Show cartoons	Advertise	
Do nothing	0	−100	−300	−300
Show cartoons	100	0	−100	−100
Advertise	350	125	50	50*
Column maximum	350	125	50*	

maximum. Both airlines will advertise. The value of the game is 50 extra passengers per year.

8-4. Mixed Strategies

The quick-witted reader may have noticed that in the first example of the previous section we went about finding the solution in a rather complicated way. It is much faster to notice that B will always play B_2, because B_1 is dominated by B_2. Whatever A does, B_2 is better for B (he pays out less) than B_1. Because A will realize that B will always play B_2, A will always choose A_2. This argument is correct, but it can break down when we add a third strategy for both players, as we did above. B_1 is then no longer dominated by B_2, because B_1 gives a better result than B_2 when A plays A_3. Further, there is no immediate reason why A should not play A_3; that is, A_3 is not dominated either. If B plays B_3, the best A can do is to play A_3. Thus the saddle-point (minimax) argument cannot usually be avoided, but, unfortunately, does not always lead smoothly to the solution.

This can be easily illustrated with the game of heads or tails. *Whatever A does, he can expect to receive at least* -1 (that is, the worst that can

Strategies of A	Strategies of B		Row minimum
	Tails	Heads	
Tails	1	-1	-1
Heads	-1	1	-1
Column maximum	1	1	

happen is that he loses 1 quarter). So what should he do? For B the problem is analogous. In the most unfavorable situation he loses 1 quarter whichever move he makes. To determine the players' strategies, we reason as follows. Suppose A considers putting tails up. If B also shows tails, A will gain a quarter (the upper left-hand 1). But if B second-guesses A, he will no doubt show heads with the result that A loses a quarter (the upper right-hand -1). If B shows heads, A should also show heads (cf. the lower right-hand 1). If B guesses that A will show heads, however, he will put up tails; but then A should also put tails up, etc. The cycle is complete; we have returned to the beginning (the upper left-hand 1) and apparently did not make much progress.

All we can say is that A's payoff depends on what B will do. If A should in one way or another discover what B was about to show next, he could profit from this knowledge by mimicking B. Also, A can profit from more subtle knowledge. Suppose A notices that B shows a definite preference for heads; three out of four times B shows heads, for example.

Then A will win three out of four times by always putting heads up. It is clearly dangerous for either player to exhibit a preference for heads or tails. Moreover, regularity is dangerous. If B shows heads and tails alternately, then, even though he shows no preference in the long run, the regularity enables A to predict B's next move and to profit from this. Hence there should be no preference and no regularity.

How can a player prevent his opponent from second-guessing his next move? The easiest suggestion is that the player himself should not know what he will show the next turn! Suppose A *flips* the coin and then puts up the result of the flip. He can be certain that in the long run heads and tails will come up with the same frequency (no preference) and that they will come up in a completely irregular series (no regularity). Thus A guarantees that his opponent will not be able (any better than he himself!) to predict what will turn up next. This strategy is known in game theory as a *mixed strategy*. It is not predetermined what A will do at any particular play of the game. It could be tails, or it could be heads. A himself does not even know; all he knows is that both moves have a probability of $\frac{1}{2}$. It is thus a mixture of the possible strategies, as the name indicates.

What is the payoff for A if he plays by flipping? That can be easily determined. If B shows tails, A's strategy will win 1 with a probability of $\frac{1}{2}$ (if his flip gives him tails)—and lose 1 with probability $\frac{1}{2}$ (if his flip gives him heads). The *expected payoff* hence is $\frac{1}{2} \times 1 + \frac{1}{2} \times (-1) = 0$ if B shows tails. And if B shows heads, the gain is also 1 with probability $\frac{1}{2}$ and -1 with probability $\frac{1}{2}$, and hence the expected payoff equals zero. Thus, a mixed strategy gives no particular result with certainty; we evaluate such a strategy by means of the *expected* payoff.

The question now is *what* mixed strategy a player should choose. In the above example it was easy enough. Both players should choose heads and tails with equal probability, because no preference should be shown either way. It is not always that simple, however. We can slightly change the payoff matrix by increasing A's profit from 1 to 2 quarters in case both players show tails. The game is then no longer symmetric, as A stands to gain. But the question is how A can realize

Strategies of A	Strategies of B		Row minimum
	Tails	Heads	
Tails	2	-1	-1
Heads	-1	1	-1
Column maximum	2	1	

this gain.   At first glance one would expect A to show a preference for tails, which enables him to cash 2 quarters (in case B also shows tails). However, this might induce B to expect that A will play tails; hence B may decide to defend himself by playing heads so that A loses 1 quarter instead of winning 2. A, in turn, realizes this, and hence might, on second thought, show heads.   We are about to get involved in a vicious circle again, and it stands to reason that a mixed strategy is called for.   The basic question has now become: What should be the mixture of the strategies?   Originally we were to specify the one particular strategy to choose; now we want to specify the probabilities with which the various strategies should appear in the mixture.   We shall show that the best policy for A is to choose tails with a probability of 0.4 and heads with a probability of 0.6.   He should show tails less often than heads, although showing tails was his first inclination.   We shall also show that the expected profit for A is 5 cents per game.

8-5. A Graphical Solution

The solution to our game for player A can be graphically determined. We draw a horizontal axis along which we measure the probability x_H

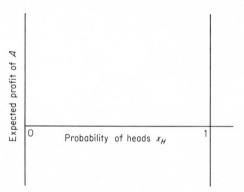

F<small>IG</small>. 8-1

that A will show heads.   Along the vertical axis we measure the expected profit of A.   Because the probability that A will show heads can never exceed 1, we can cut off the illustration at $x_H = 1$.   The resulting design is given in Fig. 8-1.   It is important for what follows to realize that whatever B does, whether he follows a mixed strategy or not, he will eventually show either tails or heads.   This is what A needs to know.   He can determine his expected profit in each of these two cases.

Let us first assume that B shows tails.   We wrote x_H for the probability in the strategy mixture that A will show heads; hence the probability that A will show tails equals $1 - x_H$.   If B shows tails, the expected profit for A is determined by the numbers in the first column of the payoff matrix:

$$(1 - x_H)2 + x_H(-1) = 2 - 3x_H$$

If B shows heads, one can derive the expected profit for A from the second column of the payoff matrix:

$$(1 - x_H)(-1) + x_H = -1 + 2x_H$$

In both cases the expected profit is given as a linear function of x_H. These functions are the straight lines in Fig. 8-2. The first begins at

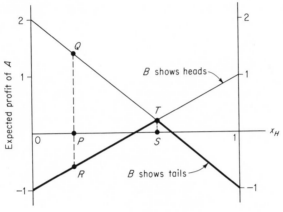

FIG. 8-2

2 (when $x_H = 0$) and ends at -1 (when $x_H = 1$). The second begins at -1 (when $x_H = 0$) and ends at 1 (when $x_H = 1$).

What can A infer from this figure? His problem is to find the best possible strategy, assuming that B plays as well as possible, i.e., assuming that A is faced with the most unfavorable situation. Consider then the point P, corresponding to $x_H = 0.2$. Player A then gets an expected profit of PQ if B shows tails, but the expected profit in the most unfavorable case is negative PR when B shows heads. This last result is quite bad for A and should be prevented. The best A can do is to go to S, corresponding with the intersection T of the two lines. *Before* S the expected profit is lower than ST when B shows heads; *after* S the expected profit is lower than ST when B shows tails.

We find the value of x_H at the intersection of the two lines by equating the expected profits of these lines:

$$2 - 3x_H = -1 + 2x_H$$

or $5x_H = 3$ with the solution $x_H = 0.6$. The probability of showing tails is then only 0.4. And the expected profit is

$$2 - 3(0.6) = -1 + 2(0.6) = 0.2$$

We conclude that A can expect to win 0.2 quarters or 5 cents per game.

For B we proceed in exactly the same way. We again construct a graph and find that B's best strategy is to play tails and heads with probabilities of 0.4 and 0.6, respectively. It is a coincidence that the optimal mixed strategy for B is the same as for A. Such a mixed strategy with these odds can be realized by rolling a five-sided pencil. In fact, there are vastly more sophisticated procedures with which to formulate decisions based on specified probabilities. Some of them will be discussed in Chap. 10.

8-6. The Minimax Theorem

We shall now consider a somewhat larger game where A has three and B has four strategies to choose from. The payoff matrix gives again the amounts A wins (and hence B loses). The largest row minimum equals 3,

Strategies of A	Strategies of B				Row minimum
	B_1	B_2	B_3	B_4	
A_1	10	1	7	8	1
A_2	3	4	5	9	3*
A_3	6	7	4	2	2
Column maximum	10	7*	7*	9	

and the smallest column maximum is 7, indicated with asterisks. These two numbers are different (and do not correspond to the same number in the payoff matrix), so there is no saddle point. Then it is always wrong to play invariably one and the same strategy, as can be easily illustrated with the following "circle" reasoning. Suppose A plays A_2, which guarantees him at least 3. Then the best B can do is to play B_1, in which case A indeed receives only 3. However, if B does play B_1, it is much better for A to play A_1 rather than A_2, because he then gains 10. Then B should play B_2, which leads to a payoff of only 1. When B plays B_2, A should counter by playing A_3; the result is 7 for A. However, then B goes to B_4 and limits his payout to only 2, unless A then plays A_2, which leads to a result of 9. Now we are back where we started and can begin anew. Such a situation cannot occur when there is a saddle point, which is a point of equilibrium where neither player can profit by changing his strategy if the other does not. Usually there is no saddle point, however, and we must search for the right strategy mixture.

For A the problem is to find the probabilities x_1, x_2, and x_3 with which he will play A_1, A_2, and A_3. These probabilities must always be positive or zero, and they add up to 1 because A must play one of these strategies. Thus

$$x_1 \geq 0 \qquad x_2 \geq 0 \qquad x_3 \geq 0 \tag{1}$$
$$x_1 + x_2 + x_3 = 1$$

A must then, subject to these restrictions, choose the x values in such a way that the minimum expected payoff is as large as possible. Let us consider the expected profits when B plays B_1. Taking the numbers from the B_1 column of the payoff matrix, we see that A wins 10 with probability x_1, 3 with probability x_2, and 6 with probability x_3. A's expected profit when B plays B_1 is therefore

$$10x_1 + 3x_2 + 6x_3$$

We can similarly compute the expected profit when B plays B_2, B_3, or B_4, with the following results:

Strategy choice of B	Expected profit of A
B_1	$10x_1 + 3x_2 + 6x_3$
B_2	$x_1 + 4x_2 + 7x_3$
B_3	$7x_1 + 5x_2 + 4x_3$
B_4	$8x_1 + 9x_2 + 2x_3$

A's object is to maximize the lowest of these four expected values. We shall write w for this minimum expected profit, that is, for the lowest of those four profits. Then, by the definition of a minimum, we find

$$10x_1 + 3x_2 + 6x_3 \geq w$$
$$x_1 + 4x_2 + 7x_3 \geq w$$
$$7x_1 + 5x_2 + 4x_3 \geq w \tag{2}$$
$$8x_1 + 9x_2 + 2x_3 \geq w$$

A's problem is now clearly formulated. He is to determine x_1, x_2, and x_3 in such a way that w (the lowest expected profit) is as large as possible, subject to the restrictions (1) and (2).

We shall not solve this problem immediately. That would not be quite fair with respect to B, who faces a similar problem. He has four strategies, and must determine the four probabilities y_1, y_2, y_3, and y_4 of his mixed strategy. These probabilities should be nonnegative and should add up to 1:

$$y_1 \geq 0 \qquad y_2 \geq 0 \qquad y_3 \geq 0 \qquad y_4 \geq 0$$
$$y_1 + y_2 + y_3 + y_4 = 1 \tag{3}$$

B also tries to maximize his lowest expected gain or—since the payoff matrix gives him no hope of winning—to minimize his highest expected loss. His expected loss when A chooses A_1 equals

$$10y_1 + y_2 + 7y_3 + 8y_4$$

as follows from the first row of the payoff matrix. For the second and third rows, corresponding to the strategies A_2 and A_3 of A, the expected profit can likewise be given. If we write v for the highest expected loss of B, it follows from the definition of a maximum that

$$10y_1 + y_2 + 7y_3 + 8y_4 \leq v$$
$$3y_1 + 4y_2 + 5y_3 + 9y_4 \leq v \tag{4}$$
$$6y_1 + 7y_2 + 4y_3 + 2y_4 \leq v$$

The problem for B now is to determine y_1, y_2, y_3, and y_4 in such a way that v (the highest possible expected loss) is as small as possible, subject to the restrictions (3) and (4).

Thus we have two different problems, one for A and one for B—two persons who have little reason to get on well and live in harmony, because the one wins at the expense of the other. However, the remarkable fact is that a sort of harmony does exist—or at least a sort of equilibrium. It is an equilibrium of mixed strategies to be compared with the saddle-point equilibrium we came across before. The result is known as the *minimax theorem* of von Neumann, which is valid for all two-person zero-sum games, independent of the number of different strategies open to the players, and irrespective of the numbers in the payoff matrix. The von Neumann theorem states that a mixed strategy for A exists (i.e., certain probabilities x_1, x_2, . . . exist) and also a mixed strategy for B exists (i.e., certain probabilities y_1, y_2, . . . exist) such that:

(1) A's expected gain is at least w, and B's expected loss is at most v.
(2) $v = w$.

(3) If A plays his optimal strategy but B does not play his best strategy, it is possible that A's expected gain will be more than w; likewise, if B plays his optimal strategy but A does not, perhaps B's expected loss will be less than v.

(4) The values v and w (which are equal) are somewhere in between the maximum of the row minima and the minimum of the column maxima.

In our example the solution for A is[1]

$$x_1 = {}^{10}\!/_{42} \qquad x_2 = {}^{9}\!/_{42} \qquad x_3 = {}^{23}\!/_{42}$$

All x values are positive, and their sum equals 1. By substitution we find the expected payoff for A for each of the strategies of B:

$$B_1: 10 \times {}^{10}\!/_{42} + 3 \times {}^{9}\!/_{42} + 6 \times {}^{23}\!/_{42} = {}^{265}\!/_{42}$$
$$B_2: \ 1 \times {}^{10}\!/_{42} + 4 \times {}^{9}\!/_{42} + 7 \times {}^{23}\!/_{42} = {}^{207}\!/_{42}$$
$$B_3: \ 7 \times {}^{10}\!/_{42} + 5 \times {}^{9}\!/_{42} + 4 \times {}^{23}\!/_{42} = {}^{207}\!/_{42}$$
$$B_4: \ 8 \times {}^{10}\!/_{42} + 9 \times {}^{9}\!/_{42} + 2 \times {}^{23}\!/_{42} = {}^{207}\!/_{42}$$

The result shows at once that A's expected gain is at least ${}^{207}\!/_{42}$, or nearly 5. For B the solution is

$$y_1 = 0 \qquad y_2 = {}^{15}\!/_{42} \qquad y_3 = {}^{24}\!/_{42} \qquad y_4 = {}^{3}\!/_{42}$$

The zero value of y_1 means that B_1 is not played at all, and we shall see shortly that B has good reasons for never playing his first strategy. The expected losses for B corresponding to the various choices of A now become:

$$A_1: 10 \times 0 + 1 \times {}^{15}\!/_{42} + 7 \times {}^{24}\!/_{42} + 8 \times {}^{3}\!/_{42} = {}^{207}\!/_{42}$$
$$A_2: \ 3 \times 0 + 4 \times {}^{15}\!/_{42} + 5 \times {}^{24}\!/_{42} + 9 \times {}^{3}\!/_{42} = {}^{207}\!/_{42}$$
$$A_3: \ 6 \times 0 + 7 \times {}^{15}\!/_{42} + 4 \times {}^{24}\!/_{42} + 2 \times {}^{3}\!/_{42} = {}^{207}\!/_{42}$$

The expected loss of B is thus ${}^{207}\!/_{42}$ whatever A does. We have herewith illustrated the points (1) and (2) of the minimax theorem. A makes at least an expected gain of $w = {}^{207}\!/_{42}$, and B has at most an expected loss of $v = {}^{207}\!/_{42}$; hence $v = w$. Also, (3) is true. If B were foolish enough to play B_1, his expected loss would increase to ${}^{265}\!/_{42}$, but the specified optimal strategy precludes this possibility. Finally, the highest

---

[1] The derivation of this solution will not be given. The reader who recalls the example of betting at Saratoga in Chap. 1 will understand that it amounts to a linear programming problem.

row minimum is 3, the lowest column maximum is 7, and $v = w$ lies in between these values.   The expected profit for A $(^{20}\!\!\not/_{4\,2})$ is the value of the game in case there is no saddle point.

Our conclusions can be summarized as follows.   If a two-person zero-sum game has a saddle point, there are two strategies, one for A and one for B, which form the minimax solution.   If there is no saddle point, such a point is generated with the help of mixed strategies.   The situation is then analogous, for there is an equilibrium in the sense that no player can improve on his expected profit when the other follows his optimal mixed strategy.[1]

8-7. More Players and Nonzero-sum Games

Some of the complications which arise when there are more than two persons or when the game is not zero-sum can be illustrated by the following example.   Consider the nonzero-sum game for a pig breeder A.   His problem is how many pigs to breed each year.   Suppose that in addition to A there are 1,000 other pig breeders, all faced with the same problem.   It would seem to be a 1,001-person game, but by combining all others under the one name "colleagues," pig breeder A can consider it as a game between himself on the one hand and his colleagues collectively on the other.

Suppose now that all pig breeders can produce either 10 or 25 pigs.   If all breeders produce 10 pigs, there will be few pigs on the market that year, and each will bring in a good price of $400.   Since the costs of breeding are $250, each pig clears a profit of $150 for his breeder.   Hence, A gains $10 \times 150 = \$1,500$.   Each and every one of his colleagues also earns a $1,500 profit.   If A decides now to start producing 25 pigs, while all his colleagues continue to breed only 10, there will be 15 more pigs on the market.   This will not perceptibly influence the price, and thus A gains $25 \times 150 = \$3,750$.   What happens, however, if every breeder produces his capacity of 25 pigs?   Then there will be a large supply, and the market price will fall sharply to $275.   This leaves a profit of $25 for each pig and of $25 \times 25 = \$625$ for each farmer.   If A in this situation were to produce only 10 pigs, his profit would drop to $10 \times 25 = \$250$.

Thus, A has two possibilities, which we shall indicate by $A10$ and $A25$. His profit depends upon what his colleagues do.   For convenience we

<hr>

[1] Note that the minimax solution need not be unique (though the value of the game is always unique).   In the game of morra, which we discussed previously, the solution is the same for A and B: They should never play the first or the last mentioned strategies; that is, they should never *show* the same as they *say*.   They should play the strategies "say 1, show 2," and "say 2, show 1" in proportion z_1 and $z_2 = 1 - z_1$, where z_1 is anywhere between $\frac{2}{5}$ and $\frac{3}{7}$, including these limits.   In morra, therefore, a certain arbitrary element remains.

assume that either all colleagues produce 10 or they all produce 25 pigs. These two possibilities will be indicated by $C10$ and $C25$. The payoff matrix, which gives the yearly profit for each farmer, then looks as follows:

	$C10$	$C25$
$A10$	A, \$1,500 C, \$1,500	A, \$250 C, \$625
$A25$	A, \$3,750 C, \$1,500	A, \$625 C, \$625

From this scheme, A concludes immediately that he should produce as many pigs as possible. Whatever his colleagues do, he is better off producing 25 rather than 10 pigs. He will make a profit of \$3,750 instead of \$1,500 if his colleagues produce only 10 pigs each, and a profit of \$625 instead of \$250 if all others produce up to capacity. In short, $A25$ dominates $A10$.

But now the tragedy. Each and every one of the individual pig breeders can make a similar payoff matrix. Each can consider the 1,000 others collectively as colleagues, and each will, just like A, decide to produce a lot of pigs. So they will all make a profit of \$625 a year. If they agreed to produce only a few pigs, however, they would all make a profit of \$1,500. The decision which is correct for each individual farmer is collectively wrong. This simple game shows one of the reasons why many people think that every now and then the government should interfere in the market of agricultural products, and in practice nearly every government does.

In conclusion, let us devote a few words to games for more than two persons. One of the complications that can arise is that it may be profitable for a number of players to form a combination or cartel. Then a new game results, with fewer participants and a modified payoff matrix. In fact, even when there are only two players, cartels cannot wholly be excluded. Two airlines competing on the same route can (and as a rule do) make some rules to mitigate the competition. Sometimes, especially in Europe, they even start working together on a specific route. Admittedly, if it is a zero-sum game, they cannot both profit from combining, but as a matter of established fact, many games are not zero-sum.

Literature

The pioneering book on game theory (more than 600 pages!) is the von Neumann–Morgenstern book already cited at the end of the previous chapter. The books of McKinsey [2] and of Luce and Raiffa [3] are easier, but still hard to digest for mathematical laymen.   The funniest book, which everybody can understand and which certainly gives a good idea about the approach, is that of Williams [4].

[1] J. von Neumann and O. Morgenstern, *Theory of Games and Economic Behavior*, 3d ed., Princeton University Press, Princeton, N.J., 1953.
[2] J. C. C. McKinsey, *Introduction to the Theory of Games*, McGraw-Hill Book Company, New York, 1952.
[3] R. D. Luce and H. Raiffa, *Games and Decisions*, John Wiley & Sons, Inc., New York, 1957.
[4] J. D. Williams, *The Compleat Strategyst*, McGraw-Hill Book Company, New York, 1954.

9

Queues

9-1. The Problem

The problem facing us in this chapter is all too familiar. We have to wait—at the barbershop, the post office, for traffic lights, for clear telephone lines, etc. Not only do *we* have to wait, but machines have to wait to be repaired, airplanes must wait for the runways to be clear, ships must wait for pilots to arrive, and trains must wait for signals. In most cases such waiting could be avoided. The barber could expand his shop and hire extra employees, traffic lights could be dispensed with by building over- and underpasses, factories could increase their repairshops, and airports could increase their capacity by building more runways.

The relevant question is whether these drastic measures are called for. If the barber does employ an extra person to prevent your waiting, it is possible that the newly employed barber will be idle much of his time. This is very bad for the barbershop's profit. Thus, the problem is to find a sort of equilibrium between, in general, the costs associated with waiting and the costs of preventing waiting. What needs to be determined, somehow, is the optimum number of pilots in New York's harbor, the optimum number of telephone lines between New York and Los Angeles, etc.

The telephone line example is appropriate because the telephone industry fathered the science which has become known as *queueing theory* and which is concerned with determining these optimum numbers. The pioneer in this field was the Dane A. K. Erlang, an employee of the Copenhagen telephone company. The *theory* is especially important because experimentation is possible only to a very limited extent. One cannot proceed by building a new runway just to see how waiting times of circling planes are influenced. To the extent that experimentation is possible, it is done with pencil and paper and computers and is called *simulation;* this will form the topic of our next chapter. In this chapter we shall give an outline of the factors that influence queueing.

The very variety of fields of application makes it desirable to establish a uniform terminology. We shall speak about *customers* and *service stations*. The customer may be you waiting in the post office, or a plane waiting for permission to land, or a machine waiting to be repaired, or a repairman waiting for a machine to break down. The service station may be a counter in the post office, a runway, or a repairman. The road traveled by the customer may be schematically indicated as follows:

arrival → (possibly) waiting → being serviced → departure

More often than not customers do not arrive at regular intervals, but more or less haphazardly. Also, some customers require more and some less time (we all are only too well aware of the fussy old lady before us in line). We shall, therefore, call on probability theory for such concepts as the probability that the customer will enter during the next minute and the probability that it will take between 3 and 4 minutes to service him. Indeed, queueing theory is a special branch of probability theory.

9-2. Arrival of Customers

The arrival of customers can be viewed in two different ways. We can ask ourselves how many customers will arrive between 9 and 9:15 A.M. The answer will by necessity be an integer, such as 0, 1, 2, 3, ... The associated probability distribution—which gives the probability that 0, 1, 2, 3, . . . customers arrive during that period—will be *discrete*. Alternatively, we can ask ourselves how long a time span elapses between the arrival of two successive customers. The answer will then be in minutes, seconds, and even milliseconds, depending upon the required accuracy. In principle we have a *continuous* distribution in this case.

In Fig. 9-1 these two points of view have been illustrated. The arrival of customers has been indicated along a time axis. On the one hand, we can count the number of customers who arrive during a 5-minute period. We then find four customers between 9 and 9:05 and also four customers between 9:05 and 9:10. (By pure coincidence, the numbers are equal; during the time interval 9:10–9:15 seven customers arrived.) On the other hand, we can record the time which passes between successive arrivals. We then find, measured in seconds,

126 (until the arrival of the first customer)
 85 (between arrival of first and second customer)
 26 (between arrival of second and third customer)
 51 (between arrival of third and fourth customer)

For the sake of brevity, we shall call the lengths of time between two successive arrivals *interarrival times*. In Fig. 9-1 they are indicated by little arrows above the time axis.

To make the problem more amenable to analysis we shall now have to say something about the probability distribution of these interarrival times. We shall have to assume certain probabilities that the interarrival time is, for example, between 0 and 10 seconds, 10 and 20, etc. This will be done with the help of Fig. 9-2, which deals with the number of arriving planes at the airport of Amsterdam during the peak hours in the foggy January month of 1950. The interarrival times in minutes have been plotted along the horizontal axis. The relative frequency of cases in which the observed interarrival time is *equal to or greater than* the time given on the horizontal axis is given along the vertical axis. Take the point P which is at the far right. This corresponds to the largest interarrival time observed. Nearly two hours elapsed between the arrival of two planes. There is only one such case; hence the position of point P is $1/N$ above the horizontal axis, where N is the total number of observa-

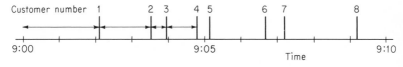

Fig. 9-1

tions (the total number of interarrival times, one less than the total number of planes that arrived during the period studied). Consider next the point Q, corresponding to the second longest interarrival time. The number of cases in which the interarrival time was at least this long was 2, and point Q is therefore $2/N$ above the horizontal axis. If the shortest interarrival time was 20 seconds, each and every one of the N interarrival times is equal to or longer than this 20 seconds, and the corresponding height is $N/N = 1$. This is indeed the height plotted at the far left of Fig. 9-2, corresponding to the shortest interarrival time.

Through these points we have drawn a smooth curve which fits rather well. The mathematical representation of the curve is given by e^{-at}, where $e = 2.71828 \ldots$, the number we introduced in our discussion of the normal probability density function. The t is the interarrival time, and a is a coefficient which determines the specific form of the function *in concreto*. In our case a is about $\frac{1}{25}$, and hence the function is $e^{-t/25}$. This implies that the probability that an interarrival time will be larger than 25 minutes is $e^{-25/25} = e^{-1} = 0.37$, or 37 out of 100 times. The probability that the interarrival time will be more than 50 minutes is $e^{-50/25} = e^{-2} = 0.14$, or about once in seven times. The reciprocal of a,

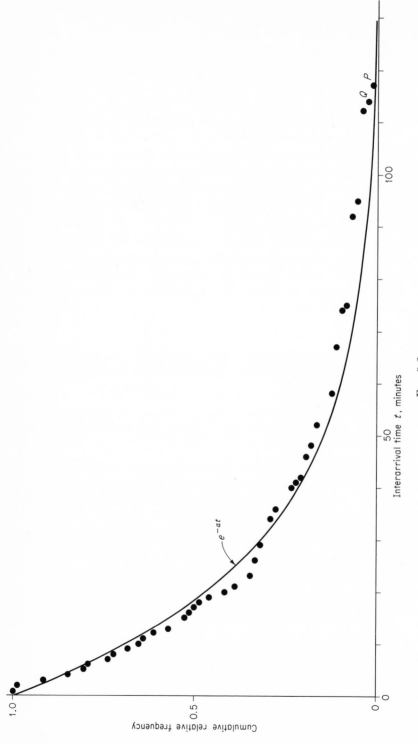

Cumulative relative frequency

e^{-at}

Q P

0   50   100

Interarrival time t, minutes

Fig. 9-2

that is, $1/a$, is equal to the mathematical expectation[1] of the interarrival time, in this particular case about 25 minutes.   Hence, on the average, we can expect one plane every 25 minutes.   (The a itself is the average number of planes that arrives per unit of time; in our case, $\frac{1}{25}$ plane arrives per minute.)   Actually, the value $1/a$ equals not only the mean but also the standard deviation of the distribution of the interarrival times.   The probability density function of the interarrival times is ae^{-at}, or in this example $\frac{1}{25}e^{-t/25}$.   This is, just as is the normal distribution, a continuous probability density function because t can in principle assume all (positive) values.   The distribution is known as the *exponential distribution*, which often fits very nicely with the actually observed arrival of customers for an appropriate choice of a.   This is not too surprising, because the results can be derived theoretically (apart from experimentally) whenever we assume that the customers arrive haphazardly, unsystematically, independently of each other.   We shall not pursue this further.   In what follows we shall assume that interarrival times are exponentially distributed.

9-3. Servicing

When a customer arrives, he usually has to wait before he is serviced. The time he has to wait depends on a number of factors such as:

1. The number of service stations (runways, repairmen, counters). Obviously, there may be more than one service station, but we shall confine our attention for the time being to the simple case in which there is only one.

2. The priority schedule, which may upset the old adage "first-come, first-served."   For example, old ladies might be dealt with on a preferential basis.   We shall assume in this section that the only priority is the time-honored first-come, first-served.

After a period of waiting, the customer is serviced.   The servicing time is usually not the same for all customers, and here again we shall use probability theory.   The probability distribution of servicing times, which determines the probability that an arbitrary customer will need less than 1, between 1 and 2, . . . minutes to be serviced, can have various forms. It turns out that two characteristics of the distribution, its mean and its standard deviation, are of special importance.   In particular, the ratio of the standard deviation to the mean will prove to be important.   This ratio is called the *coefficient of variation*, and will be denoted by v.   Thus

$$v = \frac{\text{standard deviation of servicing times}}{\text{mean servicing time}}$$

---

[1] The results which follow are given without proof.

If all servicing times are equal, the standard deviation is zero, so $v = 0$. If the servicing times are exponentially distributed (just as the interarrival times), the mean servicing time and the standard deviation of the servicing time will be equal, as we have seen, so $v = 1$. Notice that we confine our attention to the mean and the standard deviation of the distribution of servicing times. We do not specify a complete distribution. For the interarrival times we *did* specify a distribution, in fact the exponential distribution ae^{-at}. For the servicing time, only the mean and the standard deviation of the distribution are of interest to us as long as we want to determine the average number of waiting customers. This is a nice feature; the fewer the assumptions made, the better the applicability to different concrete situations.

The first question that comes to mind is whether the service station can handle its task. The answer to this question can be given by comparing interarrival times with servicing times. If more customers arrive per unit of time than can be serviced per unit of time, the mechanism will break down. The line of waiting customers then increases continually, and drastic measures are called for. Mathematically, we must compare the average interarrival time $1/a$ with the average servicing time; if the latter exceeds the former, we are headed for trouble. In the time needed to help a customer, more than one new customer arrives, at least on the average. If the mean servicing time is smaller than $1/a$, there is no trouble, although because of the variability in arrival times and servicing times, some customers may have to wait. Consider now the ratio

$$b = \frac{\text{average servicing time}}{\text{average interarrival time}} = \frac{\text{average servicing time}}{1/a}$$
$$= a \times \text{average servicing time}$$

The ratio b should be smaller than 1, lest the system get "choked." This ratio is known as the *utilization factor* of the service station. If $b = 0.7$, this means that the average time for servicing a customer is 70 per cent of the average time that elapses between the arrival of two customers. It also means, as can be shown, that the service station is utilized 70 per cent of the time on the average. The remaining 30 per cent of the time the service station waits for customers.

9-4. The Average Length of the Queue

Having discussed interarrival times and servicing times, we shall now get down to the real problem: waiting. A post office counter opens at 8:30 A.M., and from then on the customers drop in to buy stamps, claim packages, etc. If we assume that there are no people waiting before the doors open, the first customer to arrive after 8:30 is obviously in a very advantageous position. He will be immediately serviced; he does not have to wait at all. The second customer to arrive is in a somewhat different position. Perhaps he need not wait at all, but it is also possible that the first customer is still being serviced when he arrives, so that he has to wait. However, there is at most one man in front of him. For the third customer the situation is again more complicated. He may have to wait for two people or for one, or perhaps he need not wait at all. And so on for the rest of the day's customers. Apparently for each successive customer the situation is a little different, but the following important result resolves these difficulties. It can be shown that whenever the utilization factor is less than 1, the differences for successive customers become imperceptibly small after some time. What does this mean? It does *not* mean that all customers will have to wait equally long. On the contrary, some will have to wait a long time; others will hardly have to wait at all. The time the customers will have to wait is given by a probability density function, which specifies the probability that the customer will have to wait between 0 and 1 minute, 1 and 2 minutes, and so on. What *is* meant is that the probability density function becomes the same for all customers. Thus, although it remains possible that the hundredth customer will have to wait twice as long as the two-hundredth, this is not based on systematic causes. It is due to the fact that the probability density function of the time one has to wait is characterized by a certain variance.

One can visualize this situation as follows. At the entrance of the post office stands an urn filled with many numbered balls. Each customer draws a ball from this urn, and if it says "seven," he has to wait 7 minutes. He throws his ball back into the urn. Another customer now arrives and draws a ball out of the same urn. He perhaps draws a "three" and has to wait 3 minutes. The implication is that all customers draw from the *same* urn (the same distribution), though they may well draw *different* numbers (because there is a certain variance). Of course, this is true only after a certain time. The first customer certainly does not have to wait, the second at most a short time, but gradually the situation stabilizes and every additional customer is in the same situation as his predecessor. After how long a period the situation becomes stabilized or *stationary* depends very much on the utilization factor. If the factor is close to 1, it takes quite a while; if the utilization factor is far less than 1, the stationary situation is arrived at rather quickly. In what follows we shall assume that the stationary situation has been reached.

The phenomenon of waiting, just as the phenomenon of arriving, can be viewed in two different ways. As we saw in describing arrivals, either we can determine the number of people arriving in a 5-minute interval or we can determine the time elapsing between two arrivals. In describing waiting, we can count either the number of waiting people or the time a customer has to wait. It is perhaps slightly easier to focus attention on the number of people who wait in line (after the stationary situation has been reached). This may be 0, 1, 2, 3, . . . , but it will always be an integer number. The probability distribution, then, is apparently *discrete*. We shall be concerned with the mathematical expectation of this distribution, that is, with the average length of the line of waiting people. Under our assumptions of exponentially distributed interarrival times and a stationary situation, it turns out that the average length of the line (r) depends only upon the utilization factor b and the coefficient of variation v of the servicing times. The formula which results is

$$r = \frac{b(1 - \tfrac{1}{2}b) + \tfrac{1}{2}b^2v^2}{1 - b}$$

We see that (when b remains constant) r increases as v increases. A large standard deviation of the servicing times is unfavorable for the average length of the line. This could be expected, for the larger the standard deviation, the more often a customer arrives who needs an inordinate amount of time. The number of waiting people will then increase sharply. Admittedly, when the standard deviation is large, there will also be a number of customers requiring only very little time, but this does not sufficiently offset the increase resulting from very slow customers. The reason is that each fast customer reduces the line by only one person (himself) when he leaves after being quickly served, whereas the number of new customers arriving during the servicing of one slow customer may be quite large.

The relationship between r and b when v remains constant is not so easy to determine from the formula, but it stands to reason that the average number of waiting people increases when the utilization factor increases. This is confirmed by the following instructive table, which gives for various values of v and b the average number of people waiting in line:

	$b = 0.5$	$b = 0.7$	$b = 0.85$	$b = 0.95$	$b = 0.98$	$b = 0.99$
$v = 0$	0.75	1.51	3.26	10	25	50
$v = \frac{1}{2}$	0.81	1.72	3.86	12	31	62
$v = 1$	1.00	2.33	5.67	19	49	99
$v = 2$	1.75	4.78	13	46	121	246
$v = 4$	4.75	15	42	154	409	834

When we consider the columns of this table, we observe an increase in the average length of the line as v increases—a conclusion we have reached before. When the utilization factor b is 95 per cent and when all customers need the same amount of time to be serviced ($v = 0$), there are, on the average, 10 people waiting. This average increases to 19 when the coefficient of variation equals 1, which is the case when the servicing times are exponentially distributed.

When we read this table row by row, we see that the average length of the queue increases sharply as b approaches 1. The denominator $(1 - b)$ of the formula in that case approaches 0, and the situation tends to explode, so to speak. When $b = 0.99$ and $v = 4$, there are 834 impatient customers, on the *average*. (The queue might in fact be much longer, but on the average there are 834 people waiting.) This is not a realistic situation; the system is unworkable. The table indicates quite clearly that small changes can have substantial effects. If the utilization factor increases from 0.95 to 0.99, the average length of the line increases fivefold or more!

9-5. Priority

We shall now change one of our assumptions. We shall no longer assume that customers are serviced in order of arrival, but instead we shall allow priority rules. These exist in practice for various reasons. Ladies may be served first for reasons of courtesy, international flights may get landing privileges over national flights, and a defective machine may be repaired first because it is needed immediately or because it is such a small repair job that it can be done in a jiffy. We shall be concerned here with priority rules designed to decrease the average waiting time. One more or less intuitively feels that people will have to wait less on the average if the very fast customers are served on a preferential basis. The customers who need a lot of time will then have to wait longer, but because the quick customers will not have to wait until all slow ones in front of them have been taken care of, the average waiting time will be reduced. This case will be discussed in some detail.

Suppose that the customers can be split up into two groups, which we shall refer to as fast and slow customers. Let us write q for the ratio of their average servicing times:

$$q = \frac{\text{average servicing time of fast customers}}{\text{average servicing time of slow customers}}$$

The value of q will be between 0 and 1. For example, if the fast customers require, on the average, 5 minutes and the slow ones 20 minutes, then $q = 5/20 = 0.25$. This q will turn out to be the only relevant aspect of the servicing times which we need. (In general, the servicing times of both the fast and the slow groups will be characterized by some variance. It is even quite conceivable that a particular "fast" customer will need more time than a particular "slow" customer, but the variance within these groups turns out to be irrelevant to our results.)

It is also important to know the composition of the customers. We must know what percentage belongs to the fast and what percentage belongs to the slow group. We consider this as given and write f for the fraction of customers belonging to the fast group. Thus

$$f = \frac{\text{number of fast customers}}{\text{total number of customers}}$$

If f is 0.2, then 20 per cent of the customers belong to the fast group; hence 80 per cent belong to the slow group.

Our priority rule now specifies that as soon as a customer is serviced, his place is taken by the fast customer who arrived first. When there are no fast customers, the place is taken by the slow customer who arrived first. Within the two groups of slow and fast customers, in other words, the order of arrival determines the order of servicing. Once a slow customer is being serviced, he is waited on until he has finished, even if in the meantime a fast customer arrives.

It is easy to see that this rule decreases the average waiting time. As an example, consider the case where there are only two customers, whom we will call slow A and fast B. Slow A needs 20 minutes, fast B only 8, and both wait till the service station becomes free. If slow A is serviced first, fast B has to wait 20 minutes from the moment slow A arrives at the station. If fast B is serviced first, slow A needs to wait only 8 minutes from the time fast B arrives at the station. The gain in waiting time when B is serviced first is $20 - 8 = 12$ minutes. There is, to be sure, no gain for slow A; on the contrary, A has to wait 8 minutes more, but fast B gains 20 minutes, and the average waiting time of A and B is thus reduced substantially. The total time needed to service them, 28 minutes, is, of course, not influenced by the change in the order of servicing. Hence, the utilization factor of the service station does not change.

The general formula for the percentage reduction of the average waiting time which results from our priority rule depends on three factors:

1. The ratio q of the average servicing time of fast and slow customers
2. The fraction f of customers belonging to the fast group
3. The utilization factor b

The general formula reads as follows:

$$\text{Percentage reduction of the average waiting time} = \frac{100f(1-f)(1-q)b}{1-f+fq(1-b)}$$

Some numerical experimentation with the formula is useful. Assume that $q = 0.3$; the percentage reduction in the average waiting time as a function of f and b is then given in the following table:

	$b = 0.5$	$b = 0.7$	$b = 0.85$	$b = 0.95$	$b = 0.99$
$f = 0.1$	3	5	6	7	7
$f = 0.2$	7	10	12	13	14
$f = 0.3$	10	14	18	20	21
$f = 0.4$	13	18	23	26	28
$f = 0.5$	15	22	28	33	35
$f = 0.6$	17	26	33	39	41
$f = 0.7$	18	28	38	45	48
$f = 0.8$	$17\frac{1}{2}$	29	40	50	55
$f = 0.9$	13	24	38	53	61

When there are very few fast customers, that is, when f is small, the percentage reduction is only small. It varies from 3 per cent to 7 per cent depending upon the utilization factor b when $f = 0.1$. As f increases, the possible reduction also increases, but by the time nearly everybody belongs to the fast group, the possible gains decrease again. This stands to reason, for if everybody belongs to the fast group, no reduction is obtained by the priority rule, which then gives everybody priority over nobody. In general, the higher the utilization factor, the higher the percentage gain. When 70 per cent of the customers belong to the fast group and the utilization factor is 99 per cent (and $q = 0.3$), the gain is nearly 50 per cent. This is quite important, because when the utilization factor is high, the waiting times may be very long. We saw this in the previous section where we mentioned some results for the average number of people waiting. It is easy to guess what that implies for the average waiting time.

There are many situations in which reduction of the average waiting time leads to a proportional reduction in costs. By allowing priority rules one can obtain savings of 25 per cent or more in many a case. The first-come, first-served rule is by no means to be preferred in all situations.

9-6. Machines and Repairmen

Consider the concrete case of a factory with a number of identical automatic machines. When all runs smoothly, no human action is required, but in case of trouble the machine must be repaired. It cannot be predicted when a machine will break down; it may happen any moment. So we call on probability theory, and assume that the machines run uninterruptedly for a period of time which is exponentially distributed with an average of $1/a$. If $a = 0.2$ per hour, the average time during which the machine runs without interruption is 5 hours. This situation is fully analogous to the interarrival times of planes; in this case the machine "arrives" to be repaired.

The servicing of the machine is done by a repairman. Because the failure may be due to various causes which are more or less serious, the repair time may differ from case to case. To be specific, we shall assume that the repair time is exponentially distributed with a mean equal to one-tenth of the average length of an uninterrupted run; hence the mean is $1/10a$. If the machine runs an average of 5 hours without trouble, the repair time is assumed to be, on the average, half an hour. Finally, we assume that there are 6 machines and 1 repairman.

There are then seven different possibilities: the number of broken machines may be 0, 1, 2, 3, 4, 5, or 6. One possibility is that all machines run smoothly. Under our assumptions (and under the assumption that the stationary situation has been reached) we find with the help of some solid arithmetic that this will happen 48 per cent of the time. This implies that the repairman is idle almost half the time. If only 1 machine is out of order, the repairman will occupy himself with this machine, while the other 5 are working. This has a probability of 29 per cent. If 2 machines give out, the repairman will be occupied with one of them while the other must wait to be repaired. This unfortunate event happens 15 per cent of the time, and it can get even worse: 3, 4, 5, or all 6 machines may be simultaneously out of order, but the chances that these situations will occur become increasingly smaller. A complete survey is given in the following table:

Number of broken machines	Number of machines waiting to be repaired	Probability
0	0	0.48
1	0	0.29
2	1	0.15
3	2	0.058
4	3	0.018
5	4	0.0035
6	5	0.0003
Total		1

We see that 48 per cent of the time the repairman waits for a machine to break down, 29 per cent of the time neither the one repairman nor any of the machines has to wait, and in the remaining 23 per cent of the time at least 1 machine must wait to be repaired. The average number of machines waiting to be repaired equals

$$0.48 \times 0 + 0.29 \times 0 + 0.15 \times 1 + \cdots + 0.0003 \times 5 = 0.33$$

In exactly the same way we can now consider the case in which there are 20 machines and 3 repairmen, while all other assumptions remain unchanged. The situations that can then prevail are listed in the following table:

Number of broken machines	Number of machines being repaired	Number of machines waiting to be repaired	Number of idle repairmen	Probability
0	0	0	3	0.14
1	1	0	2	0.27
2	2	0	1	0.26
3	3	0	0	0.16
4	3	1	0	0.088
5	3	2	0	0.047
6	3	3	0	0.023
7	3	4	0	0.011
8	3	5	0	0.0048
9	3	6	0	0.0019
10	3	7	0	0.0007
11	3	8	0	0.0002
12	3	9	0	0.00007

It turns out that when there are 20 machines (which are each broken an average of half an hour for each 5 hours of performance), there are no broken machines 14 per cent of the time. Thus, 14 per cent of the time the 3 repairmen can play gin rummy. When 1, 2, or 3 machines fail, they can be immediately repaired. The more or less "ideal" situation occurs when 3 machines fail—no idle repairmen and no machines waiting to be serviced. This happens 16 per cent of the time. Machines have to wait as soon as 4 or more are out of order at the same time. The table ends when 12 machines are broken, since the probability that more than 12 machines will be out of order at any one time is negligible.

It is interesting to compare the two situations—1 repairman for 6 machines and 3 repairmen for 20 machines. Let us first compare the number of idle repairmen. In the first case the one repairman is idle 48 per cent of the time. In the second case the mathematical expectation of the number of idle repairmen is

$$0.14 \times 3 + 0.27 \times 2 + 0.26 \times 1 = 1.21$$

Since there are 3 repairmen, each of them is idle 40 per cent of the time $(1.21/3 = 0.40)$. This is better than the 48 per cent in the first case. Perhaps this is considered obvious, because the repairmen-machine ratio is 1 to 6 in the first case and 1 to $6\frac{2}{3}$ in the second case, so that in the latter case the repairmen will, on the average, be more fully occupied. Following this argument, we should expect the average number of waiting machines to be larger in the second case than in the first. Let us verify this.

In the first situation (1 repairman for 6 machines) we found an expected number of waiting machines equal to 0.33. Because there are 6 machines, each machine must wait to be repaired $5\frac{1}{2}$ per cent of the time $(0.33/6 = 0.055)$. In the second case (3 repairmen for 20 machines) the expected number of waiting machines is

$$0.088 \times 1 + 0.047 \times 2 + 0.023 \times 3 + \cdots = 0.34$$

Per machine, this is $0.34/20 = 0.017$ or 1.7 per cent of the time. Contrary to what we might have guessed, the average time machines have to wait for repairs is, in the second case, more than 3 times smaller. Despite the fact that there are fewer repairmen relative to the number of machines, the loss due to waiting machines is smaller (per machine). This interesting conclusion is an indication of one of the advantages of the large company over the small. It is an instance of the well-known phenomenon called "economies of scale."

Literature

A rather solid book on the topics dealt with in this chapter is Morse [1]. Chapter 11 of Saaty [2] is more specifically concerned with queueing theory. Priority models have been studied by Cobham [3]. The tables in this chapter have been taken from Koerts [4], apart from those in the last section which can be found in Feller [5]. Feller, in turn, took them from a Swedish publication by Palm.

[1] P. M. Morse, *Queues, Inventories and Maintenance*, John Wiley & Sons, Inc., New York, 1958.
[2] T. L. Saaty, *Mathematical Methods of Operations Research*, McGraw-Hill Book Company, New York, 1959.
[3] A. Cobham, "Priority Assignment in Waiting Line Problems," *Operations Research*, vol. 2 (1954), pp. 70–76 [with a correction in vol. 3 (1955), p. 547].
[4] J. Koerts, "On Mean Waiting Times and Their Reduction by Priority Procedures: An Expository Survey and Some Tables," *Statistica Neerlandica*, vol. 17 (1963), pp. 267–283.
[5] W. Feller, *An Introduction to Probability Theory and Its Applications*, vol. 1, 2d ed., John Wiley & Sons, Inc., New York, 1957.

10

Simulation and Management Games

10-1. The Pools

Millions of Britons each week play the pools, a very exciting game. In its simplest version it is played with a pencil and a list of 15 soccer matches to be played the following Saturday. All one needs to do is predict whether the home team or the visiting team will win or whether the game will end in a draw. If the home team is expected to win, one indicates this by writing a 1 beside the game; a 2 predicts that the visiting team will win; a 3 indicates a draw. After filling out the form, one thus has a list of 15 numbers, all of which are 1, 2, or 3. For example,

1   2   1   3   3   1   2   1   1   2   2   1   1   3   1

It is, indeed, quite a simple form of entertainment. The biggest thrill of it all is that when it turns out that all predictions were correct, a huge prize is received. Ordinarily, disappointment is in store, because only six or eight matches were correctly predicted, but then some solace may be found in the thought that next week there will be another chance to win the jackpot.

Unfortunately, there is one organizational problem. The weather conditions are repeatedly so unspeakably bad that the games are *not* played. The field resembles a swimming pool as a result of days of uninterrupted rain, or the field has the structure of concrete because of a long period of frost. The games are then postponed; so for the time being the predictions cannot be verified. One might think that the results of the betting game would then be delayed until the game were actually played, but this would have practical disadvantages. The slips of paper would have to be preserved, and the possibilities of fraud would increase. Apart from that, there are theoretical objections. The predictions were made for the game to be played the following Saturday. If the game is

169

played at a later date, the circumstances on which the predictions were based might change. This solution therefore does not work.

The solution which has been found is quite ingenious. Whenever a match is not played, the result is *simulated*. To that end, five experts (such as referees, players, club officials, journalists) appear together on TV to discuss the chances of the teams in each canceled match, for example, the match Arsenal-Blackpool. They take into consideration a great number of possibly relevant circumstances: results in the past, illness of certain players, etc. As a result of a penetrating discussion of the issue, the chairman of the TV panel might conclude in summary that "all things considered, the home team Arsenal had a chance of 55 per cent to win the match and a chance of only 10 per cent to lose." The probability that a draw would have occurred is thus determined at 35 per cent; one of the three mutually exclusive possibilities (Arsenal wins, loses, or draws) had to be realized. This means that the probabilities should add up to 1, as here: $55 + 10 + 35 = 100$ per cent.

The chances for a 1 (Arsenal wins), a 2 (Blackpool wins), or a 3 (draw) have thus been determined in a reasonably objective way, or at least in a fully public way. Next quite an interesting event can be seen. A large urn is brought on stage which contains 100 golfballs numbered from 1 through 100. Let us distinguish three groups—a first group of balls numbered 1 to 55, a second group numbered 56 to 65, and a third group numbered 66 and higher. These groups contain, respectively, 55, 10, and 35 balls in precisely the same ratio as the determined chances of the results 1, 2, and 3. Then the chairman draws a ball from the urn and shows the number for all to see on TV. If it happens to be any of the numbers from 1 to 55 inclusive, a "1" is counted as the correct prediction; "2" is considered the correct prediction when the result is a number in the range 56 to 65; if the number drawn is higher than 65, a "3" is considered the correct prediction. (It goes without saying that these results are only relevant for the pools, not for the league standing; the game itself will be played at a later date.)

It may seem far-fetched that if number 61 is drawn, Blackpool is considered to have won the game, even though it was agreed in advance that its chances of winning were as small as 10 per cent. But a moment's thought will convince one that this is only the logical consequence of our conviction that Blackpool has a 10 per cent chance of winning. If Blackpool has that chance, we should give it to that team. It would be definitely wrong to fill in a "1" blindly just because Arsenal is considered the most likely to win.

All in all we have given a simple but topical and realistic example of simulation. For simulation we need a *model* which represents an image

of reality as we see it. In this case the model simply consisted of the
agreed-upon chances of the results 1, 2, and 3.   For the match Arsenal-
Blackpool these chances were, respectively, 0.55, 0.10, and 0.35.   Apart
from the model, we need a *mechanism* to simulate the model.   This
mechanism was an urn with 100 consecutively numbered golf balls.
These two characteristics, a model and a mechanism to simulate the
model, are necessary for simulation.   The testing of model ships in labora-
tory bathtubs, in which waves and streams can be artificially generated, is
another example of simulation.   The models can thus be tested for maneu-
verability, stability, and so forth.   This may be called for in order to
check computations, or it may be necessary because the computations are
too complicated to be made in reality.   Perhaps the necessary computations cannot even be performed analytically at all; in that case the simulation technique can be an important way out.

10-2. The Margarine Factory

In Chap. 9 we came across the problem caused by machines that stop
functioning at arbitrary moments and then need repairs.   We distinguished two unpleasant situations: Either the repairman was idle, or a
broken machine had to wait for repairs.   Both circumstances cost money.
The problem is how many repairmen one should employ if one wants to
minimize these costs, given certain probabilities that a machine will
break down and the time then needed for repairs.   It was implied in the
previous chapter that this problem could be solved mathematically, given
such a set of judiciously chosen assumptions as exponential distributions
for both arrivals and the repair time of defects.   The computations were
not given in detail, but perhaps the impression was conveyed that they
were not really very difficult.   That impression may be correct, but it
should be born in mind that our assumptions were carefully chosen to
make them amenable for mathematical manipulations.   (It is one of the
little marvels of nature that such simple assumptions as exponentially
distributed arrival times are often amazingly realistic and lead to accurate
results!)   As the problems become more complicated, the required mathematics becomes more intricate.   It might actually become so complex as
to frustrate analytical techniques.   Furthermore, even if a mathematical
derivation of the solution is possible, this is objectionable mainly because
laymen, who have the cunning habit of being your boss, no longer understand it.   If the mathematical expert goes to his director with seven sheets
of algebra and blandly states that 4 rather than 3 repairmen will decrease
the overall costs, he may hear the director say: "Half the time the present
crew is idle as it is, and that is not changed one iota by your abracadabra."
Our mathematician will find less than a willing ear if he then tries to pro-

ceed by explaining the algebra.   Instead he should start running a simulation study of the problem.

Imagine now a margarine factory with 20 machines for packaging. These packaging machines are fully automatic; they weigh, mold, wrap up, and move the packages along the conveyor belt.   Moreover, they do it at a rate of 1 package per second, 60 per minute, 3,600 per hour, day and night, night and day—if they run at all.

There, you see, is the trouble.   A machine may start to weigh inaccurately, a wrapping paper may get in the way, the motor may fail, or there may be a congestion at the conveyor belts.   This happens at unpredictable times, but long experience may have proved that there is a 1 in 10 chance that the machine will break down during any given hour.   In such a case, a repairman is needed.   This repairman can put the machine in working order again, but that will cost time.   Depending on the type of failure, the following data are available concerning the required repair time.   The probability is

0.4 that the repair will take ½ hour
0.3 that the repair will take 1 hour
0.2 that the repair will take 1½ hours
0.1 that the repair will take 2 hours

This is our *model*.   It consists of the probability that a machine will break down and the time then required to repair the damage.   The mechanism to simulate this model can again be a bag with 100 numbered balls, 00, 01, 02, . . . , 98, 99.   The procedure is as follows:

1. Draw a number.   If the number is 90 or higher, we shall say that the *first* machine broke down during the *first* hour.   Notice that there is a chance of 1 in 10 that the randomly chosen number is 90 or higher.   This corresponds to the probability of a breakdown.

2. If the number drawn was 90 or higher, the necessary repair time is determined as follows.   When the number drawn was

90, 91, 92, or 93, the repair requires ½ hour
94, 95, or 96, the repair requires 1 hour
97 or 98, the repair requires 1½ hours
99, the repair requires 2 hours

It is immediately evident that this last rule is based on the ratio 4:3:2:1, corresponding to the probabilities of the repair times.

This procedure may be repeated 20 times, once for each of the 20 machines. The second number drawn concerns the second machine during the first hour, and so on. One can then continue to simulate the *second* hour, which again requires the drawing of 20 numbers. If one wants to simulate 30 hours, one must be patient enough to draw 20 × 30 = 600 numbers. Draw a number, record it, put it back; draw a number, record it, put it back—a rather tiresome procedure. Perhaps you may think that it would be ever so much simpler just to write down the numbers 00, 01, . . . , 99 in a random, arbitrary order instead of using a bag of numbers. Believe it or not, however, experiments have proved beyond doubt that the human mind simply cannot write these numbers down in a truly *random* order. Mechanical aid of some form or other is called for. The bag of numbers, of course, is a rather clumsy aid.

There are two satisfactory ways out, one for the amateur and one for the professional. The amateur can use a table of random numbers, such as *A Million Random Digits with 100,000 Normal Deviates*, which has been published by the RAND Corporation.[1] It contains on each page numerous two-digit figures of the form 07, 93, 65, etc. The professional may turn to his computer which, when properly instructed, produces random numbers at fantastic speeds; it can, for example, produce 5,000 two-digit numbers in a minute or so. This is what we have done for the current problem, with the following results:

Machines	Hour 1	Hour 2	Hour 3	Hour 4	Hour 5	Hour 6	Hour 7
1	04	61	29	28	87	21	93*
2	87	44	07	57	65	42	57
3	12	52	79	30	25	56	35
4	98*	58	50	86	71	03	47
5	30	09	80	28	75	73	24
6	91*	07	39	93*	90*	64	96*
7	66	45	54	31	58	58	84
8	48	62	71	50	47	73	24
9	52	46	70	19	54	37	62
10	24	40	78	91*	33	88	39
11	49	87	79	93*	04	33	76
12	20	98*	34	43	03	50	94*
13	29	05	87	34	76	74	63
14	83	94*	03	54	06	69	06
15	81	79	40	76	47	91*	55
16	86	38	79	79	56	52	33
17	54	99*	44	15	51	07	03
18	51	14	58	31	56	73	92*
19	08	76	89	60	52	88	74
20	42	99*	48	23	34	25	52

[1] The Free Press of Glencoe, New York, 1955.

The table shows that during the first hour two numbers in the 90s were drawn, 98 and 91 (the starred numbers).   Hence, 2 machines broke down during that hour.   One of these (98) required 1½ hours repair time, the other (91) only half an hour.   In the second hour there was trouble with 4 machines (98, 94, 99, 99).   With 3 of these the trouble was of such a serious nature that 1½ or 2 hours were required to repair them.   In the third hour there was no trouble at all, etc.   During the 7 hours considered, 15 machines broke down.

We are still trying to determine whether there should be 3 or 4 repairmen.   It is therefore of great importance to know how many machines are out of order at the same time.   To this end we want to know the exact time when the machines break down.   For each broken machine we are therefore going to draw a second random number (00, 01, . . . , 99), which gives the number of minutes after which, in the given hour, the machine stops.   If the first number drawn is 17, this means that the first machine that breaks down during the first hour does so after 17 minutes.   The fact that there are only 60 minutes in an hour is not a problem.   We simply disregard all numbers higher than 60 and go on to the next number:

20	24	58	(66)	(81)	07	53	(70)	47
38	26	53	(99)	01	35	(99)	12	(89)
39	(84)	51	36	28	(91)	44	15	04

The 2 machines of the first hour break down after 20 and 24 minutes, respectively.   As we saw before, it takes 1½ hours to repair the machine that stops after 20 minutes and only ½ hour to repair the machine that stops after 24 minutes.   In the next hour 4 machines need repairs after 58, 7, 53, and 47 minutes; the respective repair times are 1½, 1, 2, and 2 hours.

All the facts have now been generated.   Now we need only to plot the results along a time axis to see in one glance how many machines are broken at the same time.   This is done in Fig. 10-1, in which the time axis is drawn as a spiral to get it all on one uninterrupted axis.   The hours have been split up into 20 periods of 3 minutes.   We conclude from the figure that after 20 minutes a machine breaks down and that it needs 1½ hours to be repaired.   This is indicated by the line from 20 minutes to 1 hour and 50 minutes.   For each of the three-minute periods the number of broken machines can now be seen immediately by just counting the number of lines above the axis.   These are the numbers 0, 1, 2, 3, and 4 in the figure.   In the 7 hours considered there are $7 \times 20 = 140$ such periods.   The complete results are as follows:

Number of broken machines	Number of 3-minute periods	Percentage of working time	Hours per year of 360 days
0	28	20	1,728
1	28	20	1,728
2	33	24	2,037
3	40	30	2,469
4	11	6	679
5	0	0	0
Total	140	100	8,640

It goes without saying that these results are not very accurate, but the principle should be clear. Taking longer periods, one will find that it occasionally happens that 5 or 6 machines are out of order at the same time.

Finally, we come back to the question of the number of repairmen.

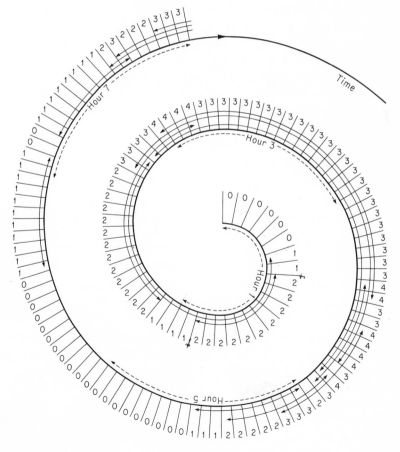

Fig. 10-1

The factory works with three shifts.   We see that during 679 hours per year, or 226 hours per shift, the 4 repairmen (if present) are all needed. If only 3 repairmen are present, the loss will therefore be at least 226 hours per shift.   Actually, it is even more, the reason being the following. Suppose that 3 machines are broken, so that no repairman is available for a fourth machine.   Suppose that nevertheless a fourth machine breaks down.   Then it has to wait before being repaired, and the time during which it is out of order exceeds the time indicated in the figure.   During that additional period there may be other machines which get out of order, in which case the number of broken machines increases above the levels indicated.

Now each lost hour costs $50, and a repairman costs the factory $7,200 a year.   Clearly $226 \times 50 = \$11,300$ is substantially more than $7,200, so that the fourth man should certainly be employed on each shift.   The savings will then be at least $11,300 - 7,200 = \$4,100$ (actually even more). This all is true despite the fact that all 4 repairmen will be idle 20 per cent of the time.

10-3. Further Subtleties

The reader may be tempted to think that these results were so easily derived because the problem was relatively simple.   This proposition is true in mathematics, but it is hardly true in the case of simulation.   Just as it is almost as easy to experiment with a model row boat as with a model carrier in a tub, so we can admit a far more refined model here without overly complicating the mechanism.   Let us, then, introduce some further refinements, which will, no doubt, make the model more realistic.

1. A suspicious mind may have discovered a mistake in the previous model.   A machine that is already broken cannot break again before it has been repaired.   Yet we drew a number for machine 20 in the third hour, while during that entire hour machine 20 was out of order.   It turned out that the number was 48, but suppose it had been 91?   We shall take this factor into account in what follows, so that no machines which are already out of order can break down again.

2. The distribution of repair times will generally be vastly more complicated.   This is also taken in stride by the simulation technique.

3. Not all machines will have the same probability of breaking down. After all, there are old and new machines, lemons and peaches.

All these subtleties—which are really not so subtle at all—are very disturbing complications when we follow the mathematical (analytical) approach.   They can all be easily incorporated in the simulation technique, however; we do this simply by drawing random numbers with more digits. Let us take the example of an arbitrary machine during the third hour; this machine is out of order during the first 7 minutes of that hour. The other data are as follows.

The machine has a probability of 0.14 of breaking down during an hour. The occurrence of this event will be indicated by the first and second digits of the random number drawn. If these are 00, 01, . . . , 85, everything is in order; if 86 or higher is drawn, the machine stops functioning during the third hour. (We can, of course, work with different probabilities for different machines.)

The third and fourth digits, as listed in the following table, indicate the required repair time *if* the machine breaks down. Again, the distribution of repair times may very well differ from machine to machine.

Repair time (in minutes)	Probability	3d and 4th digits of random number
10	0.01	00
20	0.03	01–03
30	0.05	04–08
40	0.07	09–15
50	0.09	16–24
60	0.11	25–35
70	0.13	36–48
80	0.13	49–61
90	0.11	62–72
100	0.09	73–81
110	0.07	82–88
120	0.05	89–93
130	0.03	94–96
140	0.01	97
150	0.01	98
160	0.01	99

Finally, the fifth and sixth digits of the random number indicate at what time during the hour the machine breaks down *if* it breaks down at all. We divide the hour in 100 periods of 36 seconds each. Thus, if the digits drawn are 2 and 5, this concerns the twenty-fifth period of 36 seconds in the third hour. We can now easily incorporate the fact that the machine is out of order during the first 7 minutes, i.e., during the first 12 periods of 36 seconds. We simply disregard the breakdown if the last two digits are anywhere from 00 to 11.

As examples:

077631: the machine does not break down, for 07 is one of the numbers 00, 01, . . . , 85.

937910: the first two digits indicate that the machine breaks down, but the last two (10) negate this information, since it is one of the numbers 00, 01, . . . , 11.

898876: the machine breaks down (89), this is not contradicted by the last two digits (76), and 110 minutes are needed for the repair (88).

So one can continue. By drawing (generating with a computer) random numbers of more and more digits, many other complications can be incorporated. The principle remains simple. When the random numbers have been drawn, all that remains to be done is to administer and interpret them carefully. The question remains how long one should continue to simulate. Is 7 hours sufficient to get reliable results? Or are 70 hours required? Or are 700 hours still too few to trust the results? This question can be answered pragmatically. In our case the only relevant problem is to determine the percentage of the time that 0, 1, 2, 3, . . . machines are simultaneously defected. One may then begin to simulate 3 hours and determine these percentages. Then one adds 3 hours—to get 6 hours—and recomputes the percentages. Next one simulates 9 hours and again computes the percentages of the time during which 0, 1, 2, . . . machines are broken down. After a little while the consecutive results will not perceptibly or appreciably differ—according to the basic statistical "law of large numbers"—and one can safely stop.

10-4. Chess and Monopoly

Simulation is not limited to the pools, the model-ship tank, or to machines. After all, nearly everything can be simulated, from illness to bank notes. The following application of simulation, which we shall introduce with the examples of chess and Monopoly, perhaps does not come to mind immediately.

With some fantasy the game of chess can be viewed as a miniature war; the symbolism is the same. Admittedly the comparison is somewhat far-fetched; real war with invasions and bombings has little in common with a relaxed game of chess, during which the players puff cigars and sip whisky. To some extent a war has more in common with roulette: one has hardly any hope of really winning. Perhaps chess should rather be considered as the predecessor of the modern war games, which have an amazing reality content. These war games, despite their realism, are more peaceful than an American college football game, or even children's wild west games. Yet the thought of playing war games is frightening. Aren't we all a little pacifistic? The point to be made here, however, is that they are useful.

Indeed, one cannot start a real war, shooting with live ammunition, just for the sake of an exercise.   Nevertheless, we must have military officers who, if necessary, would be able to wage a war in all its aspects, centered around the questions when, where, and how to defend or attack.   These aspects are simulated in war games, with maps, armies, planes, bridges, spies, bombings, and all.   Sometimes the simulations are based on historic events; usually they are based purely on imagination.   In this way the future officers are trained in the complicated art—unfelicitous word—of war.

If chess can be viewed as the predecessor of war games, the Monopoly game may be considered as an early example of a business game.   While the first complicated war game was already produced in 1780 in Prussia, business or management games became popular only after 1955.   This is rather surprising, because the business world with its life-or-death competition involving millions of dollars is strikingly similar to military science.   Moreover, business students cannot be educated by receiving a real business in which to show their genius.   Again, they must learn to swim without water, and this is done with management or business games. They are a sort of complicated Monopoly, as we shall now show by a typical example.

10-5. Freezers

The management of an industrial concern has two basic objectives: to produce and to sell.   Production often requires careful planning far in advance, because of the time needed for the production process.   Whether cars, books, or fertilizers are produced, the raw materials needed for today's production should have been received yesterday, and these raw materials should have been ordered the day before yesterday—or even months ago when delivery times are as long as for manuscripts of books, for example. Moreover, one should try to produce regularly.   Production cannot follow each variation in demand, thus creating inventory problems.   If the inventories are small, one might not be able to satisfy the forthcoming demand.   If the inventories are large, they cost a lot of money (insurance, pilferage, tied up capital).

The other principal objective is selling.   The main instruments of the sales division are the price, advertising, distribution channels, installment plan, and, to some extent, quality.   Obviously, the sales manager and the production manager must coordinate their efforts.   The sales manager should tell the production manager what quality, color, style, size, and material are in demand.   In his turn, the production manager will have to tell the salesman what is technically feasible, what is very expensive to

produce, and so on.   Together they will aim at maximizing profit.   The
receipts from the sales should cover the expenses of production and the
selling costs.   All these aspects are simulated in games.

In the prototype of a management game you are the director of a firm
producing a product on a so-called *oligopolistic market*—that is, a market
where there are only a few competitors.   Let us assume that the market of
freezers in the United States is an example.   Such a market leaves some
room for an independent sales policy (within limits you can fix your own
price), but your results will also partly depend on the behavior of
your competitors, such as the price they ask for their product or their
advertising efforts.

As a director you will obviously be aware of some of the more important
aspects of the market for freezers; in any case, these are given in the rules
of the game.   These rules specify that there are only four different
producers, who each had 25 per cent of the market last year—which
means that each firm sold 10,000 freezers.   During the past year the
capacities of each of the factories as well as the sales efforts were comparable.
Each factory can produce up to 1,000 freezers a month.   The fixed costs
are given, as are the variable costs per freezer.   These variable costs may
depend on the total production.   It is quite possible, for example, that
they will increase when the production capacity of the factory is approached.

The rules of the game also specify that at the beginning of the year each
factory has 1,000 freezers in stock and that the total market is expected to
grow.   There is a sharp seasonal fluctuation in the sales, however; usually
four times as many freezers are sold in April as in November.   If desired
and if the money can be put up, the capacity of the factory can be increased
to 1,500 freezers each month.   This will influence both the fixed and the
variable costs.   The costs of carrying inventories are $10 for each freezer
in stock at the end of the month.   Each firm in the past year charged
$500 for a freezer.   Further details concerning installment payment
plans, possible distribution channels, advertising possibilities, and research
possibilities are mentioned in the rules.   Thus, the rules may state that
research might lead to the development of a superior freezer.   In complicated cases the market may be divided geographically, and prices of
advertising may differ from area to area.   In short, there is a vast body of
data.   It is your task to direct the business with three colleagues during
the coming years.   The objectives are to make profits and to increase your
market share, in short, to make the factory a prosperous concern.

The first problem in such a game is to agree on a task distribution within
the team.   In this case it stands to reason to appoint a production manager, a sales manager, an administrative manager (for bookkeeping,
computing the profits, determining the cash balance), and a president to

coordinate the decisions and map out the long-run decisions, such as expansion of the factory or the incurring of research expenditures. Many teams fail at this stage; they do not provide for a division of duties, and all managers concern themselves with every decision that is to be made. When the jobs have been divided, the real game begins.

Decisions have to be made for the first month, January. What price should be set? How much should you advertise? How much will you produce? Will you plan to expand? You should also take into account the possible lags; for example, the freezers produced during this month cannot be sold until the next month. The decisions you make then go to an umpire, which may be an electronic computer or a secretary equipped with a slide rule. The umpire also receives all the decisions of the other companies, such as their prices, their advertising expenditures, their quality. *All* these decisions influence the sales of *each* firm. A computer is required when the interdependencies get complicated. The umpire can give the total sales for each of the companies in a number of minutes. The management is then informed about its sales as well as about other factors, such as the prices and advertising budgets of its competitors. No information is provided about the production decisions of the competitors. Sometimes further information can be bought, just as one pays for a market analysis study.

The management then is allowed some time to analyze data and to draw conclusions from them for the next period, February. This procedure is followed a number of times, a whole month of business life being simulated each half an hour or so. Management is confronted with a whole array of problems that might occur in reality, although the environment is not always wholly realistic. In fact, of course, complete reality cannot be reached and is not even strived for. The purpose of these games is to learn; thus, there must be specific problems.

10-6. Problems Facing the Players

There are internal problems, corresponding to the desire to produce as efficiently and cheaply as possible. There are also external problems, corresponding to the desire to sell the product with profit despite the competition. Production and sales should be more or less attuned to each other; to the extent that they are not, there will be inventory problems. Then there are the more weighty policy problems, such as the expansion and research programs. Finally, there are administrative problems, but these are more prevalent in the construction of the game than in the actual playing. As a rule, the teams work with prefabricated standard forms, which ease the task of the umpire who calculates the monthly sales of each company. There is still room for initiative on the part of administrative management, however, with respect to making graphs of the development of the market share or the long-run inventory costs. These graphs, when cleverly laid out, can be very useful in the shaping of decisions.

In most games there is a built-in friction between production and sales. During the peak season, demand exceeds capacity; during the slack season, capacity exceeds demand. The production policy, the sales policy, and the seasonal fluctuations in demand then determine the inventory. In this area there are vast possibilities for management to fail, usually because of insufficient coordination. It frequently happens that a firm advertises prodigiously while it is not able to satisfy demand. It happens even more often that, despite ever increasing inventories, production is kept steady at the level where the sum of fixed and variable costs per freezer attains its minimum value. The production manager apparently forgets that inventory costs also add up. Liquid funds may also prove a problem. The time lapse between the payments for raw materials, on the one hand, and the receipt of money from the consumer, on the other hand, may be a matter of months. An all too liberal installment plan, which the sales manager advocates to entice customers, may necessitate expensive loans or even precipitate bankruptcy. Such results *can* be foreseen, but experience shows that management seldom fully recognizes them.

Long-range policy is an important aspect of the game. As a rule the games are constructed in such a way that with prudent and intelligent financial management expansion is feasible as well as desirable. If a decision to expand is made blindly, however, disaster waits just around the corner. After all, an investment ties up a lot of capital which trickles back slowly and with delays. Suppose that freezer sales are high in spring and summer, but low in autumn and winter. Suppose further that if you decide to expand, the new factory will be ready four months later. Then a decision to expand is best made in November when sales are low; the factory is then ready in March, nicely in time for the peak season. It is tempting, however, to expand in June or July at the end of the season when sales are still brisk and inventories low. However, one would then have a new factory in November when only few people buy freezers; the high fixed costs would be a heavy burden. Management would be the victim of a lack of foresight.

The problems seem very simple, but in practice they are not. The coordination of decisions, the necessity to look ahead, the need to analyze the results, the required speed in making decisions, and the somewhat tense atmosphere all combined usually prove too much for management. That is not to say that the game is without learning value. This type of learning is especially helpful because the players are so involved themselves that they will not soon forget the lessons. In class, it can be stated time and again that good management should plan ahead. Once you have gone bankrupt because this wisdom was temporarily forgotten, or at least not applied, the need to plan ahead will always be obvious.

The analysis of the results has been dealt with only in passing. Yet, these analyses are needed to make good decisions. You will, for example, have to try to determine in the course of the game with the help of the gathered evidence how sensitive the demand is with respect to price changes. Does a price decrease of $10 (2 per cent) increase demand by 1, 2, or perhaps 3 per cent? Are there equal advantages to building a new shop in Rochester, New York, at the cost of $60,000 and to spending that amount on ads? Of course, there is a whole range of similar questions. It goes without saying that they cannot all be directly (and correctly) answered, but in the course of the game you might get a pretty good idea about the answers if you analyze perceptively.

Without a complete and detailed specification of the rules, it is obviously impossible to play such a game or to analyze the results here in any detail. The following discussion in the directors' office, however, is illustrative of the type of conversation one might hear from a team of less than excellent players.

10-7. In the Directors' Office

After a number of months have been simulated, the administrative director suddenly comes forward with a dismal graph of the development of the market share (cf. Fig. 10-2). Where did the management fail? This is the question managers A, B, C, and D discuss.

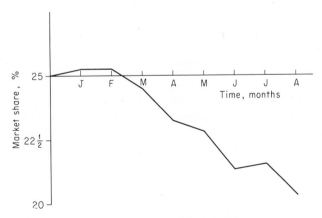

Fig. 10-2

A: Apparently our price is too high. When the chips are down, the price is all the buyers are really interested in.

B: But according to our data, our price is on the low side compared with the prices of our competitors. We charge $490, while their prices are $480, $500, and $520. No, no, it can't be the price. And anyway our profit margin is small as it is. I don't think we should further lower the price. We probably don't advertise enough.

A: But advertising is terribly expensive, and we have no idea about its effect. I for one don't think it amounts to much. During the first two months we didn't advertise more than we do now, and we did pretty well then.

C: Be that as it may, what we do have to know is our relative position with respect to our competitors. How much did the others advertise in the beginning, and how much do they advertise now?

A: That we just don't know.

B: No, we don't *know* it. But there must be *some* reason for our declining percentage. Since it can't be the price, it stands to reason that it's advertising.

A: Why? Why? It can just as well be our installment plan. Or perhaps our quality is too low.

D: Possibly. We haven't done anything about product development and research. Maybe we should.

C: I don't really think research will solve the problems. In the rules of the game it says that research expenditures below $150,000 are not likely to result in much. And $150,000 is a lot of cash. That's going to be a long-run solution at best.

D: Well, we've got to start sometime. Otherwise we're bound to become stagnant.

C: But we just don't have the money for research.

D: Let's give less credit to the consumers.

A: And sell even less?

D: It will hurt, of course. But it has to be done, and perhaps we can negotiate a loan.

B: So we'll reduce the credit to consumers from four to two months and spend $30,000 on research.

D: Oh, come on. A little more. Say, $50,000. Would that be possible?

B: If we take out a loan.

D: O.K. We'll leave the price at $490. And there is no impelling reason to change the advertising policy either. But we should cut back on production since inventories are high. Let's decide to produce 700 freezers this month.

This simulated discussion resembles reality and, as such, properly belongs in this chapter. For real games with rules and forms we refer to the literature. Some of the games mentioned in the bibliography can be played without computers or even desk calculators.

Literature

A collection of essays concerning simulation techniques applied to a wide range of problems can be found in Guetzkow [1]. Simulation techniques—especially when computers are applied—are often referred to as *Monte Carlo methods*.   A good, though technical, book in this field is Schreider [2].

The history of management games and some examples can be found in Cohen and Rhenman [3]; theoretical backgrounds are illuminated in Kibbee and others [4]. A small collection of management games, some of which are very simple and none of which requires the use of a computer, can be found in Greene and Sisson [5].

[1] H. Guetzkow (ed.), *Simulation in Social Sciences: Readings*, Prentice-Hall, Inc., Englewood Cliffs, N.J., 1962.

[2] Y. A. Schreider (ed.), *Methods of Statistical Testing*, American Elsevier Publishing Company of New York, 1964.

[3] K. J. Cohen and E. Rhenman, "The Role of Management Games in Education and Research," *Management Science*, vol. 7 (1961), pp. 131–166.

[4] J. M. Kibbee, C. J. Kraft, and B. Nanus, *Management Games*, Reinhold Publishing Corporation, New York, 1961.

[5] J. R. Greene and R. L. Sisson, *Dynamic Management Decision Games*, John Wiley & Sons, Inc., New York, 1959.

11

Production and Inventory Decisions

11-1. The Optimum Lot Size

A radio factory produces 12,000 radios per year. Each radio has many knobs. The same on-off knob is used for all of them. Thus, 12,000 of these knobs are needed per year, or 40 per working day. The knobs are produced by a machine, which can also make all the other required types of knobs. This particular on-off knob is fabricated very quickly once the machine has been set up for its production. A knob will usually have to be stored before being placed on one of the 12,000 radios that move along the conveyor belt each year. Schematically,

fast machine → warehouse → conveyor belt

Adjusting the knob machine from the production of one type of knob to another costs money. As far as these set-up costs are concerned, it is best to produce a large quantity of one kind of knob at a time. However, since only about 40 knobs are used per working day, the production of a large quantity leads to stock piling. These stocks also cost money: tied up capital, administrative costs, etc. The larger the quantity produced (the lot size), the larger the average inventory, and hence the higher the inventory costs. Small lot sizes lead to high set-up costs, large lot sizes to high inventory costs. The problem is to find the optimum lot size to minimize the sum total of set-up costs and inventory costs.

To derive this optimum lot size algebraically, we shall write n for the number of knobs needed per year; in our example, $n = 12,000$. We write x for the lot size; the optimum x value is unknown and must be determined. When a lot size x has been produced, it goes to the stocks. The stocks decrease at a rate equal to the production rate of the radios—in our example, 40 per working day, 12,000 per year. When the inventory is gone, a new batch of x knobs is produced, and the cycle starts anew. This can be depicted in a diagram, as in Fig. 11-1. After each cycle we begin

186

with an inventory equal to the lot size x.   The inventory declines regularly until it reaches the zero level, at which moment a new batch of size x is produced, etc.   The average inventory is equal to $\frac{1}{2}x$.

If the lot size is x and n knobs are needed per year, the number of series produced per year clearly equals n/x.   For example, if each batch consists of 4,000 knobs and 12,000 knobs are needed per year, there will be $n/x = 12,000/4,000 = 3$ series each year.   Hence, set-up costs will be

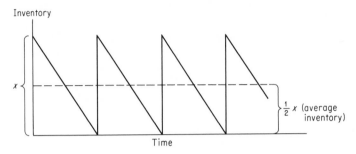

Fig. 11-1

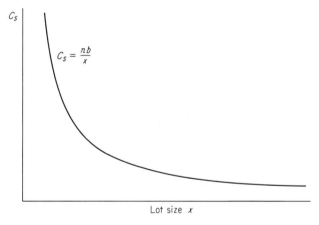

Fig. 11-2

incurred n/x times during the year.   If each time this costs b dollars, the yearly set-up costs C_s are

$$C_s = \frac{n}{x} \times b = \frac{nb}{x}$$

These costs clearly diminish as x increases; they approach zero as the lot size is increased more and more.   This stands to reason.   If one produces 1.2 million knobs in one batch, no new series will be needed for another century, and hence the set-up costs will be well-nigh zero, as illustrated in Fig. 11-2.

Furthermore, suppose that it costs c dollars to have 1 knob in stock during one year. Because we have on the average $\frac{1}{2}x$ knobs in inventory, the yearly inventory costs C_i are

$$C_i = \frac{1}{2}cx$$

It follows that C_i increases linearly with x, as shown graphically in Fig.

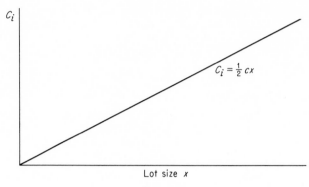

Fig. 11-3

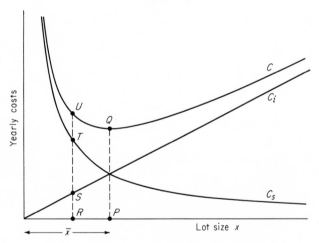

Fig. 11-4

11-3. We now want to minimize the sum total C of the set-up costs C_s and the inventory costs C_i. In other words we want to determine x such that

$$C = C_s + C_i = \frac{nb}{x} + \frac{1}{2}cx \qquad (1)$$

takes on its minimum value.

If we combine the graphs of Figs. 11-2 and 11-3 and add the curves C_s and C_i to get C, we arrive at Fig. 11-4.   For example, we obtain the point U on the C curve by adding to RT (the set-up costs for a lot size corresponding to R) the line segment $TU = RS$ (the inventory costs for the lot size R).   This illustration suggests (as will be verified algebraically in the next section) that the optimum value of x is to be found where $C_s = C_i$, that is, where the yearly set-up costs are equal to the yearly inventory costs.   When $C_s = C_i$, we have

$$\frac{nb}{x} = \tfrac{1}{2}cx$$

or, multiplying both sides by x,

$$nb = \tfrac{1}{2}cx^2$$

or, dividing both sides by $\tfrac{1}{2}c$,

$$\frac{2nb}{c} = x^2$$

The optimum x value is now found by taking the square root.   If we write $\bar{x}$ for the optimum lot size, we have

$$\bar{x} = \sqrt{\frac{2nb}{c}} \tag{2}$$

If n, as in our example, equals 12,000 and the cost of adjusting the machine is \$40 ($b = 40$) and the cost of each unit in inventory during one year is \$6 ($c = 6$), then the optimum lot size equals

$$\bar{x} = \sqrt{\frac{2 \times 12{,}000 \times 40}{6}} = \sqrt{160{,}000} = 400$$

which is enough for 10 working days (40 for each working day).   The average inventory equals $\tfrac{1}{2}\bar{x} = 200$ units and thus costs $200 \times 6 = \$1{,}200$ yearly.   Each year there will be $12{,}000/400 = 30$ series costing

$$30 \times 40 = \$1{,}200$$

for machine adjustments.   The two amounts C_s and C_i are indeed equal, which is a check on our computations.   The total yearly cost when the lot size is $\bar{x}$ equals

$$\sqrt{2nbc} \qquad (3)$$

as can be verified by simple substitution of $x = \bar{x}$ into formula (1).

Formula (2) confirms what one would expect. The optimum lot size increases as the set-up costs b increase, but the lot size decreases as the costs of holding inventories c increase. The lot size also increases, quite logically, when the yearly requirement n increases. However, this simple kind of intuitive logic is not sufficient to arrive at the precise relationship which (2) specifies.

11-2. Sensitivity Analysis

It was just stated that formula (2) gives the optimum lot size. However, that must still be proved; that is, we shall have to show that any other lot size leads to a higher sum of inventory and set-up costs. Also, we need to know how *"sensitive"* the solution is; that term can be illustrated by the following example. If the size of the series actually produced is 10 per cent higher than the optimum value $\bar{x}$, the total cost will no doubt be higher—but *how much* higher? If a 10 per cent deviation from $\bar{x}$ results in only a 1 per cent increase in cost, the solution is not very sensitive. If a 10 per cent error should double the total cost, however, the solution is very sensitive indeed.

It is best if the solution is not very sensitive, because it is possible that in fact the manufacturer will not produce the optimum lot size $\bar{x}$. Recall that $\bar{x}$ depends on n, b, and c. Although the yearly demand for radio knobs is estimated at 12,000, it may turn out that only 9,000 radios will be produced because demand is slow. On the other hand, perhaps demand is underestimated, and it will turn out that no less than 16,000 radios can be sold, requiring 16,000 knobs. It is also possible that the cost figures b and c are not precisely known. In practice it is especially difficult to determine c, the cost of storing one unit during one year, in view of the fact that fixed costs must be allocated to the various kinds of knobs stored in the warehouse. Thus, because n is incorrectly predicted or because c is vaguely known, the numerical value which is computed for $\bar{x}$ will not be the actual optimum value. Then the question is by how much the costs will increase.

It is a matter of algebra to grind out the answer. Suppose that the lot size is 10 per cent too high; then it can be written as $1.1\bar{x}$. If the lot size turns out to be 30 per cent below the optimum, the value is $0.7\bar{x}$. In general, the size of the lot actually produced will be indicated as $(1 + \delta)\bar{x}$, in which δ is a measure of the percentage deviation from the optimum value.   If $\delta = 0.1$, the lot size is 10 per cent too high; if $\delta = -0.3$, it is 30 per cent too low.   The total cost then according to formula (1) is

$$C = \frac{nb}{\bar{x}(1 + \delta)} + \tfrac{1}{2}c\bar{x}(1 + \delta)$$

If in accordance with (2) we substitute for $\bar{x}$ the value $\sqrt{2nb/c}$, we find

$$
\begin{aligned}
C &= \frac{nb}{1 + \delta}\sqrt{\frac{c}{2nb}} + \tfrac{1}{2}(1 + \delta)c\sqrt{\frac{2nb}{c}} \\
&= \left(\frac{1}{1 + \delta} + 1 + \delta\right)\sqrt{\frac{nbc}{2}} \qquad (4) \\
&= \left(1 + \frac{\tfrac{1}{2}\delta^2}{1 + \delta}\right)\sqrt{2nbc}
\end{aligned}
$$

This expression takes on its minimum value when $\delta = 0$, which confirms our statement that $\bar{x}$ as given in (2) is the optimum lot size.   The minimum value itself is $\sqrt{2nbc}$ in accordance with (3).

When the lot size equals $\bar{x}(1 + \delta)$ rather than $\bar{x}$, we conclude from (4) that there is a percentage increase in cost equal to

$$\frac{\tfrac{1}{2}\delta^2}{1 + \delta} \times 100 \text{ per cent}$$

All we need to do now is evaluate this expression for various values of δ. If $\delta = 0.1$, so that the lot produced is 10 per cent more than the optimum, cost increases by

$$\frac{\tfrac{1}{2}(0.1)^2}{1 + 0.1} \times 100 \text{ per cent} = 0.45 \text{ per cent}$$

This result is comforting, as the solution is seen to be very insensitive. If we repeat this computation for various other values of δ, we find

Value of δ	0.2	0.3	0.4	0.5	0.6	0.7	0.8	0.9	1
% of cost increase	1.7	3.5	5.7	8.3	11	14	18	21	25

If we produce a lot double the optimum size [$\delta = 1$ implying $(1 + \delta)\bar{x} = 2\bar{x}$], the cost is increased by 25 per cent.   Only when one goes to extremes does the cost start rising quickly.   If the value of $\delta = 9$, that is, if the size is 10 times the optimum, the cost is 505 per cent as large, or more than five times the minimum cost.

For deviations below the optimum size, the derivations are quite similar. The results are then

Value of δ	-0.1	-0.2	-0.3	-0.4	-0.5
% of cost increase	0.6	2.5	6.4	13	25

Again, we notice that the extra cost incurred is reasonably small as long as the deviations are not excessive. The results seem to indicate that deviations below the optimum are more serious than deviations above the optimum. When $\delta = +1$, the cost increases by 25 per cent, but the cost also increases by 25 per cent when δ is only -0.5 (rather than -1). If we agree, however, to consider as equally serious deviations half of the optimum size ($\delta = -0.5$) and double the optimum size ($\delta = 1$), we see that the effects on cost are precisely the same.

We conclude that the formula for the optimum lot size is very insensitive: deviations from the optimum increase the cost by relatively small amounts. Thus, it is not necessary to know the exact values of n, b, and c. Only when one really goes wild will the cost increase substantially.

11-3. A More Elaborate Cost Function

The analysis so far has been based on very simple assumptions. We assumed the yearly demand n to be known, and sensitivity analysis taught us that even if the actual demand differs moderately from the anticipated demand, the cost will not be greatly influenced. Nevertheless, a more sensible attitude is to revise the size of the series as soon as it becomes evident that n actually differs from the original estimate. When we formulate *in advance* how the lot size should change—given the evidence (the sales figures) that becomes available in the course of time—we in fact formulate a *strategy*. In other words, we formulate a strategy if we determine for each month, say, the lot size as a function of the information on future sales which is available at that time, whatever the content of this information may be. We shall formulate such a strategy in an example with a more complicated and a more realistic cost function. The cost function will be explained in this section. It is based on the work of Holt, Modigliani, Muth, and Simon, and the numerical data refer to the paint department of the Pittsburgh Plate Glass Company. The object is to produce at minimum cost. Four different categories of costs are distinguished.

1. *Regular payroll costs.* If the manager decides to produce more, more man-hours are required. This implies either overtime work for the existing labor force or additions to the labor force, or a combination of these two measures. Costs for overtime will be discussed under point 3 below.

The regular payroll costs are considered as a function of the number of employees. These costs are approximated by a linear function of the number of employees,

$$c_1 + c_2 q$$

in which q stands for the number of employees and c_1 and c_2 are constants. The function is illustrated in Fig. 11-5. Obviously, the constants c_1 and c_2 will change when wages change. This means that the computations to be discussed in this chapter will have to be revised if wages increase.

2. *Hiring and layoff costs.* When a new worker comes on the job, he begins with a training period, during which he receives full wages. Hence

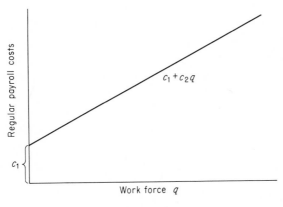

FIG. 11-5

a new worker is expensive. Even *before* he is employed costs are incurred—interviews, aptitude tests, medical checkups, etc. Thus, additions to the labor force cost money. There is also a price to be paid for decreasing the labor force. The dismissed employee often receives severance pay when he leaves, the production line may have to be reorganized, union contracts may specify further expenses to be incurred by the company, and there will be intangible costs, such as loss of goodwill and increased difficulty in attracting new personnel in favorable times. (It may not be easy to evaluate these latter costs numerically, but a rough guess is preferable to neglecting them.) All combined we conclude that dismissing employees costs money—indeed, more money when more employees are dismissed.

If we assume that both hiring and layoff costs increase linearly with the number of employees hired or fired, we get a V-formed cost function as illustrated in Fig. 11-6. Along the horizontal axis we have indicated the monthly changes in the labor force, $q - q_{-1}$, where q_{-1} indicates the size of the labor force during the previous month. The costs are measured along the vertical axis. To the right of that axis are the costs of hiring new employees, to the left the costs of laying off employees. Such a straight-line function implies that the costs are proportional to the size of the change. (In Fig. 11-6 we drew the lines in such a way that the costs of hiring and firing people are equal.)

In the figure we have also drawn a dashed curve, which is more or less

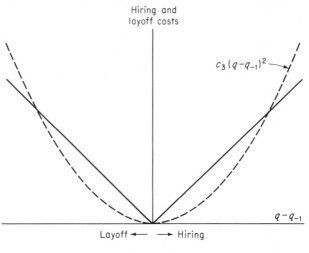

Hiring and layoff costs

$c_3(q-q_{-1})^2$

$q-q_{-1}$

Layoff ← → Hiring

Fig. 11-6

closely adapted to these straight lines. The equation of this curve is given by

$$c_3(q - q_{-1})^2$$

in which c_3 is a constant. In contrast with the V-line, this curve implies that the costs increase more than proportionally when the difference $q - q_{-1}$ increases. Small changes cost relatively little, but large deviations between q and q_{-1} result in sharply increasing costs. Such a specification may well be realistic in this case. It may be quite true that it becomes increasingly more difficult and expensive to hire new employees when their numbers get larger and larger. In what follows, we shall continue to use the curved line $c_3(q - q_{-1})^2$ as an appropriate description of the costs incurred for hiring and firing personnel.

It will be noticed that this specification implies that the costs of employing, for example, 17 new employees are equal to the costs of dismissing 17 employees. In the one case the costs are $c_3 \times 17^2$, in the other case $c_3 \times (-17)^2$, and both are equal to $289c_3$. This symmetry need not be realistic. The specification can be amended to incorporate possible differences between costs of hiring and firing umpteen workers, but this refinement will not be made here.

3. *Overtime and idle-time costs.* We already pointed out that hiring employees entails costs. The alternative is overtime, but this also costs extra money. As a rule, overtime is 50 per cent as expensive as work during regular hours. Formally, the costs of overtime are determined as follows. Let us write c_5 for the normal production of one employee working all regular hours. If there are q employees, the total normal production will be $c_5 q$. Let us now write p for the actual production. Then overtime is necessary as soon as p exceeds $c_5 q$, in other words when $p - c_5 q$ is positive. One procedure is to work with an upward-sloping

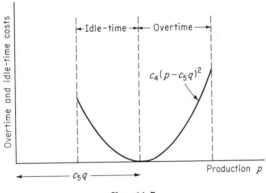

FIG. 11-7

straight line as in Fig. 11-6. This would imply that overtime costs are assumed to be proportional to the excess of actual over normal production. It happens frequently, however, that each additional amount of overwork is characterized by less efficiency, so that a quadratic curve is more appropriate. Note that such a curve also implies costs when $p - c_5 q$ is negative, which corresponds to idle time rather than overtime. This, too, is an undesirable situation. Although the wages paid to those who are idle are accounted for by the regular payroll costs and although it is frequently possible to "hide" the slack by organizing all kinds of little odd cleaning and repair jobs, it is nevertheless a costly situation because those who are not idle will work less efficiently for fear of layoff. This moral disorganization will be more and more serious when there is more idle time. So we arrive at a quadratic approximation to overtime and idle-time costs,

$$c_4(p - c_5 q)^2$$

shown graphically in Fig. 11-7.

4. *Inventory and machine set-up costs.* The Pittsburgh Plate Glass Company produces paint for the market. If the demand is smaller than expected, the inventories will increase; if the demand exceeds expectations, inventories will be exhausted and deliveries delayed. We have already seen that under certain conditions the average inventory equals half the lot size and that the optimum lot size is proportional to the square root of the demand per unit of time (the n value in the first section of this chapter). Under these conditions the optimum inventory value will therefore be proportional to the same square root. We also established that the optimum lot size is fairly flexible, in the sense that deviations from the

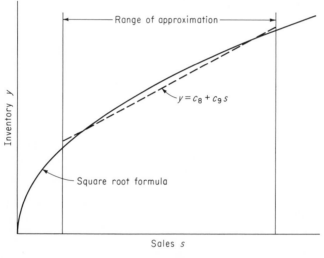

Fig. 11-8

optimum do not result in large increases in costs; the same is true of the optimum inventory level, which enables us to use with confidence the following convenient approximation. Instead of writing the optimum inventory level as proportional to the square root of the sales, we shall use a linear approximation. For the optimum inventory level we write $c_8 + c_9 s$, in which the c's are coefficients and the s stands for the monthly sales of paint. Fig. 11-8 clearly shows that this approximation is quite accurate for considerable variations of s, provided the coefficients c_8 and c_9 are well chosen. As long as the sales do not fluctuate too wildly, the linear approximation is certainly justified. Furthermore, we should not forget that even rather substantial deviations from the optimum lead to a relatively small increase in the costs.

The inventory and machine set-up costs can be written as the sum of two terms. The minimum possible value of this sum will be indicated by c_6.

Besides these minimum costs there will be extra costs as soon as the optimum inventory $c_8 + c_9s$ deviates from the actual inventory y. If $y - (c_8 + c_9s)$ is positive, the inventory is higher than the optimum, and the inventory costs are unnecessarily high. If $y - (c_8 + c_9s)$ is negative, the inventory is too low. Then the chances are that during the next period the demand will exceed the delivery potential, and the necessary crash-production program or delayed deliveries will lead to a loss of goodwill and extra costs. Again, the chosen mathematical function is quadratic in the deviation between the actual inventory y and the optimum inventory $c_8 + c_9s$:

$$c_6 + c_7[y - (c_8 + c_9s)]^2$$

as seen in the graph of Fig. 11-9. The graph clearly shows that c_6 is the minimum possible sum of inventory and adjustment costs. This value

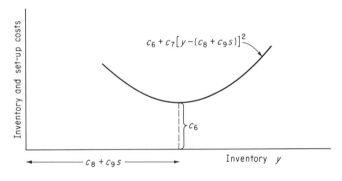

Fig. 11-9

c_6 is actually reached only when $y = c_8 + c_9s$, that is, when the inventory is at its optimum level.

In summary, we distinguish four categories of costs, all determined by certain coefficients (c_1, c_2, . . . , c_9) and by four monthly variables: production p, the work force q, the inventory y, and the sales s. The total costs can be found by addition. We have

Total costs per month

$$= c_1 + c_2q \qquad \text{(regular payroll costs)}$$
$$+ c_3(q - q_{-1})^2 \qquad \text{(hiring and layoff costs)}$$
$$+ c_4(p - c_5q)^2 \qquad \text{(overtime and idle-time costs)}$$
$$+ c_6 + c_7[y - (c_8 + c_9s)]^2 \qquad \text{(inventory and set-up costs)}$$

11-4. The Problem of Cost Minimization

In our discussion on inventory and set-up costs we just used the term optimum inventory. We concluded that if we let inventories y vary with sales s according to the formula $y = c_8 + c_9 s$, the sum of inventory and set-up costs would attain its minimum value c_6. So the question is, why don't we do precisely that? We have a similar situation in the case of overtime and idle-time costs. If the manager always produces an amount p equal to $c_5 q$, that is, the production which will be achieved when all people work without overtime or idle time, this category of costs reaches its minimum value, zero. Again, the question is, why doesn't the manager do precisely that?

The object for the manager is not to minimize the costs in one category or another, but the total, overall cost. Let us see what happens if the manager should adapt the inventory y to sales according to the formula $y = c_8 + c_9 s$ and if he should produce according to $p = c_5 q$. Then each change in sales s leads to a change in y, which in turn necessitates a certain change in production p in order to realize that inventory change; but p is given as $c_5 q$, so if p changes, the work force q must also change. In fact, q will then probably fluctuate wildly from month to month, so that the costs of hiring and firing personnel will be excessive. By minimizing two cost categories, the manager has allowed a third to become high, and the sum of all costs may well be substantially larger than necessary. In short, we must minimize the overall costs, and this cannot be achieved by separately minimizing some individual cost categories. Another procedure must be followed, which will give rise to the following problems:

1. There is a definite relationship between inventory y, sales s, and production p, which we already alluded to in the previous paragraph. When the production in any given month is 100 and sales equal only 80, the inventory will increase by 20 during that month. In general, the change in inventory from month to month ($y - y_{-1}$) equals the difference between production p and sales s:

$$y - y_{-1} = p - s$$

Obviously, y_{-1} stands for the inventory at the end of the previous month. It is clear that $y - y_{-1}$ will be negative when the monthly sales exceed the monthly production.

2. We therefore have to minimize the total costs subject to the restriction which links changes in inventories to levels of production and sales. There is a further complication, however: The manager should minimize

the total costs *in the long run.*   It would be very shortsighted to minimize the costs only for the next month—an *après nous le déluge* attitude. Instead, the manager should make his decisions (how much to produce, how many workers to employ) to minimize costs over the next 6 or 12 months, or even over an indefinite number of months ahead.   The number of future periods the manager takes into consideration constitutes his *time horizon.*   In practice a time horizon of 12 months gives frequently accurate results.   This implies that whether the manager plans 12 or 100 months ahead, the same decisions regarding production and employment will be made.

Our looking ahead introduces two new tasks.   First, we should find the total of future costs with the object of minimizing the sum of all costs over the total period.   Second, it becomes necessary to *date* our variables. We must take into consideration not only the production p_0 during the next month (the only production decision that must be made today) but also production p_1 for the following month, also p_2, etc.   The production level in the successive months is thus denoted by $p_0, p_1, p_2, \ldots$, in which p_0 stands for the production in the month immediately ahead.   For the number of workers to be employed in the successive months, we write analogously $q_0, q_1, q_2, \ldots$.   For the inventories we write $y_0, y_1, y_2, \ldots$, and for the sales $s_0, s_1, s_2, \ldots$.   The values of the p and q variables have to be determined by the manager; the values of the s variables are unknown to him, but nevertheless important.   The values of y are determined by the rule which states that the inventory change is equal to the deviation between production and sales.   There is one such restriction for every month.

3. The problem is thus to minimize the total costs over a long period up to the time horizon, subject to all monthly restrictions dealing with inventory change as a function of production and sales.   We must now face the problem of uncertainty.   The future sales $s_0, s_1, s_2, \ldots$ are unknown. This implies that the manager will be unable to determine with certainty the costs associated with his production and work force decisions.   He is thus unable to specify at this moment all decisions $p_0, p_1, p_2, \ldots$ and $q_0, q_1, q_2, \ldots$, which will lead to the smallest costs, because these depend on the unknown future development of sales.   Under these circumstances we may advise the manager to base his decision on minimizing the mathematical expectation of total costs, which is possible, if he can make probability statements about the future sales.   These statements might be of the following type:

The sales of next month s_0 are normally distributed, with a mean equal to 95 per cent of this month's sales and a standard deviation of 4 per cent of this level;

the sales for the following month s_1 are normally distributed, with a mean equal to 96 per cent of this month's sales and a standard deviation of 6 per cent of this level;

etc.

In this example the standard deviation increases over time (from 4 to 6 per cent). This stands to reason, because the standard deviation is a measure for the uncertainty concerning the future sales, and it is to be expected that this uncertainty increases the further we look ahead.

The problem is now well defined. We want to minimize the mathematical expectation of the total costs over time subject to the restrictions regarding the changes in inventory levels. How should we now proceed? In order to understand the solution procedure, we must distinguish two groups of variables. On the one hand, we have the variables which the manager must decide upon, viz., the production level p and the work force q. (We assume that the manager can determine the production level each month and that he can hire and dismiss personnel as he sees fit.) On the other hand, there are the variables s and y which are not, or at least not completely, under the control of the manager. For sales s this is self-evident. The inventories depend on s in view of the above-mentioned restrictions; hence they are not under the manager's complete control either.

This distinction between the variables is of fundamental importance because the manager can satisfy the criterion of minimizing expected costs only by judiciously determining the variables which he controls, p and q. Regarding the others, mainly s, he can do nothing more than hope that they will behave more or less according to his expectations. In short, he controls the values of the variables

$$p_0, \ p_1, \ p_2, \ \ldots \text{ as well as } q_0, \ q_1, \ q_2, \ \ldots$$

and he must now choose the values for these variables such that the expected total long-run costs are minimized (subject to the restrictions which define the changes in inventory from month to month). How does the manager go about doing this? It is tempting to say that he should do so by picking p and q values such that, subject to the aforesaid restrictions and given his ideas regarding future sales, the expected total costs will be minimized. We know that this is wrong, however, for we saw in Chap. 7 that the best procedure is to develop a *strategy* which determines each decision as a function of the information that will be available when the decision actually needs to be made. In the present application this information deals with the development of sales over time. Take the situation of this moment when the manager has to decide on p_0 and q_0. This information consists of (1) the development of sales in the past and (2) his ideas regarding sales in successive future months (in the form of probability distributions). One month later the manager knows the sales s_0 in the month which has just passed; in addition, his probabilistic ideas regarding the sales of paint in later months may have become different (e.g., because construction plans of new buildings have been announced). This new information can and should be used by the manager when he makes his p_1 and q_1 decisions. That process is repeated month after month—each time the manager collects the sales figure of the most recent month and reformulates his ideas on sales in the future, and he makes his production and work force decisions dependent on these new data.

11-5. Linear Decision Rules

We want to find the decision rule which minimizes the expected total costs subject to the restrictions concerning changes in inventories. These restrictions are *linear;* moreover, the cost function to be minimized is *quadratic.* Under these two conditions (a quadratic function to be minimized subject to linear constraints), an important result, known as *certainty equivalence*, holds. This result implies, roughly speaking, that we get the solution by acting as if future sales coincide with their expected value.

Let us be quite specific. The immediate problem facing the manager is to find the values p_0 and q_0 of the optimum strategy, which minimizes the expected costs (subject to the well-known restrictions) over time. In our present application the future sales are the sole source of uncertainty. If the manager now neglects this uncertainty by acting *as if* the future sales coincide with their expected value and if he then minimizes the total costs subject to the linear restrictions, he will find p_0 and q_0 values which coincide with those of the optimum strategy. Take, for example, the specific probability distributions that were mentioned under point (3) of the previous section. They imply that the expected value of s_0 equals 95 per cent of the most recently observed sales level, that the expectation of s_1 is 96 per cent, and so on. The theorem just mentioned states that the manager is able to compute p_0 and q_0 of the optimum strategy by forgetting all about the uncertainty and just acting as if $s_0 = 95$ per cent, $s_1 = 96$ per cent, etc. "Forgetting all about the uncertainty" implies that the standard deviations of the distributions of future sales are irrelevant from the point of view of finding the appropriate p_0 and q_0. It may be that they increase from 4 to 6 per cent as in our example, they may increase from 2 to 8 per cent, and they may be constant or even decrease—in all cases we have the same p_0 and q_0 because only the expected values of $s_0, s_1, \ldots$ do really matter.

The theorem described in the preceding paragraph is aptly called that of "certainty equivalence." By acting as if there is certainty, i.e., by acting as if future sales are certainly equal to their expected values, the manager decides optimally. Of course, "acting as if" is not the same as assuming that the future sales will really coincide with their expectations. The probability that they will is very small, if not zero—but it simply does not matter for p_0 and q_0.

We now proceed to the actual determination of p_0 and q_0 as a function of the relevant information. It goes without saying that they will depend on the expected sales volumes in the future months, which will be written $Es_0, Es_1, Es_2, \ldots$. It can further be shown that the relationship is linear; that is, p_0 and q_0 are linear functions of $Es_0, Es_1, Es_2, \ldots$, hence the term *linear decision rule*. This result also holds generally whenever a *quadratic* cost function is minimized subject to constraints which are *linear* in sales. Finally, there are the initial conditions. The manager makes his decisions given an existing situation, in particular given y_{-1} (initial inventory on hand) and q_{-1} (the number of workers currently employed). It stands to reason that the larger the inventory on hand (y_{-1}), the lower the production next month (p_0). This will indeed prove to be the case.

Holt and others have calculated the decision rules for p_0 and q_0 numerically for the paint factory here considered. To this end they have first specified the cost coefficients $c_1, c_2, \ldots, c_9$ on the basis of the internal financial data provided by the firm. They also assumed an infinite horizon, so that in principle all future sales expectations $Es_0, Es_1, Es_2, \ldots$ enter the decision. In fact, however, the influence of future sales becomes imperceptible after a little while. If we record only those future sales which have a coefficient of more than 0.01, the linear decision rule specifies p_0 as

$$p_0 = \begin{Bmatrix} 0.464Es_0 \\ +0.236Es_1 \\ +0.112Es_2 \\ +0.047Es_3 \\ +0.014Es_4 \end{Bmatrix} - 0.464y_{-1} + 1.007q_{-1} + 153.1$$

This decision rule describes the production level for the next month as the sum of three terms. Reading backwards, we first have a constant term (153.1). Secondly, there are the initial conditions. The rule states that if the initial inventory y_{-1} is 1 unit larger, the production level should be 0.464 unit lower.   This confirms our expectations.   Furthermore, we see that the bigger the work force q_{-1}, the higher the production p_0; this follows from the positive coefficient (1.007) of q_{-1}.   This result is intuitively plausible.   For the higher q_{-1}, the higher q_0 unless the manager is willing to incur layoff costs, and the higher q_0, the higher production unless the manager is willing to incur idle-time costs.

Thirdly, there are the terms in the expected sales in the successive months.   When the expected sales next month (Es_0) are 1 unit higher, the production is increased by nearly half a unit (0.464 unit, to be exact). This extra unit of expected demand is apparently not fully produced at the cost of overtime or hiring new employees.   Instead, it is partly provided from inventory.   The influence of expected demand one month later (Es_1) is about half the influence of Es_0.   After that the coefficients decrease at a faster rate, until the influence of Es_5, Es_6, . . . becomes very small indeed.   Terms involving Es_5, Es_6, . . . have not been reproduced here.

The decision rule for the size of the work force is as follows:

$$q_0 = \begin{Bmatrix} 0.0100Es_0 \\ +0.0087Es_1 \\ +0.0070Es_2 \\ +0.0054Es_3 \\ +0.0041Es_4 \\ +0.0030Es_5 \\ +0.0022Es_6 \\ +0.0016Es_7 \\ +0.0011Es_8 \end{Bmatrix} - 0.0100y_{-1} + 0.742q_{-1} + 2.00$$

This decision rule contains the same terms as the previous one, but with different coefficients.   We again have a constant term (2.00) and two coefficients associated with the initial conditions y_{-1} and q_{-1}.   The coefficient of q_{-1} is rather sizable, 0.742.   This can be ascribed largely to the costs of hiring or firing employees.   The coefficient of the initial inventory is negative.   The explanation for this is that the larger the inventory, the smaller the production, and hence the smaller the work force.   Finally, the expectations concerning future sales enter the decision again in a linear way.   The influence of expected sales on the work force is positive, as is its influence on production.   It tapers off the further ahead we look, but the decrease is very gradual.   In the case of production, each successive coefficient is usually about half as small as its predecessor, whereas here the successive coefficients are only 10 to 30 per cent smaller than their predecessors, with the following implication.   Suppose the expected demand from month to month varies sharply (as is the case with many products subject to seasonal demand). Then it is more advantageous to adapt the production than the work force to these short-run fluctuations. To be sure, even production does not fluctuate as wildly as demand (cf. the coefficient 0.464 of the decision rule for production, which is indeed far

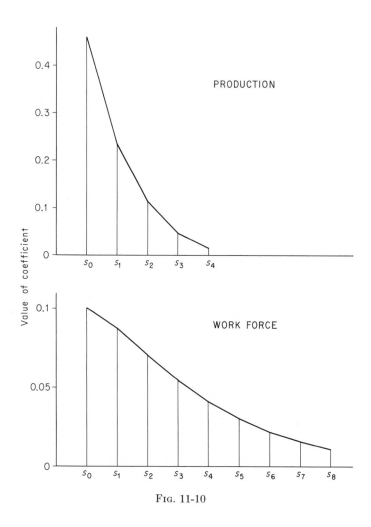

FIG. 11-10

less than 1), but given the cost structure, changes in work force are apparently extremely objectionable. The decision rule for q_0 has the tendency to spread out the fluctuations in expected demand. The successive expectations have slowly decreasing coefficients, and one or two exceptionally high or low values have a relatively mild effect on q_0.

The difference between the two patterns of reaction to changes in expected sales can be shown graphically.   In Fig. 11-10 the height of each vertical bar indicates the value of the coefficient associated with the expected sales in each future month.   For the sake of clarity, we connect tops of successive bars by straight lines.   The decrease in the graph of production is seen to be much faster than the decrease in the graph of the work force.

11-6. Concrete Examples

Let us consider the implications of these decision rules by reference to an easy numerical example.   Assume that monthly sales are constant except during May, when they are 100 units higher.   In order to keep matters simple we shall assume that future sales are known in advance. Hence the expected value of sales in any future month, including memorable May, coincides with the corresponding actual value.

The problem facing the manager is how his production and work force should react to demand.   The answer can be read from the decision rules: He should produce 1.4 extra units in January, four months before the sudden increase in demand.   This follows from the coefficient of Es_4 in the production decision rule, 0.014.   Thus 100 more units four months from now should increase present production by 1.4 units.   In February 4.7 extra units should be produced, since the coefficient of Es_3 is 0.047; and so on.   The procedure is analogous for the work force.   Consequently, the inventory increases before May.   During May the inventory decreases sharply to a value below original level.   After May, the production also decreases, but it remains above the original level for a number of months. During these months inventories increase again.   In the meantime, the work force will also come back to the normal level after an original increase. The complete details can be read from Fig. 11-11.   The horizontal axes are put at the equilibrium level corresponding to the constant sales level (May being excluded).   Therefore, the vertical axes measure the various variables as deviations from their long-run equilibrium level.   It is clear from the graphs that the deviations are more or less symmetrical around the month of May.   The effect is spread over time.

Let us now consider the same situation, with the exception that the manager does not know in advance about the extra sales in May.   For all he knows, May sales will be the same as previous monthly sales.   He is taken by surprise.   What will now be the course of production, work force, and inventories?   The effects are drawn in Fig. 11-12.   The explanation is as follows.   All of a sudden the extra order for 100 units comes in.   Before May all variables were at their equilibrium level, so during May only the sales are different from usual.   At the end of May the inventory is 100 units below its initial, normal level.   According to

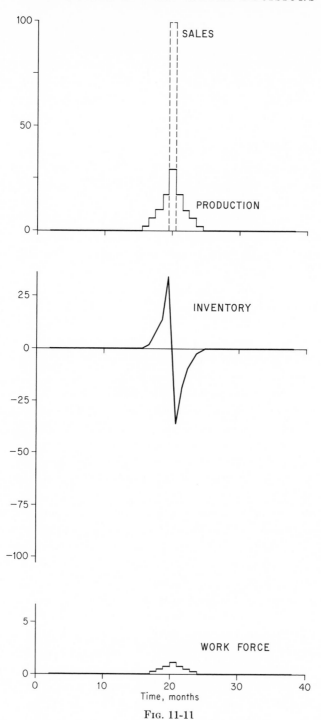

FIG. 11-11

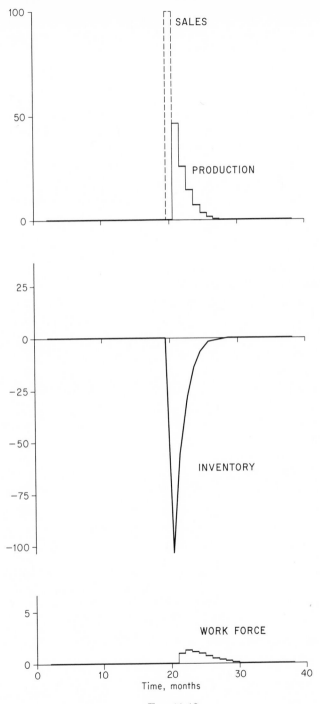

FIG. 11-12

our decision rule, the June production should now increase by

$$100 \times 0.464 = 46.4 \text{ units}$$

because y_{-1} is decreased by 100 and its coefficient is -0.464. This is, as far as the production in June is concerned, all there is to it, because the expected sales in future months are all unchanged, as was the work force in May. Further computations along these lines result in the given figures. The most striking difference between the two cases is that the deviation in inventory is much larger in the case without perfect foresight. The total costs, of course, are higher in the second case.

The most obvious way to demonstrate the use of these decision rules is the pragmatic one. Had the paint factory actually applied these rules, would the shareholders then have profited? This is surely an important question. Holt and others have investigated this by comparing the costs actually incurred over a three-year period with the costs that would have resulted from the use of their decision rules. The results should be cautiously interpreted, but are not without illustrative value. Caution is called for because cost determination is always to some extent arbitrary and less than fully accurate; furthermore, managers do not always make a habit of recording their expectations of future monthly sales. This last problem was tackled by working with two different assumptions: (1) an optimistic assumption that presumes that future sales were exactly and correctly known in advance, (2) a more pessimistic assumption that managers predicted future sales in a purely mechanical way on the basis of past evidence.

We thus obtain three configurations of costs. Firstly there are the actual costs. Secondly there are the costs that would have resulted from using the decision rule and a mechanical prediction technique for future sales. Thirdly there are the costs that would have been made had the decision rule been used and had perfect sales forecasts been made. If costs are expressed in units of $1,000, the results are as follows:

Cost categories	Actual costs	Based on a mechanical prediction of future sales	Based on a perfect sales forecast
Regular payroll	$1,940	$1,834	$1,888
Hiring and layoff	22	25	20
Overtime and idle time	196	296	167
Inventory and adjustment	361	451	454
Back orders	1,566	616	400
Total	$4,085	$3,222	$2,929

As we could expect, the total costs are smallest when the decision rules are used and the sales predictions are perfect. The mechanical prediction procedure reduces the advantage somewhat; its overall costs are 10 per cent higher. Actual costs, however, are 25 per cent higher than that, which suggests that using the decision rules is more important than making perfect predictions. The differences in costs are mainly due to difference in back orders, or negative inventory. For this reason the costs of back orders have been mentioned separately from the costs of carrying a positive inventory. The decision rules indicate that one should have kept larger inventories (compare 451 and 454 with 361), which would have drastically reduced back orders. This result is due in part to the fact that one of the three years considered was 1951 during the Korean conflict. Another investigation not including the year 1951 gave a cost reduction of nearly 10 per cent when decisions were based on the decision rule. This is certainly still worthwhile for shareholders.

11-7. Predictions of Future Decisions

In the previous section the decision rule was applied month after month, so that each month the meaning of p_0 and q_0 changed. At the beginning of a new year p_0 and q_0 stand for the production and work force decisions for January, a month later they represent the decisions for February, etc. This is how the decision rules are used in practice. The computational procedure, however, also gives other interesting results. For one thing, it is possible to make a prediction about the optimum decisions that should be made in later months. We recall that the present determinations of p_0 and q_0 were arrived at as follows: We minimized the total costs (subject to the restrictions concerning changes in inventories) after having substituted the expected values of the uncertain future sales. The results p_0 and q_0 then coincide, according to the certainty equivalence theory, with the decisions prescribed by the use of the optimum strategy. The same minimization procedure, however, determines values for p_1 and q_1 as well. Do these values also coincide with the p_1 and q_1 of the optimum strategy? No, of course not, because the procedure cannot take into account the information that will become available during the coming month, in particular the actual sales figure s_0. Nevertheless, the values p_1 and q_1 which are computed in this way are important, if only because they are available now, whereas the "true" figures of the optimum strategy can be computed only after a month. A more fundamental reason for the importance of the preliminary figures is that it is possible to make a simple probability statement on the discrepancies. If we take the p_1 value of the optimum strategy (available after a month) and the p_1 value computed as indicated above (available now), we find that their difference is sometimes positive and sometimes negative, but the expected value of the difference is zero. Hence the preliminary p_1 is a prediction of the definitive value with the special property that the prediction error has zero expectation (which is expressed by saying that the prediction is *unbiased*).

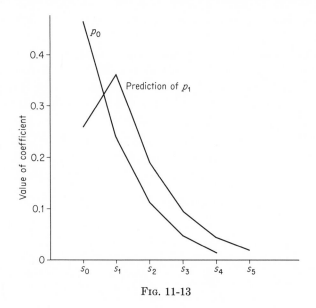

FIG. 11-13

In the present case we find the prediction of p_1 by applying the following formula:

$$\text{Prediction of } p_1 = \begin{Bmatrix} 0.259Es_0 \\ +0.363Es_1 \\ +0.191Es_2 \\ +0.096Es_3 \\ +0.044Es_4 \\ +0.018Es_5 \end{Bmatrix} - 0.259y_{-1} + 0.280q_{-1} + 84.1$$

The structure of this formula is fully analogous to the decision rule for p_0; only the coefficients differ. In the first place the coefficients of the initial conditions (-0.259 and 0.280) are closer to zero than the corresponding coefficients in the equation for p_0. This is only common sense, for the level of inventories and the work force at the beginning of the first month are of less importance to the decisions to be made in the second month than to those in the first month. Furthermore, the coefficients for the expected sales are different from those in the decision rule for p_0. The largest coefficient is the one corresponding to Es_1 for the expected sales in

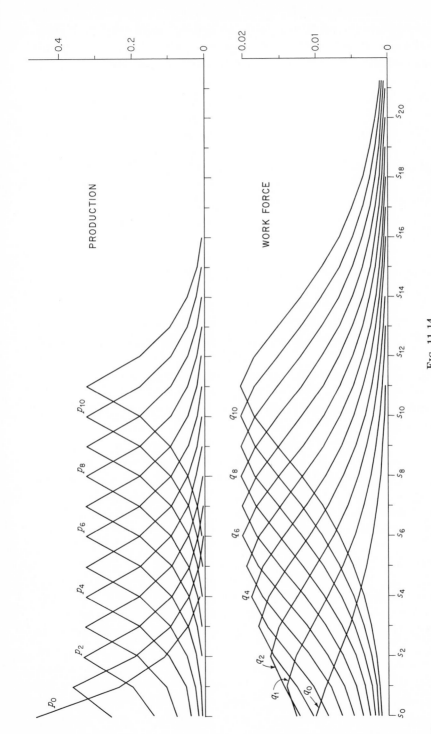

PRODUCTION

WORK FORCE

FIG. 11-14

211

the month for which we predict the production p_1.   By attaching great weight to the expected sales Es_1 in determining p_1, we mitigate changes in inventories.   Both series of coefficients together (on the one hand, those of expected sales in the decision rule for p_0 and, on the other hand, those of expected sales in the prediction equation for p_1) can be compared by plotting them in a diagram similar to Fig. 11-10.   The result is shown in Fig. 11-13.   We see clearly that the successive coefficients of p_0 have their top at s_0, and those of p_1 at s_1.   The decrease from the top is gradual, as is proved to be generally true.   We can also predict the production decisions in the second month (p_2), the third month (p_3), etc.   The coefficients of expected sales are recorded in Fig. 11-14 both for the production and for the work force predictions.   The resulting figures look like rolling waves. The waves of the work force are smooth compared with the peaked ones of the production predictions.

So we see that this procedure enables the manager not only to compute what he should do right now $(p_0$ and $q_0)$, but also to compute a forecast of what he will do in the future $(p_1, q_1; p_2, q_2; \ . \ . \ .)$.   These predictions are not necessarily perfect, of course, since sales expectations change over time.   The necessary data are the initial conditions q_{-1} and y_{-1}, the expected future sales $Es_0, Es_1, \ . \ . \ . \ ,$ and the coefficients by which these factors are multiplied.   These coefficients are the outcome of the computations performed in minimizing the quadratic cost function subject to the linear constraints.   The result is that on January 1 the decisions p_0 and q_0 are determined and predictions of the later decisions $p_1, q_1; p_2, q_2;$ $. \ . \ .$ are available.   The predictions are then successively revised.   On February 1, we compute p_0 and q_0, which may differ from the p_1 and q_1 determined on January 1 because sales in January and sales expectations may have taken on different values from those originally formulated on January 1.   Again, on February 1, the decisions p_1 and q_1 (*now* the decisions concerning March), $p_2, q_2, \ . \ . \ .$ are recomputed, so that the March predictions, April predictions, etc., are also revised.

Literature

The square-root formula for the optimum lot size was derived by F. Harris in 1915. Several extensions for more complicated cases have been formulated since then; reference is made to the textbook by Hadley and Whitin [1].   The paint factory and its cost function have been discussed by Holt and others [2].   The first step toward the certainty equivalence theory was made by Theil [3], who considered the so-called static case in which the minimization process is confined to only one period.   For the dynamic (multi-period) generalization see Simon [4] and Theil [5].   An extensive treatment of the subject can be found in Theil [6], which contains *inter alia* an account of some investigations by C. van de Panne, P. J. M. van den Bogaard, and A. P. Barten.   The first of these authors analyzed the losses incurred in a number of suboptimal situations: when the manager's decisions deviate from the optimum p_0 and

q_0, when the sales forecasts are subject to error, and when the cost coefficients (the c's) are erroneously specified. Van den Bogaard and Barten made a macroeconomic application dealing with the Dutch economy in the three-year period 1957 through 1959, using three alternative quadratic social preference functions which are each maximized over time, subject to the constraints implied by an econometric model.

[1] G. Hadley and T. M. Whitin, *Analysis of Inventory Systems*, Prentice-Hall, Inc., Englewood Cliffs, N.J., 1963.

[2] C. C. Holt, F. Modigliani, J. F. Muth, and H. A. Simon, *Planning Production, Inventories, and Work Force*, Prentice-Hall, Inc., Englewood Cliffs, N.J., 1960.

[3] H. Theil, "Econometric Models and Welfare Maximization," *Weltwirtschaftliches Archiv*, vol. 72 (1954), pp. 60–83.

[4] H. A. Simon, "Dynamic Programming under Uncertainty with a Quadratic Criterion Function," *Econometrica*, vol. 24 (1956), pp. 74–81.

[5] H. Theil, "Note on Certainty Equivalence in Dynamic Economic Planning," *Econometrica*, vol. 25 (1957), pp. 346–349.

[6] H. Theil, *Optimal Decision Rules for Government and Industry*, North Holland Publishing Company, Amsterdam, and Rand McNally & Company, Chicago, 1964.

12

The Statistical Specification of Economic Relations

12-1. The Problem

Throughout this book we have been repeatedly concerned with relationships between economic variables. In input-output analysis, for example, we specified a relationship between the deliveries from sector i to sector j and the total production in sector j. The relationship specified was the very simple one of proportionality. The coefficient of proportionality was called the technical coefficient, which was easily determined by means of the input-output table of one single year. Often, however, the numerical specification of the relationship between economic variables poses far greater problems. This is particularly the case in determining the numerical coefficients of econometric macromodels (cf. Chap. 4), which is our present topic. To keep the discussion reasonably simple, we shall take up the case in which there is only one equation of an uncomplicated nature. Three phases will be dealt with:

1. We shall start by discussing the sources of information on which the procedure is based. It will be obvious that statistical data are one of these sources.

2. Given the statistical data, we shall consider the numerical computation of the coefficients of the relationship.

3. When this has been accomplished, we shall feel less than satisfied, because we know so very little about the reliability of the result. This reliability, or the faith we have in the answer, is our final topic.

12-2. Two Sources of Information

One source of information consists of the things that one already knows about the relationship concerned and the things that can reasonably be assumed to be true a priori. This will be considered in the next para-

214

graph.   Another source consists of statistical data, which may take differ-ent forms.   We may have household data on expenditures on various commodities supplied by families which participated in a budget survey. Another example is investment data supplied by firms which participated in an investment survey.   A third (and very important) source of sta-tistical information is the time series of economic variables constructed by official statistical bureaus.   Suppose, for example, that we are interested in the relation between per capita consumption and per capita income in the United States since World War II and that the Department of Com-merce provides us with annual data on both these variables.   Then it should be possible to use these data in the specification of the relationship.

This consumption-income example is also appropriate to illustrate the first source of information.   As stated, this source consists of what is already known or assumed to be known about the relationship.   In our example this could take the following form: Per capita consumption is a linear function of per capita income.   Or perhaps: Per capita consumption is a quadratic function of per capita income.   It is also conceivable that the investigator feels that a distinction should be made between wage income and nonwage income, because the consumption reactions to changes in wage income are considered to be different from those to changes in nonwage income.   The relation could then be: Per capita consumption is a linear function of per capita wage income and per capita nonwage income. One may also decide to use income of the previous year besides current income, etc.   Evidently, there are numerous possibilities.   Which one is the favorite choice depends partly on considerations of economic theory, partly on considerations of simplicity.   It is, in principle, possible to test the validity of the choice made on the basis of the computations that will be described in this chapter.

The rules in econometric investigations can be summarized as follows. The object of the study is to explain the variation of an economic variable. This is the variable "to be explained," or the *dependent variable*.   In our example we want to explain the changes over time in consumption per capita.   Of course, the variable to be explained could also be the changes in investments over time, the fluctuations in the price of butter, the course of the interest rate, or, in fact, any other economic variable one can think of.   To this end one specifies (1) the variables with which one hopes to explain the variations in the dependent variable, referred to as *explanatory variables*, and (2) the mathematical form in which the explanatory varia-bles influence the dependent variable.   In our example, we first select income per capita as an explanatory variable.   Secondly, we specify that the relationship is linear or quadratic or log-linear, for example.   The actual relationship chosen depends on theoretical considerations.   In case these do not give a clear-cut answer, experience, intuition, and considerations of simplicity will guide our choice.

Even if we know the structure of the relationship, we do not yet know its numerical coefficients. We do know, for example, that the dependent variable y depends upon the explanatory variable x according to the linear equation $y = a + bx$, but the values of a and b are not yet known. Our next task is to determine these values with the help of our numerical data on y and x. This is the second phase of our econometric investigation.

12-3. The Scatter Diagram

We shall consider the easy case of one explanatory variable x (income per capita) and one variable to be explained, the dependent variable y (consumption per capita). We assume that observations on these variables are available. In the first year, income x equaled 77, and consumption y was equal to 70. In the second year, the values observed for x and y were 83 and 68, respectively, and so on. The observed values for seven consecutive years are recorded below:

Year	x	y
1	77	70
2	83	68
3	90	85
4	70	65
5	73	72
6	95	78
7	68	55

These pairs of numbers are now plotted in a diagram. Along the horizontal axis we measure income, the explanatory variable x, and along the vertical axis consumption, the dependent variable y. The first point lies at 77 to the right of the vertical axis and at 70 above the horizontal axis. In this way all points can be plotted. We then get Fig. 12-1, a so-called *scatter diagram*. If only all points in the scatter diagram were situated on a straight line, our problem would be solved. We would draw that line and interpret it as the relationship between x and y. But the points do not all lie on a straight line, and experience teaches that they virtually never do. At this point the objection may be raised that there is no impelling reason for the relationship to be linear. When we allow curved lines, it is not very hard to draw one which fits the points precisely. This is done in Fig. 12-2. The points are the same as those in the previous figure. A freehand line has been drawn through them. However, the very fact that an infinite number of such lines can be drawn through all these seven points is one important objection to this procedure.   There are also other difficulties.   For one thing, do we think this curve establishes the actual relationship between x and y?   Granted, the line has the virtue that it fits the observations, but its shortcomings are serious.   The curve alternately increases and decreases.   This implies that if we interpret the curve as giving the true relationship between y and x, an increase in x would sometimes lead to a decrease in y and at other times to an increase in y, which is not very plausible for a consumption-income relationship.

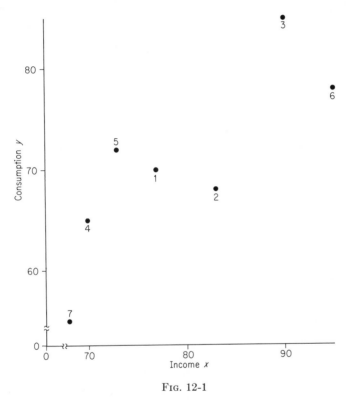

FIG. 12-1

There is another objection.   Suppose a new observation becomes available, for example, the observation $x = 88$.   Then, according to our curve, the associated y value should be 75.   Do we really believe this is true? What do we do if the value turns out to be 70?   Do we then draw a new line, and do we repeat this whenever a new observation does not fit the line?

These objections weigh so heavily that the curve of Fig. 12-2 cannot be seriously considered.   In practice one tries to fit a straight line or a curve of simple structure (a quadratic curve, for example) to the points.   Since, however, it is impossible to find a straight line which fits all points, the

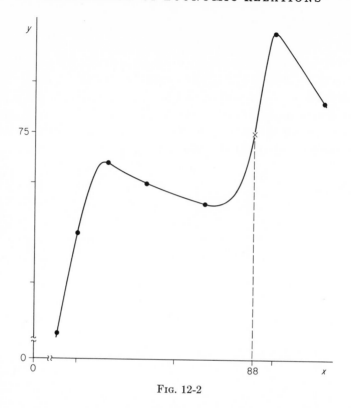

Fig. 12-2

question is which straight line should be chosen. Even if the "best" straight line is chosen, there will be deviations between the actually observed values and the systematic relationship described by the line.

12-4. The Least-squares Method

In what follows we shall assume that there is a linear relation between x and y. The structure of the equation is thus determined as $y = a + bx$, but the values of a and b are yet to be specified. The first problem is what criterion should be used to determine a and b. Our criterion will be based on the wish that the (inevitable) deviations be as small as possible in some appropriate sense. In Fig. 12-3 we have drawn two straight lines to fit the points of Fig. 12-1, and each point has a certain deviation from both lines. The point P deviates a little bit from the second line and substantially from the first. Note that the deviations are measured vertically. This should be obvious, for the variable y, measured vertically, is the variable we want to explain. Given a value x, the variable y should according to the first line take on the value given by Q, whereas in fact it is as high as P; the deviation therefore equals PQ.

In Fig. 12-3 line I performs on the whole better than line II. This is not true as far as point P is concerned. When all points are considered, however, the overall deviations from line I are smaller than those from line II. Of course, a reasonable procedure should not just focus attention on one or two points, but it should take all points into account.

By far the best-known procedure of adapting a straight line to a number of points is known as the *least-squares method*. This consists of minimizing the sum of squares of the deviations—the name is thus telltale. Consider then all possible straight lines. For each line, measure the deviations (the

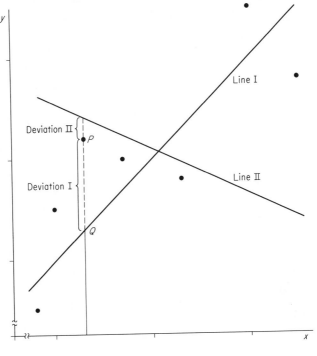

FIG. 12-3

vertical distances) from the points to the line. Square these deviations and add them. Then pick the line for which this sum of squares of deviations is as small as possible. This method can be traced to the famous mathematician Gauss (1777–1855), and has since been applied in many fields.

Our above formulation may have suggested that it is necessary to draw a great many straight lines and compute the sum of squares of the deviations for each of these. This would hardly be feasible, and fortunately it is not necessary. We shall derive the construction of the least-squares line for the very simple case where the straight line $y = a + bx$ is assumed to go through the origin. Hence when $x = 0$, we must have $y = 0$, so that $0 = a + b \times 0$. Our assumption therefore says that $a = 0$. It remains for us to determine the b value of the relationship $y = bx$. This b must be determined in such a way as to minimize the sum of the squared deviations.

The derivation is illustrated with Fig. 12-4 where x_1 and y_1 are the coordinates of the first observation, x_2 and y_2 the coordinates of the second observation. Let us now consider an arbitrary straight line through the origin. The equation of such a line is $y = bx$. If $x = x_1$, the associated y value is accordingly bx_1. In fact, y is equal to y_1, and so the deviation

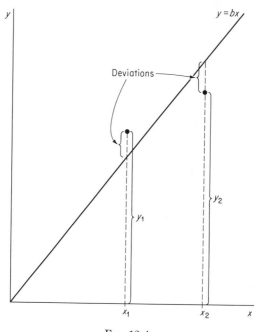

FIG. 12-4

is $y_1 - bx_1$. The deviation of the second point from the line is similarly seen to equal $y_2 - bx_2$. The sum of the squared deviations is therefore

$$(y_1 - bx_1)^2 + (y_2 - bx_2)^2$$

We must now, according to the least-squares criterion, determine b to minimize this expression. The solution can be found algebraically, the following being an elementary derivation.

First, let us actually take the square of $y_1 - bx_1$ plus $y_2 - bx_2$:

$$(y_1^2 - 2bx_1y_1 + b^2x_1^2) + (y_2^2 - 2bx_2y_2 + b^2x_2^2)$$
$$= (y_1^2 + y_2^2) - 2b(x_1y_1 + x_2y_2) + b^2(x_1^2 + x_2^2)$$

We have thus split up the sum of squares of the deviations into three terms. The first term does not involve b at all. Whatever value for b we care to pick, that term will remain unchanged. We can influence, however, the values of the other two terms by our choice of b. The problem has become to choose b to minimize

$$-2b(x_1y_1 + x_2y_2) + b^2(x_1^2 + x_2^2)$$

These terms can again be written in such a way that the first part is wholly independent of our choice of b. It can be verified by straightforward algebra that this expression is equivalent to

$$-\frac{(x_1y_1 + x_2y_2)^2}{x_1^2 + x_2^2} + (x_1^2 + x_2^2)\left[b - \frac{x_1y_1 + x_2y_2}{x_1^2 + x_2^2}\right]^2$$

Since the first part is indeed independent of b, we must now determine b to minimize

$$(x_1^2 + x_2^2)\left[b - \frac{x_1y_1 + x_2y_2}{x_1^2 + x_2^2}\right]^2$$

This expression is always positive, unless

$$b = \frac{x_1y_1 + x_2y_2}{x_1^2 + x_2^2}$$

in which case it assumes the value zero. Zero is thus its minimum value, which is attained for the specified b value. Because x_1, y_1, x_2, and y_2 are all known numbers, b is now numerically specified.

When there are more than two observations, the same procedure, but slightly more complicated mathematics, gives the following more general result. If there are n pairs of observations $y_1, x_1; y_2, x_2; \ldots ; y_n, x_n,$ then we should determine b as

$$b = \frac{x_1y_1 + x_2y_2 + \cdots + x_ny_n}{x_1^2 + x_2^2 + \cdots + x_n^2}$$

Thus, we take all available pairs of observations, compute their products $x_1y_1; x_2y_2; \ldots ; x_ny_n$, and add these. We also add the sum of squares of the values taken by the explanatory variable to get $x_1^2 + x_2^2 + \cdots + x_n^2$. We then divide the sum of products by this sum of squares to get b. The numerical example for the case depicted in Fig. 12-1 gives

$$77 \times 70 + 83 \times 68 + \cdots + 68 \times 55 = 39{,}640$$
and
$$77^2 + 83^2 + \cdots + 68^2 = 44{,}796$$

and hence $b = 39{,}640/44{,}796 = 0.885$. The conclusion is that given our observations and the proportionality between y and x, the consumption varies with income according to the equation $y = 0.885x$. This implies that, as a rule, 88.5 per cent of the income is consumed; but there will be deviations to this rule (whose sum of squares has been minimized).

The equation $y = bx$ with b as specified above is called a *least-squares regression equation*. The straight line which represents the equation graphically is called the *regression line*, and b is called the *regression coefficient*. The term "regression" was coined by the English statistician Galton (1822–1911). He applied the least-squares technique to a description of the relationship between the heights of fathers and sons. His conclusion was that the sons of tall fathers were also tall, but not—as a rule—quite as tall as their fathers. Sons of short fathers similarly tended to be short, yet a little taller than their fathers. Thus, there is a tendency to *regress* to the average, which explains the choice of the term. At present, regression analysis is applied in many fields; the specific interpretation of Galton is of little importance to us; indeed, it is frowned upon in modern statistics.

We have confined ourselves to the very simplest case of a straight line through the origin. When the straight line is not prescribed to go through the origin, the equation is $y = a + bx$, and we then need to determine two coefficients, a and b. When there are more explanatory variables, the number of coefficients becomes even larger; the computations then become more complicated, but no new principles are involved. The task is always to minimize the sum of the squared deviations between the observed values of the dependent variable and the corresponding values according to the regression equation. *All* these coefficients are determined *simultaneously* by this criterion.

12-5. The Philosophy of Statistical Estimation

We shall now concern ourselves with the reliability of the obtained result. This is the third phase of the program which we announced at the outset of the chapter. As we saw, the least-squares procedure leads to a unique numerical value of the coefficient b, given the pairs of observations $x_1, y_1; x_2, y_2; \ldots .$ The relevant question is to what extent we can trust this result. Does it give the real relationship between y and x?

If not, if it is only an estimate of the actual relationship, how much faith should we have in this estimate?

The philosophy of statistical estimation can most easily be explained when we work with only one variable. In regression analysis there are at least two variables—a dependent and an explanatory variable. We shall therefore return to regression analysis after a detour via a one-variable problem. Again we use the example of the 50 families whose monthly expenditures are listed in Sec. 6-5. All families had a monthly income of $1,000, and each family consisted of two parents and two children.

If we want to characterize the monthly expenditures of these 50 families with one number, we can use the average expenditures. Algebraically, if $r_1, r_2, \ldots, r_{50}$ stand for the 50 expenditures, the average is

$$m = \frac{r_1 + r_2 + \cdots + r_{50}}{50}$$

The numerical average of the data given in Sec. 6-5 is

$$m = \frac{716 + 937 + \cdots + 839}{50} = \frac{41,048}{50} = 820.96$$

The average expenditures of these 50 families thus equal (about) $821. This conclusion is important if we are specifically interested in these 50 families, but there is no reason why we should single them out as being of special importance. It is, however, quite conceivable that we are interested in the average expenditures of all American families with two children and a monthly income of $1,000. The statistical theory now considers the 50 families as a *sample* from the *population* consisting of all American families with husband, wife, two children, and $1,000 income. More precisely, in the present case the population consists of the monthly expenditures of all such families, and the sample is a part of the population. In other examples the population might be the heights of all persons over 21, and the sample might consist of the heights of 75 persons who were actually measured. The population might be the sugar content of a shipment of sugarbeets delivered to a factory. The sample might then consist of the sugar content in 25 beets that were actually analyzed for sugar content. More abstractly, one can consider the result of 10 flips of a coin as a sample of the population of all conceivable results that would be obtained by flipping the coin an infinite number of times.

The theory of statistical estimation owes its existence to the problem of incomplete knowledge. Our knowledge is confined to the information provided by the sample, but the sample *as such* does not interest us. We

use the sample only to draw conclusions concerning the population characteristics in which we are interested. The sugar factory is interested in
the sugar content of the whole shipment, not in the sugar content of the
25 analyzed beets. Better, one is interested in the sugar content of the
25 analyzed beets only to the extent that it gives information about the
sugar content of the whole shipment. Quite analogously, the expenditures of the 50 families interest us only in so far as they help us to get a
better idea of the expenditures of the population as a whole. In our
particular case the expenditures of the population as a whole are *known*
to be normally distributed, with an average of $800 and a standard deviation of $100. (Our data were generated by a computer according to these
specifications; see Sec. 6-5.) This is a very unusual situation, however.
In practice, the characteristics of the population are unknown, and the
sample is used to infer conclusions about them.

We shall suppose that *all* we are interested in is the determination of the
average expenditures in the complete population. One might wonder
why we then do not include all families—i.e., the complete population—in
our sample. The answer is, of course, that it would be very costly. In
other cases it would be physically impossible. This happens when the
sample information can be obtained only by destroying every item in the
sample; e.g., in the case of the average lifetime of lamps. It is also impossible when the population is in principle infinitely large, e.g., when it consists of all conceivable results of flipping a coin.

What can we say about the quality of the figure obtained for the sample
average ($821) as an approximation to the population average ($800)?
In this case, of course, we know the error ($21) precisely. That is true
because we happen to know the population average; but the problem in
general is to make statements about the population average, given the
sample average, if we do not know the population average. Let us then
suppose that we draw a second sample of 50 families (same composition,
same income) and determine the average of the expenditures of that
group. Obviously, it would be a pure coincidence if this second sample
average were to coincide either with the first or with the population average.
Let us assume that the second sample average is $803. We can continue
in this way, taking many samples of 50 families and time and again computing their average expenditures. These averages will usually differ
from each other, but they will generally be fairly close to $800. Such
averages will certainly cluster more closely around $800 than the expenditures of individual families listed in Sec. 6-5. At least, this will be the
case if we take *random* samples, that is, if we sample in such a way that
every family of the population has the same chance of being included in
the sample. We shall elaborate on this procedure in the next section.

12-6. Random Samples and Unbiased Estimates

Let us suppose that our sample of 50 families was randomly taken as follows. After having (somehow) written down the complete list of all United States families with a monthly income of $1,000 and composed of husband, wife, and two children, we chose 50 of these families at random. This gave us the Dailey family in San Antonio, Texas, the Bartleson family in Spokane, Washington, the Crommelin family from Tampa, Florida, the Adams family from Maplewood, New Jersey, etc. Next we asked these families their monthly expenditures, and these gave us the numerical results which are recorded in Sec. 6-5.

Let us now consider the following case. We have written down the list of all American families that meet our specifications, but we have not yet actually chosen the sample. As long as no families have actually been chosen, the expenditures are random variables, which we indicated before by $r_1, r_2, \ldots, r_{50}$. (After the sample had been drawn, these values were specified at $716, $937, $\ldots$, $839, but even without this numerical specification we can proceed *in abstracto* with the numbers $r_1, r_2, \ldots,$ r_{50}.) Then r_1 is a symbolic way of writing the expenditure of the first family *to be chosen* in the sample, r_2 is a symbolic way of writing the expenditure of the second family *to be chosen*, etc. The $r_1, r_2, \ldots, r_{50}$ are then random variables. In fact, since all families have an equal chance of being chosen, these random variables are all subject to the same distribution as the population distribution. This can be illustrated as follows. Let us make the simplifying assumption that there are only 100 families in the population with the following monthly expenditures:

Number of families	Average monthly expenditures
2	Less than $600
14	$600–$700
34	$700–$800
34	$800–$900
14	$900–$1,000
2	More than $1,000

Consider then r_1, the random variable which stands for the expenditure of the first family to be chosen. What is the distribution of r_1? This distribution is precisely the same as the distribution of the population, because there is a 2 per cent chance that the family picked will spend less than $600, a 14 per cent chance of hitting a family with expenditures between $600 and $700, etc. This is true simply because each family has an equal probability (0.01 to be precise) of being the first to be incorporated into the sample.   The same holds for the second choice (r_2), the third (r_3), etc.[1]   We repeat for emphasis: Each of the random variables r_1, r_2, . . . , r_{50} is subject to a distribution identical with the population distribution.   In particular, all these 50 random variables have an expected value of $\mu = \$800$ (because that is the expected value of the population distribution).

We can now obtain results.   Let us forget the simple distribution of the previous paragraph and assume again that the monthly family expenditures are normally distributed, but that the mean of this distribution is unknown.   We want to know, or at least approximate, the value of μ. To that end we take, at random, a sample of 50 families and compute the sample average of the expenditures:

$$m = \frac{r_1 + r_2 + \cdots + r_{50}}{50} = \tfrac{1}{50}r_1 + \tfrac{1}{50}r_2 + \cdots + \tfrac{1}{50}r_{50}$$

The r_1, r_2, . . . , r_{50} are random variables as long as the sample has not actually been drawn.   After it has been drawn we know, for example, that $r_1 = \$716$.   It is then determined.   Before the sample is drawn, however, m is simply a linear combination of the random variables r_1 through r_{50}.   Therefore, m is also a random variable.   We can then ask for the expected value of m, which is thus equal to the expected value of a linear combination of r_1, . . . , r_{50} (with all weights equal to $\tfrac{1}{50}$). We now use a well-known theorem which reads as follows: The expected value of a linear combination of random variables is equal to the same linear combination of the expected values of these random variables.   In this case the implication is that the expected value of m equals

$$\tfrac{1}{50}\mu + \tfrac{1}{50}\mu + \cdots + \tfrac{1}{50}\mu = 50(\tfrac{1}{50}\mu) = \mu$$

because—as stated at the end of the previous paragraph—the expected value of each of the r's equals μ.

Our conclusion is that the expected value of m (the sample average) coincides with μ (the population average) provided that we take a random sample.   The actual value of m when the sample has been drawn may well be above or below μ.   But we know that the random sampling procedure guarantees that on the average the mean of the sample will coin-

---

[1] When we draw 50 times from a population consisting of 100 families, we face the problem of sampling the same family twice or even more often (assuming that each time we draw from the same 100-family population, the family being sampled last time is "returned" to the population).   This problem is not important when the population is sufficiently large; we shall disregard it here.

cide with the population mean. In such a case we speak of an *unbiased estimate*. The sample mean m is an unbiased estimate of the population mean μ.[1]

Armed with these results, let us return to regression analysis.

12-7. Estimation in Regression Analysis

Suppose that we have data on expenditures of three families. In contrast with the previous examples we shall no longer assume that they all have a monthly income equal to $1,000. Instead, we assume that the families have monthly incomes of $1,000, $1,500, and $2,500. Our data tell us that their respective monthly expenditures are $716, $1,268, and $2,011. On the basis of this evidence we are requested to determine the relationship between income and expenditures, using the least-squares regression analysis. We shall assume for convenience that the mathematical form is one of proportionality, so that we have $y = bx$. Here y, the dependent variable, stands for the expenditures, and x, the explanatory variable, stands for monthly income. We thus have the following pairs of observations:

$$x_1 = \$1,000 \qquad y_1 = \$716$$
$$x_2 = \$1,500 \qquad y_2 = \$1,268$$
$$x_3 = \$2,500 \qquad y_3 = \$2,011$$

If we apply the formula derived in Sec. 12-4, we find for the regression coefficient

$$b = \frac{x_1y_1 + x_2y_2 + x_3y_3}{x_1^2 + x_2^2 + x_3^2}$$
$$= \frac{1,000 \times 716 + 1,500 \times 1,268 + 2,500 \times 2,011}{(1,000)^2 + (1,500)^2 + (2,500)^2} = 0.8048$$

Our conclusion is that expenditures can be derived from income x by multiplying x by 0.8048.

It will be evident that the reliability of this result is still open to question. The conclusion is based on only three observations, one on a family with a $1,000 income, one on a family with a $1,500 income, and one on a family with a $2,500 income. We continue, then, by increasing the number of observations, as we did in the previous section when we considered more and more samples. Specifically, we assume that we have another

---

[1] In Sec. 11-7, we were concerned with unbiased prediction of future production and work-force decisions. It will be obvious that unbiased estimation and unbiased prediction are related concepts.

three families with monthly incomes of $1,000, $1,500, and $2,500. Their expenditures happen to be $937, $1,123, and $1,911, respectively. Again, we can compute the regression coefficient b under the hypothesis of strict proportionality between income x and consumption y. We then find

$$b = \frac{1,000 \times 937 + 1,500 \times 1,123 + 2,500 \times 1,911}{(1,000)^2 + (1,500)^2 + (2,500)^2} = 0.7788$$

The result is now slightly different. Based on these data we should estimate that consumption is found by multiplying income by 0.7788.

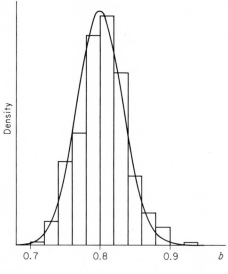

Fig. 12-5

This numerical result contradicts the previous result. In fact, we have repeated the same procedure no less than 50 times and found only contradictions, since the regression coefficient b changed from sample to sample. All data and results are reproduced in the table opposite; the first two rows give the results we already established; the other 48 results are derived similarly, based on 48 new random samples of the same type.

In fact, we did not stop with 50 samples, but took a grand total of 500. The remaining 450 have not been listed. It is quite interesting, however, to see graphically the results of all these 500 regression coefficients in Fig. 12-5. There are only very few coefficients between 0.70 and 0.72, but a large number fall in the range 0.78 to 0.82. (In the figure we have drawn a smooth, normal curve which closely fits the data.)

Number of sample	Expenditures when income equals			Regression coefficient (b)
	$1,000	$1,500	$2,500	
1	$716	$1,268	$2,011	0.8048
2	937	1,123	1,911	0.7788
3	782	1,061	2,099	0.8022
4	835	1,009	2,050	0.7867
5	1,082	1,205	1,905	0.8055
6	1,012	1,332	2,081	0.8645
7	701	1,133	1,972	0.7716
8	834	1,119	1,836	0.7476
9	864	1,296	1,856	0.7840
10	811	1,176	2,001	0.7976
11	798	1,134	2,024	0.7957
12	714	1,308	2,046	0.8201
13	801	1,227	2,002	0.8049
14	797	1,246	1,791	0.7519
15	759	1,123	2,208	0.8383
16	862	1,200	1,920	0.7855
17	883	1,301	2,027	0.8318
18	722	1,108	2,021	0.7828
19	803	1,298	1,867	0.7808
20	570	1,224	2,170	0.8243
21	878	1,301	1,908	0.7999
22	866	1,349	2,173	0.8760
23	766	1,316	2,066	0.8321
24	916	1,248	1,831	0.7753
25	876	1,240	2,213	0.8704
26	700	1,188	1,780	0.7297
27	768	1,115	2,157	0.8245
28	818	1,154	1,815	0.7459
29	808	1,235	1,776	0.7474
30	998	1,223	1,985	0.8205
31	891	1,220	1,955	0.8009
32	768	1,183	1,997	0.7932
33	623	1,212	2,101	0.8098
34	816	1,052	2,119	0.8096
35	879	1,252	1,897	0.7894
36	820	1,356	2,035	0.8359
37	931	1,304	1,918	0.8086
38	835	1,182	2,176	0.8472
39	874	1,174	1,932	0.7858
40	827	1,300	1,912	0.7955
41	939	1,149	1,986	0.8029
42	786	1,205	2,077	0.8196
43	724	1,131	1,839	0.7387
44	837	1,142	1,933	0.7771
45	572	1,131	2,058	0.7804
46	836	1,059	1,894	0.7536
47	937	1,224	2,021	0.8316
48	904	1,241	1,976	0.8111
49	733	1,215	1,840	0.7532
50	839	1,176	2,029	0.8079

How are we to interpret these results? As one would expect, these results have been obtained by random sampling groups of three observations, one each out of the populations of families whose incomes were $1,000, $1,500, and $2,500, respectively. Thus, the numerical data of the first row ($716, $1,268, and $2,011) are the result of a random sample from three different populations. All these populations are normal and have a

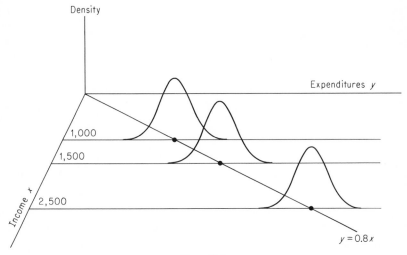

FIG. 12-6

standard deviation of $100. They have different expected values, however, which (when we artificially generated these data) we chose as follows:

Income	Expected expenditure
$1,000	$ 800
$1,500	$1,200
$2,500	$2,000

These three populations are depicted graphically in three dimensions; cf. Fig. 12-6. Along two axes we measure the income x and the expenditures y. Along the third axis we measure the densities of the three normal distributions. There are only three relevant levels of income, $1,000, $1,500, and $2,500, indicated by the straight lines parallel to the expenditure axis. Suppose now that we take a family from the population of families with an income of $2,500. We find an expenditure corresponding to a certain point on the line marked 2,500. When we choose the family at random, we interpret its expenditures as a random variable of which the distribution is drawn above the line marked 2,500. This is a normal density with an expected value of 2,000 and a standard deviation of 100.

In the figure we have indicated three points corresponding to the expected expenditures: \$800 when income is \$1,000, \$1,200 when income is \$1,500, and \$2,000 when income is \$2,500.   These three points lie on a straight line through the origin, as a consequence of the way in which we specified our numbers: for each of the three populations the expected value of expenditure is 80 per cent of the corresponding income.   This is, of course, a very special situation, but nonetheless one of crucial importance for what follows.   Let us also write the regression coefficient in more elaborate form such that it becomes quite clear that this coefficient is a linear combination of y_1, y_2, and y_3:

$$b = \frac{x_1 y_1 + x_2 y_2 + x_3 y_3}{x_1^2 + x_2^2 + x_3^2}$$

$$= \frac{x_1}{x_1^2 + x_2^2 + x_3^2} y_1 + \frac{x_2}{x_1^2 + x_2^2 + x_3^2} y_2 + \frac{x_3}{x_1^2 + x_2^2 + x_3^2} y_3$$

The incomes x_1, x_2, and x_3 are, in view of our procedure, fixed numbers, to wit, \$1,000, \$1,500, and \$2,500.   The expenditures y_1, y_2, and y_3 are the result of the random sampling procedure, however, and they are random variables as long as no actual sample has been drawn.   Then b is also a random variable; it is, in fact, a linear combination of the random variables y_1, y_2, and y_3 with the respective coefficients

$$\frac{x_1}{x_1^2 + x_2^2 + x_3^2} = \frac{1,000}{9,500,000}$$

$$\frac{x_2}{x_1^2 + x_2^2 + x_3^2} = \frac{1,500}{9,500,000}$$

$$\frac{x_3}{x_1^2 + x_2^2 + x_3^2} = \frac{2,500}{9,500,000}$$

We use again the result that the expected value of a linear combination of random variables is equal to the same linear combination of expected values of the random variables.   Furthermore, we recall that these expected values of the random variables y_1, y_2, and y_3 are equal to $0.8x_1$, $0.8x_2$, $0.8x_3$ in that order.   Thus the expected value of b is

$$\frac{x_1}{x_1^2 + x_2^2 + x_3^2} (0.8x_1) + \frac{x_2}{x_1^2 + x_2^2 + x_3^2} (0.8x_2)$$

$$+ \frac{x_3}{x_1^2 + x_2^2 + x_3^2} (0.8x_3) = \frac{0.8(x_1^2 + x_2^2 + x_3^2)}{x_1^2 + x_2^2 + x_3^2} = 0.8$$

The conclusion is that the expected value of the regression coefficient is equal to 0.8, that is, equal to the coefficient of proportionality between

income and expected expenditure.   We shall now analyze this result in a
more general context.

This more general situation is, of course, the one in which the proportionality coefficient is unknown.   This is fully comparable with the situation in the two previous sections when we were interested in the unknown
μ.   Let us agree to write β (the Greek letter beta) for the unknown proportionality coefficient, so that βx_1 is the expected value of expenditures
for an income of x_1 and analogously βx_2 and βx_3 stand for expected expenditures when incomes are x_2 and x_3, respectively.   The expected value of b
now becomes

$$\frac{x_1}{x_1^2 + x_2^2 + x_3^2} (\beta x_1) + \frac{x_2}{x_1^2 + x_2^2 + x_3^2} (\beta x_2) + \frac{x_3}{x_1^2 + x_2^2 + x_3^2} (\beta x_3) = \beta$$

The conclusion is that the expected value of the regression coefficient b is
equal to the unknown proportionality coefficient β.   In other words, b is
an unbiased estimate of β in the same way as m was shown to be an unbiased
estimate of μ in the previous section.

Let us pause a minute for a review.   Our point of departure was to
specify a relationship of the type $y = bx$, based on pairs of observations
$y_1, x_1; y_2, x_2; \ldots$ We used the least-squares method, which led to a
unique numerical determination of the coefficient b, given the observations
on x and y.   Then we started to question this uniqueness.   There can
be no doubt about the uniqueness as long as we accept the observations as
fixed data; however, we did not accept the observations as fixed.   We did
consider as fixed the values of income x (more generally, the values taken
by the explanatory variable), but not the values assumed by the expenditures y (the dependent variable).   Instead, we postulated that the expenditures can vary even when income is fixed.   Thus we decided to make
probability statements about the expenditures.   We did so by specifying
that the expected expenditures equal βx where x is the given value of
income.   The coefficient β is unknown and should be statistically estimated.   At this moment the whole character of regression analysis
changes.   At the outset it was a method of adapting lines to given observations.   As long as this is the case, given the observations on x and y
and the least-squares method, b is fixed.   Now, however, we assume β
to be fixed, albeit unknown.   The task of b is to give us information about
β in much the same way as it was the task of the sample average m to give
us information about the population mean μ.   We interpreted m as a
random variable and showed that the expected value of m coincided with
μ.   In short, m was an unbiased estimate of μ.   Here we interpret b as a
random variable because b is a linear combination of the expenditures

which themselves are—in our revised interpretation—random variables. Furthermore, it turned out, subject to the assumptions made, that b is an unbiased estimate of β, the coefficient which purports to measure the relation between income and expected expenditures.   Regression analysis has thus developed from a method of fitting straight lines to a method of statistical estimation.

12-8. Standard Errors

The variability in the determination of b from sample to sample remains perhaps hard to digest.   This is especially true because in actual practice we do not have 50 samples, leading to 50 estimates, giving us a rough idea about the variability, but only one sample leading to one estimate b.   It is pleasant to know that the expected value of b coincides with β.   The deviation of the actually computed b from β may well be substantial, however; we surely should know a little more about the possible deviation.

The list of 50 b values given in Sec. 12-7 illustrates the difficulty.   We know that the results have been generated from a model in which $\beta = 0.8$. The b values vary around this value, but any particular b value may deviate substantially from 0.8.   Thus, one b value was computed as low as 0.7297. Another randomly taken sample gave a b value of no less than 0.8760. By drawing more and more samples one would almost surely find still larger deviations from 0.8.   We introduce the following formula as a measure of this variability:

$$\sqrt{\tfrac{1}{50}(b_1 - 0.8)^2 + \tfrac{1}{50}(b_2 - 0.8)^2 + \cdots + \tfrac{1}{50}(b_{50} - 0.8)^2}$$
$$= \sqrt{\tfrac{1}{50}(0.8048 - 0.8)^2 + \tfrac{1}{50}(0.7788 - 0.8)^2 + \cdots + \tfrac{1}{50}(0.8079 - 0.8)^2}$$
$$= 0.0329$$

The b_1, b_2, . . . , b_{50} stand for the numerical outcomes recorded above. These are measured as deviations from their expected value 0.8, squared, added, and divided by 50.   The procedure is analogous to that of computing the variance where we deduct the values taken by the random variables from their expected value, square these differences, weight them with their probabilities, and add them.   In the present case the probabilities have been replaced by the relative frequencies.   Each of the 50 outcomes is recorded only once, so that they each have a relative frequency of $\tfrac{1}{50}$.   Finally, we take the square root, so that the result corresponds to the standard deviation.   We see that the standard deviation, as computed numerically from the 50 recorded results, equals 0.0329.

We can also derive the standard deviation of the distribution of b *theoretically*, just as we theoretically determined that the mean of the distribution of b is β. The theoretical result (which will not be proved here) is that the standard deviation of b equals

$$\sqrt{\frac{\sigma^2}{x_1^2 + x_2^2 + x_3^2}}$$

where σ^2 is the variance in the populations and x_1, x_2, and x_3 are the values taken by the explanatory variable, income. In our example x_1, x_2, and x_3 are \$1,000, \$1,500, and \$2,500, respectively, whereas σ is \$100 for each of these populations. If we substitute these values in the formula, we find that the theoretical standard deviation equals 0.0324, which is very close to the standard deviation found on the basis of a sample of 50 b values, 0.0329. We shall henceforth work with the theoretical standard deviation of 0.0324 (known as the *standard error* of b) because it has a more essential meaning.

The use made of the standard error is interesting. The coefficient b is a random variable, whose distribution is such that the mean is $\beta = 0.8$, for b is unbiased. As we have just seen, the standard deviation of the distribution (the standard error of b) is 0.0324. Let us further assume that b is normally distributed. (This assumption is actually true when the expenditures at the various levels of income are normally distributed. The empirical distribution in Fig. 12-5 resembles the normal distribution, as indicated by the smooth curve.) We know that in a normal distribution the chance of finding a result that is more than 2 standard deviations away from the mean is 0.0455 (or slightly less than once in 20 times). In this case the chance that the random sampling procedure will give us a b value which deviates more than $2 \times 0.0324 = 0.065$ from $\beta = 0.8$ is 0.0455. In other words, the chance is only 0.0455 that b will be either higher than 0.865 or lower than 0.735. The probability is thus $1 - 0.0455 = 0.9545$ that the b value actually found will be between 0.735 and 0.865. It is thus possible to make probability statements about the value which b will assume, given the expectation 0.8 and the standard deviation 0.0324. The only trouble is that in actual fact the value 0.8 is unknown. If this value were known, there would have been no problem in the first place.

Let us now turn the problem around. We recall that b does not differ by more than twice the standard error (2×0.0324) from β, except for a 0.0455 chance. This can be reformulated as follows: If we consider taking a random sample, we know that, apart from a chance of 0.0455, the b value of the sample will be less than 2 standard errors from β. For example, let us take the first sample result $b_1 = 0.8048$. If we deduct and add twice the standard error, we find the limits 0.7400 and 0.8696. Our conclusion is that the unknown β lies in between these limits, with only a 0.0455 chance that it does not. In this example we know that the statement is correct because $\beta = 0.8$. Had we applied the same argument to sample 26, however, we should have argued that the unknown β is between $0.7297 - 0.0648 = 0.6649$ and $0.7297 + 0.0648 = 0.7945$, apart from a chance of 0.0455. In this case we would have had bad luck; however, this will not happen more than once in 20 times on the average. (Samples 22, 25, and 26, or 3 out of 50, lead to a false conclusion in our numerical examples.)

We shall summarize the highlights of our arguments:

Assuming that the expenditures for each level of income x_1, x_2, . . . are normally distributed, that these populations of expenditures have an expected value proportional to the income, that is, βx_1, βx_2, . . . , and that the variances σ^2 of the populations are all the same,

the *problem* is to estimate β, the coefficient of proportionality which specifies the relationship between income and expected expenditure, and

the *procedure* amounts to taking a random sample, which gives for each level of income x_1, x_2, . . . a corresponding expenditure y_1, y_2, ...

The *first computation* determines the regression coefficient b on the basis of these numerical observations (0.8048 in our example),

the *second computation* determines the standard error (0.0324 in our case), and

the *conclusion* follows that 0.8048 is an unbiased estimate of β and that the standard error is 0.0324.

The implication of this conclusion (given that b is normally distributed) is that β lies within the limits 0.7400 and 0.8696, obtained from 0.8048 by deducting and adding twice the standard error, apart from a chance of 0.0455 that β lies outside these limits.

12-9. Concluding Remarks

We conclude this chapter with some remarks.

1. We have confined our attention to the case in which one deducts from and adds to the estimate twice the standard error. This is conventional, but one can also, for example, take 3 times the standard error both ways. The chance of falling outside the 3-standard-error limits is only 3 in 1,000, so that the procedure is much more reliable—but there is a price to be paid. The interval becomes wider, so that there is less

accuracy. The optimum mixture of reliability and accuracy depends upon the use that is to be made of the outcome.

2. The accuracy is influenced by the number of observations and by the magnitude of the population variance σ^2. If there are n observations, $x_1, x_2, \ldots, x_n$, the standard error of the regression coefficient equals

$$\sqrt{\frac{\sigma^2}{x_1^2 + x_2^2 + \cdots + x_n^2}}$$

The standard error is thus seen to be smaller when the population variance σ^2 is smaller and/or when there are more observations $x_1, x_2, \ldots$. Thus the result tends to become more reliable as it is based on more observations.

3. We have confined our attention to the simplest case, viz., a straight line through the origin. The line need not necessarily go through the origin. There may also be more explanatory variables, in which case the number of coefficients to be estimated increases. Each of these coefficients describes the influence of an explanatory variable on the dependent variable. For each we have a regression coefficient which is an unbiased estimate, and each estimate has its standard error. The philosophy remains unchanged.

4. Finally, our results have been derived under assumptions which need not necessarily be correct. Is the relationship truly linear? Has the sample really been drawn at random? Do all populations really have the same variance σ^2? What if we do not know that σ equals $100? (Answer: The variance in turn is estimated.) These are all quite legitimate questions, but we pass them by because they fall outside the scope of the present book.

Literature

The statistical textbooks usually cover regression analysis at a rather advanced stage. A case in point is Mood and Graybill [1] and also the rather more elementary book of Moroney [2]. Johnston's book [3] is just about exclusively devoted to regression analysis and its extensions, but is very advanced. Another recent book by Goldberger [4] is also advanced. The Wallis and Roberts book [5] gives a good elementary introduction.

[1] A. M. Mood and F. A. Graybill, *Introduction to the Theory of Statistics*, 2d ed., McGraw-Hill Book Company, New York, 1963.
[2] M. J. Moroney, *Facts from Figures*, 3d rev. ed., Penguin Books, Inc., Baltimore, 1956.
[3] J. Johnston, *Econometric Methods*, McGraw-Hill Book Company, New York, 1963.
[4] A. S. Goldberger, *Econometric Theory*, John Wiley & Sons, Inc., New York, 1964.
[5] W. A. Wallis and H. V. Roberts, *Statistics, A New Approach*, The Free Press of Glencoe, New York, 1956.

13

The Consumer's Dollar

13-1. The Behavior of the Consumer

In this chapter we shall deal with the way in which the consumer spends his income. The decisions to be made by the consumer concern the quantities he buys of each of the commodities, be it socks, sugar, or swimming pools. Within the limits imposed by his income and the prices of the various commodities, the consumer can freely decide what quantities he will buy. It is important to know what the consumer will decide. Perhaps it is not really important to know how many shirts of a given brand Mr. Smith from Boulder, Colorado, will buy next year, but the manufacturers of that brand of shirts will certainly be very much interested in knowing—or in having an idea about—the aggregate sales of all their shirts next year. The government, in turn, may not be interested in the aggregate sales of one brand of shirts, but it will be interested in the aggregate textile sales. In fact, the government might be interested in the total consumers' demand for textile products with an eye on input-output predictions (cf. Chap. 3).

In Chap. 4 we were also concerned with consumption, but there we really considered aggregate consumption not only of all consumers but also of all different commodities. Here we consider the various commodities in greater detail. We shall continue, however, to lump all consumers together—the consumption expenditures of Mr. Mays, Mr. Nixon, and Mr. Sinatra, and all 200,000,000 other Americans are considered collectively.

It will be clear that income and prices play an important role in explaining consumption. A complicating factor is that the value of the dollar is not constant. It will therefore be necessary to work with the concepts of real income and relative prices.

13-2. Real Income and Relative Prices

Most people have grown wise to the fact that an increase in income of 5 per cent means precious little when all prices simultaneously increase by

5 per cent.   In that case the consumer's purchasing power remains the
same.   Since all prices and income rise in the same proportion, there is no
sense in changing the buying pattern.   If income rises without accompany-
ing increases in prices, this will be an undisguised blessing.   One can buy
more and fulfill long-felt wishes.   There is no need to elaborate on the
new vistas.   Let it suffice to mention the phenomenon of replacement—
margarine will be replaced by butter, public transport by a private car, a
vacation in Florida by a trip through Europe.   Precisely the opposite is
the case when prices rise but income remains constant.   This is the plight
of the fixed-income groups.   In such a situation the consumer has to
tighten his belt, give a bit here and a bit there, and replace butter by
margarine.

Apparently it is not so much the money income which is important, but
rather what can be bought with that income.   This is the reason for
introducing the concept of *real income* in economics.   Henceforth, we shall
indicate real income by the symbol $\bar{m}$.   It is computed by dividing the
money income m (the pay one receives) by a price index as an indicator of
the price level.   We write i_p for the price index, so that

$$\text{Real income} = \frac{\text{money income}}{\text{price index}} \quad \text{or} \quad \bar{m} = \frac{m}{i_p}$$

If an individual's yearly income increases from \$10,000 to \$10,700 (i.e., by
7 per cent) and if the price level simultaneously increases by 4 per cent
(from 1 to 1.04), the real income (expressed in dollars of constant value)
has increased to 10,700/1.04 = \$10,288, or by nearly 3 per cent.

The construction of a price index (i_p) is a far more subtle and difficult
project.   It is still a hotly debated issue in economics.   Since it has been
established that a truly ideal price index which meets all desirable criteria
does not yet exist, it may remain an unsettled issue.   The Laspeyres
price index is the most widely used.   It strikes a balance between simplicity and intuitive appeal (with a somewhat larger emphasis on simplicity).   To explain the construction of this index, we compare two
situations which we shall refer to as the base-year situation and the new
situation.   All quantities and prices referring to the base-year values will be
starred.   If p_1 stands for the price of milk, p_1^* stands for the price of milk in
the base year.   Similarly the prices p_2, p_3, . . . in the base year are indicated by $p_2^*, p_3^*,$ . . . .   For the quantities bought we write $x_1, x_2, x_3,$ . . .
and $x_1^*, x_2^*, x_3^*,$ . . . .   We can now ask what a batch of commodities
$x_1^*, x_2^*,$ . . . , x_n^* bought in the base year would cost at the prices $p_1, p_2,$
. . . , p_n which prevail in the new situation.   The answer is, of course,

that the batch would cost

$$p_1 x_1^* + p_2 x_2^* + \cdots + p_n x_n^*$$

We can compare this with the amount the commodities x_1^*, x_2^*, . . . , x_n^* actually did cost during the base year. Since prices in that year were p_1^*, p_2^*, . . . , p_n^*, the total expenses were

$$p_1^* x_1^* + p_2^* x_2^* + \cdots + p_n^* x_n^*$$

The price index is now the ratio of these two amounts. The numerator gives the costs of the base-year quantities at new prices; the denominator gives the costs of the base-year batch at base-year prices:

$$i_p = \frac{p_1 x_1^* + p_2 x_2^* + \cdots + p_n x_n^*}{p_1^* x_1^* + p_2^* x_2^* + \cdots + p_n^* x_n^*}$$

If we find $i_p = 1.04$, we conclude that the prices have increased on the average by 4 per cent compared with the base situation. For convenience this ratio is usually multiplied through by 100, so that the price index is given as 104.

The price index takes into consideration all price changes and boils these down to one single number. The changes in the prices of the *individual* commodities are also of interest. Such price changes will often induce the customer to make changes in the quantities he buys of various commodities. Suppose that the price of cheese increases by 2 per cent but that the general price level as measured by the price index increases by 10 per cent. Then cheese, though it has increased in price, becomes less expensive relative to the general price level. Such relative price changes are important. The same price index i_p is often used to obtain a measure for this relative price. If p stands for the price of cheese, $\bar{p} = p/i_p$ expresses the price of cheese in relation to the general price level. The value $\bar{p}$ is called the *relative price*. Its construction is analogous to that of the real income $\bar{m} = m/i_p$. In both cases the actual money income and prices are divided by the price index, which gives us the real income and the relative prices in comparison with a base-year situation which was used in constructing the price index i_p.

13-3. The Quantities Bought

Let us now consider bread. We want to determine the yearly quantity of bread bought per capita as a function of both the real income per capita and the relative price of bread. The quantity of bread bought per capita will be indicated by $\bar{x}$, the real income per capita by $\bar{m}$, and the relative price of bread by $\bar{p}$. We shall express these variables in terms of yearly percentage changes, which is easy to accomplish. From the real income $\bar{m}$ in a given year, we deduct the real income $\bar{m}_{-1}$ in the previous year, divide this difference by $\bar{m}_{-1}$, and multiply by 100. For the result we write $\bar{\bar{m}}$:

$$\bar{\bar{m}} = \frac{\bar{m} - \bar{m}_{-1}}{\bar{m}_{-1}} \times 100$$

This $\bar{\bar{m}}$ gives the percentage change of real income compared with that of the previous year. If real income last year was \$3,000 and this year is \$3,090, then

$$\bar{\bar{m}} = \frac{3,090 - 3,000}{3,000} \times 100 = \frac{90}{3,000} \times 100 = 3$$

so that the real income has risen by 3 per cent during this year. The percentage change in the quantity bought ($\bar{x}$) and the percentage change in the relative price ($\bar{p}$) are determined in the same way. Thus

$$\bar{\bar{x}} = \frac{\bar{x} - \bar{x}_{-1}}{\bar{x}_{-1}} \times 100 \quad \text{and} \quad \bar{\bar{p}} = \frac{\bar{p} - \bar{p}_{-1}}{\bar{p}_{-1}} \times 100$$

We shall now assume that a linear relationship exists between the variables $\bar{x}$, $\bar{m}$, and $\bar{p}$. If we have data for a number of years on these yearly percentage changes, we can apply the least-squares regression procedure. Suppose we get the following result:

$$\bar{x} = 0.122\bar{\bar{m}} - 0.053\bar{\bar{p}}$$
$$(0.064) \quad (0.029)$$

The numbers in parenthesis are the standard errors, which are an indication of the reliability of the results.

If we disregard for the time being the standard errors, we can interpret this result as follows. The equation says that we must multiply the percentage change in real income ($\bar{\bar{m}}$) by a factor 0.122 and the percentage change in the relative price ($\bar{\bar{p}}$) by a factor -0.053 to obtain the percentage change in the quantity of bread bought. In other words, each per cent increase in real income leads to a 0.122 per cent increase in the demand for bread. This is expressed by saying that the *income elasticity* of bread is 0.122. The *price elasticity* of bread equals −0.053. This implies that each per cent increase in the relative price of bread—when real income remains constant—decreases consumption by 0.053 per cent. The addition of the clause "when *real* income remains constant" is not trivial. Suppose the price of bread increases while all other prices and the *money* income remain constant. Then the increase in the price of bread decreases the real income. The eventual effect of the price increase of bread is then twofold: the direct effect of a relative price increase and the indirect effect of a decrease in real income.

Furthermore, we know from the previous chapter that the coefficients 0.122 and −0.053 are only estimates of income and price elasticity, subject to fluctuations from sample to sample. The income elasticity was estimated at 0.122, but the standard error of this estimate is 0.064. If we apply the rule of deducting and adding twice the standard error, we find that there is a 20 to 1 chance that the interval from 0 to 0.25 contains the true value of the income elasticity. There is no greater precision than this.

13-4. Income Elasticities

We shall now study more closely the income elasticities of various commodities. As we have seen, the value of the income elasticity of commodity h answers the question: With what percentage will the demand for h change when income increases by 1 per cent? We found that the (estimated) income elasticity of bread equals 0.122. When real income increases by 1 per cent, bread consumption increases by 0.122 per cent. The amount of money spent on bread increases by the same percentage; that is, it increases from g, say, to $1.00122g$. The *proportion* of income spent on bread was originally equal to g/m and has now become

$$\frac{1.00122g}{1.01m} = 0.991\,\frac{g}{m}$$

which is *smaller* than the original proportion g/m. This situation always prevails when a commodity has an income elasticity less than 1. Whenever this is the case, a 1 per cent increase in income is followed by a smaller percentage increase in demand, so that the relative proportion of income spent on that commodity has declined. The converse holds when the income elasticity is larger than 1: the proportion of the budget allotted to that commodity will increase as real income increases. This is the case with vacation expenditures, for example. Goods with an income elasticity larger than 1 are called *luxury goods*, and we speak of *necessary goods* when the income elasticity is below 1.   Bread is a necessary commodity; thus the relative amount of income spent on bread decreases as real income increases.   A subgroup of necessary goods is formed by *inferior goods*.   In the case of inferior goods it is not only the share of income that decreases but even the absolute amount of income spent on inferior goods decreases as income increases.   Margarine provides a good example of this phenomenon.   The income elasticity of inferior goods is *negative* (and hence *a fortiori* less than 1).   The terms luxury, necessary, and inferior are, incidentally, technical terms.   They are not to be regarded as value judgments.

To give a rough idea of the value of the income elasticities for various goods, we have reproduced a list below.   The elasticities quoted are based on statistical data of the Netherlands, and have been estimated by A. P. Barten by means of a sophisticated regression procedure.   The standard errors of the estimates appear in parenthesis.

Goods	*Elasticities, with standard errors*
Bread	0.12 (0.06)
Dairy products	0.56 (0.13)
Tobacco products	0.62 (0.15)
Candies, chocolate, and ice cream	0.62 (0.15)
Groceries	0.67 (0.15)
Fuel and utilities	0.69 (0.10)
Vegetables and fruits	0.84 (0.17)
Fish	0.88 (0.41)
Beverages	0.89 (0.19)
Meat and meat products	0.92 (0.19)
Footwear	1.01 (0.20)
Household articles and furniture	1.27 (0.18)
Other durables	1.49 (0.23)
Textile and clothing	1.83 (0.12)

All elasticities are positive, which means that the list contains no inferior goods.   This is partly because the commodities have been arranged in rather large groups.   Inferior goods are then mixed with noninferior goods, and the group as a whole is not inferior.   Below, we shall work with a more detailed list of commodities and come across some examples of negative income elasticities.

The list shows further that values above 1 are found for durable goods, which agrees with introspection.   If income increases, a substantial part tends to be used for durable commodities.   The standard errors are normally of the order of 0.1 or 0.2.   There is an exception in the case of fish, where the standard error is so large that the estimate should be used with the greatest care, if at all.

13-5. Price Elasticities

We shall now discuss price elasticities in greater detail. For convenience, we reproduce the equation describing bread consumption:

$$\bar{x} = 0.122\bar{m} - 0.053\bar{p}$$
$$(0.064) \quad (0.029)$$

The only price explicitly mentioned in this equation is the price of bread. The other prices play their role implicitly, because the real income and the relative price of bread are determined by dividing the money income and the actual price by a price index and this index involves *all* prices. In fact, therefore, the price of bread appears three times in the equation, and the other prices twice. The money income is divided by a price index because only the purchasing power of the income interests us. The price has been divided by a price index because only the relative prices interest us. We care only about the *relative* prices because *all* goods compete for the consumer's dollar.

Although all goods compete for the consumer's dollar, some compete more than others do. Margarine and butter compete more than margarine and theater tickets. In still other instances, goods supplement each other, such as cars and gas. In all such cases there is a special relation between two commodities, quite apart from the more general competition of all goods for the same dollar. When butter increases in price but margarine does not, one can expect a shift from butter to margarine. The goods butter and margarine *substitute* for each other. When cars increase in price, fewer cars will be bought, and as a consequence less gas will be bought. Cars and gas are called *complementary goods*.

In Barten's investigations the commodities are grouped together in rather large classes. The specific effects of price changes of substitutes or complementary goods then do not show up very clearly. We only give one instance in which such a specific effect can be seen, concerning the consumption of candies, chocolate, and ice cream. The percentage change in this consumption will be indicated by $\bar{x}_1$, and the percentage change in the relative price by $\bar{p}_1$. The equation is

$$\bar{x}_1 = 0.624\bar{m} - 0.487\bar{p}_1 + 0.076\bar{p}_2 + 0.123\bar{p}_3$$
$$(0.150) \quad (0.108) \quad (0.052) \quad (0.079)$$

The income elasticity is estimated at slightly more than 0.6; the price elasticity is estimated at about −0.5. Furthermore, there are two other explicit prices: $\bar{p}_2$ stands for the percentage change in the relative price of tobacco, and $\bar{p}_3$ for the percentage change in the relative price of drinks. The idea is that these last two categories of goods are substitutes for candies, chocolate, and ice cream. The equation confirms this because the associated price elasticities are positive. Thus, an increase in the price of tobacco leads to an increase in the purchases of candies which then substitute for tobacco. The coefficients should be cautiously interpreted, however; in both cases the rule of adding and deducting twice the standard error leaves room for negative values. One usually expresses this by saying that the coefficients do not *significantly* differ from zero.

If the groups of commodities were subdivided in greater detail, specific effects would be more noticeable. In dealing with aggregated groups of commodities it usually suffices to work only with the single price of the group, as was done in our bread equation.

13-6. Budget Surveys

All results recorded so far were based on data provided by economic time series. We can also obtain data from budget surveys, however, in which the figures are provided by individual families. A great number of families are asked to cooperate by recording *all* their expenses, up to and including nickels spent on ice-cream cones. Obviously, some families will refuse, and others will be incapable of cooperating. The resulting sample will therefore not be a true *random* sample in which each family has the same probability of participating. Sloppy housewives do not usually participate; prudent housewives do. The results obtained from the surveys indicate that the participating families typically buy more books and less alcohol than an average family. A budget survey study is thus of moderate interest to a brewery. Despite these shortcomings, budget surveys have proved their value and deserve careful study. In most cases the survey is limited to a period of one or two years because it is difficult to find families who will cooperate for longer periods. In these small time periods there will usually be only few and small price fluctuations. A budget survey does not therefore help very much in obtaining information about price elasticities. There are important differences in incomes from family to family, however, and apart from that, there are important differences in the compositions of the various families and in their tastes and habits.

We shall now present some results of an investigation by R. Stone, concerning consumption habits of British consumers. Differences in tastes were incorporated in the study by distinguishing two categories of families: working-class families on the one hand and middle-class families on the other. This is a rough-and-ready device to obtain at least some distinction in tastes.   It is, of course, impossible to take into account all individual tastes.

The composition of the families must also be taken into account.   Given the same income, a large family will spend more on food than a small family.   A family with two children over 16 will have different needs than one with two children under 5.   To incorporate these differences, at least quantitatively, a scale was constructed which equates a woman to 0.9 of a man, for the purpose of consumption.   (Many husbands may wonder why.)   The complete scale that was used describes everybody as a proportion of an adult male, as follows:

Age group	Working-class families		Middle-class families	
	Men	Women	Men	Women
Below 5 years	0.52	0.52	0.28	0.28
5–13 years	0.52	0.52	0.65	0.65
14–17 years	0.98	0.90	0.98	0.90
18 years and over	1.00	0.90	1.00	0.90

For purposes of consumption a working-class family consisting of two parents, a son and a daughter between 14 and 17, and three children under 14 is considered to be equivalent to a family consisting of

$$1.00 + 0.90 + 0.98 + 0.90 + 3 \times 0.52 = 5.34 \text{ adult males}$$

The scale is only a rather coarse instrument and is unlikely to be satisfactory for particular commodities such as milk or tobacco.

Stone computed the income elasticities from budget survey data.   He tried to explain the *amount spent* on the various commodities rather than the *quantity bought*.   In this context one speaks of income elasticities of expenditures to distinguish them from income elasticities of quantities bought, which we mentioned before.   It was assumed that the income elasticity of each commodity was the same for the two groups of families.   However, it appeared that working-class families spend more on food than middle-class families with the same income.   This is ascribed to the fact that more food is required by people performing physical labor and that middle-class families spend relatively more on education and "culture," so that less remains for food.

Now for the numerical results, which have all been computed with the least-squares method.   The dependent variable was the expenditures per adult male; the explanatory variable was the income per adult male. For all foods together, the income elasticity was estimated at 0.53 with a standard error of only 0.04.   This value of the income elasticity for food has been found repeatedly in countries where the level of income is approximately the same as in Britain.   Middle-class families spend about 10 per cent less on food than working-class families of the same composition. For some individual commodities the results are recorded below.   The goods have been ranked in order of income elasticities of expenditures. The standard error is given in parenthesis after the estimates; in the last column we have indicated whether the middle-class families consume significantly more or significantly less of the good concerned than working-class families with the same income.   (The difference is considered significant if it is more than twice the standard error.)

Goods	Elasticities, with standard error	
Skimmed milk	−0.59 (0.76)	
Fried fish and chips	−0.45 (0.51)	
Margarine	−0.16 (0.11)	less
Flour	−0.15 (0.11)	
Cocoa	−0.10 (0.24)	
Bread	−0.05 (0.04)	less
Tea	0.04 (0.04)	
Canned meat	0.27 (0.12)	
Marmalade	0.30 (0.05)	less
Beef and veal	0.34 (0.06)	less
Milk	0.50 (0.18)	
Eggs	0.54 (0.07)	less
Pork	0.58 (0.24)	less
Mutton and lamb	0.70 (0.12)	
Cookies	0.71 (0.16)	more
Fish	0.88 (0.07)	less
Vegetables	0.93 (0.14)	less
Fruit and nuts	1.21 (0.16)	
Coffee	1.42 (0.30)	
Cream	1.71 (0.29)	
Meals away from home	2.39 (0.18)	less

There are six negative income elasticities (inferior goods), including bread. None of the negative elasticities differ significantly (more than twice the standard error) from zero, however.   The commodity with the highest income elasticity is "meals away from home."   Middle-class families spend less on meals outside their homes than working-class families because the latter families frequently use factory lunchrooms.   It may seem surprising that coffee has such a high elasticity; in fact, in the tea-drinking nation of Britain coffee is apparently a luxury good.

13-7. Quality and Quantity

As we have said, budget surveys usually consider the expenditures for various commodities rather than the quantity bought. The computed elasticities indicate by what percentage the expenditures increase when income increases by 1 per cent; they do not necessarily coincide with the income elasticities of the quantities bought. The two elasticities may diverge because the consumer will react to income increases not only by buying *more* but also by buying *better quality.* In the latter case the expenses increase while the quantity bought remains unchanged. If our studies were so detailed that various brands of coffee were distinguished, there would be no problem. Usually our data are not so detailed, however, and all qualities of coffee are lumped together.

To analyze the influence of income on the quality bought, we shall assume that the differences in price between the various brands of coffee, types of meat, kinds of cheese, etc., are indicative of differences in quality. The budget surveys enable us to investigate the relationship between the average price paid for a commodity (as an indicator of its quality) and income.

We shall consider this case in some detail. Let us take a family that buys coffee at the price of p cents per pound. If the family consumes q pounds per year, the total amount spent on coffee each year in that family is $p \times q$ cents. Suppose now that the family income increases by 10 per cent—or suppose we have another family in the budget survey with a 10 per cent higher annual income. One will presumably then notice two effects: The richer family will buy *more* and *better* coffee. If the income elasticity of the quantity bought is 0.5, the quantity bought will be $0.5 \times 10 = 5$ per cent larger. Apart from this we also introduce an income elasticity of the quality, which is the percentage change in the price paid for a pound of coffee when income increases by 1 per cent. If this income elasticity of the quality is 0.25, the price paid for a pound of coffee increases by $0.25 \times 10 = 2.5$ per cent. The total expenditures thus increase because the quantity q increases by 5 per cent to $1.05q$ and the price p increases by 2.5 per cent to $1.025p$. Hence the expenditures increase from $p \times q$ to $1.05q \times 1.025p = 1.07625pq$, or by (roughly) 7.5 per cent. This 7.5 per cent is then the income elasticity of the expenditures. In general the income elasticity of expenditures is equal to the income elasticity of the quantity plus the income elasticity of the quality. We present a table, based on a budget survey of white-collar employees in 1934–1935 in Amsterdam. The results show substantial variations. As a rule, the income elasticities of the qualities have small standard errors and are of the order of 0.1 or 0.2. For the nine commodities considered here the two sorts of income elasticity are on the average roughly equal. When income increases, then, the total expenditures increase because *both* the quantity *and* the quality of purchases increase.

Commodity groups	Income elasticity of		
	Quantity	Quality	Expenditures
Meat products	−0.11 (0.03)	0.21 (0.02)	0.11
Tea	0.09 (0.05)	0.04 (0.02)	0.13
Cookies	0.01 (0.05)	0.21 (0.02)	0.22
Cheese	0.09 (0.07)	0.14 (0.02)	0.23
Chocolate	0.13 (0.13)	0.16 (0.03)	0.29
Meat	0.07 (0.04)	0.22 (0.03)	0.29
Coffee	0.25 (0.07)	0.10 (0.04)	0.35
Cocoa	0.29 (0.15)	0.10 (0.04)	0.40
Cake	0.31 (0.09)	0.13 (0.03)	0.44

13-8. Other Factors Influencing Consumer Demand

Consumption expenditures have been explained largely on the basis of income and prices. If we want to predict consumption expenditures, then, we can proceed in a roundabout way by predicting the future developments in prices and income. This might be done with an econometric model, provided it is sufficiently detailed with respect to prices. That is hardly ever the case, but the increasing quantity and quality of relevant data and the promising development of electronic computers do not preclude the construction of such detailed econometric models in the not too distant future.

Apart from prices and income, however, there are many other factors influencing consumers' behavior. Producers spend millions on advertisements to persuade the consumer that their products deserve his dollar. They are convinced that these millions are not spent in vain, but very little is known as yet about the quantitative influence of advertisements on sales. We only mention this fact in passing.

We should also mention that the reactions of consumers are often slow. There is a psychological delay before expenditures are adapted to rising incomes. The delay is even more evident if incomes decline; it is very difficult to adapt oneself to lower standards of living. Time may be needed before price changes have their full effect, if only because they are not immediately known or because it is difficult to switch to other products. If gas becomes cheaper but one has just bought a brand-new electric stove, one will not immediately switch to a gas stove.

This example illustrates the last point we wish to make. Durable consumer goods present their own problems.   It is hardly feasible to buy $\frac{1}{10}$ of a car.   The decision is of the zero-one type (to buy or not to buy). It depends on present income, income expected in the future, prices, the state of the present car (if any), the size of the family, the need for transportation, and also, perhaps, such factors as keeping up with the Joneses.

Literature

A monumental, but not easy work on the theory of consumer demand is that of Stone [1].   Some of his results have been incorporated in the present chapter.   Other results have been taken from Barten [2], whose paper has been elaborated upon by Theil [3].   Houthakker [4] and Theil [5] simultaneously but independently investigated the influence of income on the quality bought.   The numerical results mentioned in this chapter can be found in [5].

[1] R. Stone, *The Measurement of Consumers' Expenditure and Behaviour in the United Kingdom, 1920–1938*, vol. 1, Cambridge University Press, London, 1954.

[2] A. P. Barten, "Consumer Demand Functions under Conditions of Almost Additive Preferences," *Econometrica*, vol. 32 (1964), pp. 1–38.

[3] H. Theil, "The Information Approach to Demand Analysis," *Econometrica*, vol. 33 (1965), pp. 67–87.

[4] H. S. Houthakker, "Compensated Changes in Quantities and Qualities Consumed," *Review of Economic Studies*, vol. 19 (1951–52), pp. 155–164.

[5] H. Theil, "Qualities, Prices, and Budget Enquiries," *Review of Economic Studies*, vol. 19 (1951–52), pp. 129–147.

Epilogue

Both the beginning and the end of this book concern the person in whom economics is ultimately interested: the consumer. At the outset we discussed the problem of the housewife who wants to minimize the expenses on food without forfeiting the health of the family. At the end we discussed the vastly more complicated problem of how the consumer spends his income on the various commodities and services and how his expenditure pattern changes when his income and the prices change. In between the first and the last chapters the consumer also occasionally played his role. In the chapters on probability theory and the specification of economic relationships we considered the variability of family expenditures, and in the chapter on econometric macromodels we gave a central role to the consumption equation.

Quite a number of somewhat flippant games were discussed at length: a quiz, betting at Saratoga, a soccer pool, morra in Italy, ticktacktoe, and (rather less flippant) chess. These games were not introduced for their own intrinsic interest, but because their structure and solution techniques correspond to similar situations in business and government. In the chapter on game theory, for example, besides morra and ticktacktoe, we discussed competing airlines and the plight of pig breeders.

The concept of a strategy was introduced with the game of chess. We continued to show that a wise choice between investment opportunities should be made strategically, just as the adaptation of production and work force to varying levels of demand at a paint factory should be formulated as a strategy. Such problems associated with production, incidentally, kept us repeatedly busy. A radio manufacturer wondered how to maximize his profit. Another manufacturer wanted to schedule production over the various quarters to minimize the sum of inventory and adjustment costs. A third manufacturer had to decide how many radio knobs should be produced in one batch to minimize the costs. A fourth had to decide how many repairmen to employ to minimize the sum of the costs of the delayed repair of defective machines, on the one hand, and that of his repairmen, on the other. This is a special instance of queueing or waiting problems, which were considered in some detail.

Our problems were sometimes macroeconomic, sometimes microeconomic. What the individual housewife should buy is a micro-problem (though for the housewife concerned the problem may seem very important indeed). But it is a macroeconomic problem to describe the total consumption in a country in terms of relevant factors, such as incomes of various kinds (wages, profits, etc.). In the sphere of production the same distinction is appropriate. The input-output analysis is a macroeconomic topic, since it concerns whole sectors of the economy, such as agriculture and the textile industry. The critical-path method, on the other hand, is a microeconomic technique used to produce as efficiently as possible. The building of an econometric macromodel is a prototype of a macroeconomic problem. Microeconomic is the questionnaire which the firms complete about their anticipated and realized investment level. The published report based on such a survey is macroeconomic, however, since it "aggregates" the information of all participating firms.

Predictions have been another prime concern throughout the book. Whether based on input-output models or on other econometric macromodels or on investment surveys, the results are surely not perfect, although they are generally much better than those of simple extrapolation techniques. One aspect of the imperfection is the tendency toward the underestimation of changes: In most cases the direction of change is predicted correctly, but more often than not the *size* of the change turns out to be larger than predicted. This is ultimately due to the fact that prediction procedures assume that somewhere "something" remains constant—which is in real life usually untrue.

The imperfect predictions led us to consider the uncertainty problem in detail in a chapter on uncertainty and probability. By associating probability statements with predictions, one is able to raise the scientific value of the latter. An example is provided by the way in which the paint manufacturer can forecast his own future behavior with respect to production and work force when he proceeds strategically. Such forecasts are "unbiased," which means that the discrepancy between the prediction and the corresponding actual decision has an expected value of zero (i.e., is zero on the average in a sufficiently long series of forecasts).

The chapter on uncertainty and probability takes a very central place in the book since all later chapters use this subject as their mathematical base. Needless to say, the use of probability theory—like any other mathematical tool—presupposes that the problem concerned is simplified to a level where it is manageable from the standpoint of that theory.

We should be careful here.   If we abstract too much, the model may not be sufficiently descriptive of reality any longer.   A way out is the simulation technique, which is somewhat similar to the experimental testing of model planes in wind tunnels.

All these topics, varied as they are, have in common their method of solution, which is clearly mathematically oriented, and their concern with either micro- or macro-economics.   This does not imply that the same techniques and the same concepts could not be or are not applied in other fields.   Take, for example, a judge who pronounces a conditional sentence —this is an example of a strategy because it tells the police what to do as a function of information that may become available in the future.   In fact, it is quite conceivable that the similarity of techniques used will lead to a unification of several areas in the behavioral field that are now far apart.

Index